Building Mathematical Competence
in the Elementary School

There are so many things to learn . . .

Building Mathematical Competence in the Elementary School

Revised Edition

Peter Lincoln Spencer

Claremont Graduate School

Marguerite Brydegaard

San Diego State College

Holt, Rinehart and Winston, Inc.

New York • Chicago • San Francisco • Toronto • London

Preface

This book was written by experienced teachers as an aid to other teachers and to persons preparing to teach mathematics in the elementary schools. It is a revision of our earlier book, *Building Mathematical Concepts in the Elementary School*, which presented broad and functional ideas of the nature of mathematics, as well as teaching procedures.

During the years following publication of *Building Mathematical Concepts*, changes began that led to many new developments in the teaching of mathematics in the elementary and junior high schools: developments in ways of perceiving and interpreting mathematical meanings, developments in our conception of how and why children learn, and developments of procedures for teaching mathematics at all levels. These changes, to which the original text hopefully contributed, led to an almost complete rewriting for the present text, *Building Mathematical Competence in the Elementary School.* New chapters have been added on the topics of sets, algebra, geometry, principles and relations of whole numbers, and mathematical communication. In addition, all of the chapters of the original text have been largely rewritten to incorporate new mathematical ideas and to suggest new ways for building mathematical competence.

Today's school program emphasizes problem-solving procedures in which the learner is challenged to question, to experiment, and to explore, in order to find basic ways of attacking problems. Learning is conceived to be a personal achievement that can be accomplished only through problem-solving behavior on the part of the learner. These ideas are illustrated and developed in the revised text.

A dynamic approach to teaching mathematics is stressed. Mathematical ideas as they occur in simple, and often intuitive, behavior are observed, and the ideas are developed by inferential processes into abstract and general concepts. This approach is applied, for example, in building number scales from the simple ideas of the grouping of ones, which leads to the customary counting number scale. The ideas are then extended to a logical interpretation of fraction-number scales,

v

denominate-number scales, and number scales for bases other than ten. These ideas are further extended to interpret the directional (signed)-number scale.

A very important part of mathematical competence consists in a reasonable mastery of its special language forms and symbols. A chapter of this book is devoted to the topic of languages and mathematical communication.

The measurement of understanding and computational skill is an important part of instruction. An analytical study of pupil errors is basic in determining deficiencies in instruction and learning. This text includes suggestions for constructing tests for diagnostic purposes.

Mathematical experience includes conceptual and computational aspects of mathematical behavior; these experiences are tied to applications from the physical world. The applications, wisely selected, facilitate interpretation of the concepts and computation. This point of view has been brought out by groups devoted to mathematics education, such as the University of Illinois Committee on School Mathematics, the Madison Project, and the School Mathematics Study Group. The procedure of using the many and obvious things of human experience, combined with the ability to infer and to hypothesize, characterize problem-solving behavior. This method is developed in the illustrative lessons and discussions in this text.

The authors believe that teachers who have a sound knowledge of mathematics can create classrooms that are laboratories in which their students will develop mathematical competence. This competence will lead to continuous growth in the appreciation and understanding of mathematics.

The authors wish to express their sincere appreciation to Irene Spencer who helped with each aspect in the production of this book, to Harry Crosby who produced the photographs, and to the many persons from San Diego State College, San Diego City and County Schools, and other locations, who offered helpful suggestions.

Claremont, California   P. L. S.
San Diego, California
January 1966   M. B.

Contents

CHAPTER 10   CONCEPTS UNDERLYING COMPUTATION:
DENOMINATE NUMBERS   255

CHAPTER 11   ALGEBRA: A WAY OF
MATHEMATICKING   279

1

Introduction

1.1 MATHEMATICS: CONCEALED or REVEALED?

In the fourth century B.C., Hippasus, a great mathematician, was drowned in his bath by members of his own secret brotherhood. He was guilty of divulging mathematical secrets when he publicly announced that he had added a new element — a regular solid with 12 faces — to the list of elements started by Pythagoras, founder of the brotherhood.

In those days mathematics was for the *few*. Hippasus had erred by making public a mathematical finding; by drowning him, his associates practiced a primitive but effective form of punishment for his transgression.

Now, mathematics is for *all*. Times have changed since the followers of Pythagoras bound themselves with a pledge not to reveal mathematical ideas unless they were adequately paid to do so. Today there is both an urgent need and the desire to make mathematical ideas available to everyone and to see that they are competently applied. Whenever an error or a deficiency is revealed, a diagnosis of the trouble is made and then intelligent correction is undertaken.

1.2 MATHEMATICAL EXPERIENCE IDENTIFIED

Throughout his existence, man — wherever he may be and in whatever he does — experiences quantity. His behavior is constantly being affected by awareness of position, form, or quantitative aspects from which questions such as, "how much," "how many," "where," "when," and "what" arise. Sensing, reading, and coping with quantitative situations constitute mathematical experience.

Although everyone performs mathematical discriminations ("mathematicks") in some degree daily, few people pursue their development

1

beyond relatively simple needs. For example, everyone is aware of variations in size and amount of things they experience, but few ever by themselves evolve a comprehensive number scale or devise a general schema of weights and measures. Likewise, many people become adept in measuring or quantifying things, but they may be unable to express their ideas of their findings in the conventional mathematical language forms. Mathematical competence requires both clear conceptions of the ideas themselves and an awareness and understanding of the instruments, devices, and procedures that implement and facilitate their application in behavior.

The responsibility for leading elementary school pupils to attain a reasonable degree of mathematical competence is basically one of mathematics instruction. However, the responsibility is also a function of the entire instructional offering. Every phase of the daily experience offers an opportunity to develop some aspect of mathematical competence, because mathematics is a "social study," a "language art," a "science," an "esthetic art," and a "recreational activity":

Mathematics is a social study because it has been developed to serve the personal and social needs of human kind.

Mathematics is a language art because special forms have been devised for expressing and communicating mathematical messages.

Mathematics is a science because it is produced by discovery and experimentation, and because its content is systematically organized.

Mathematics is an integral part of esthetic arts because it is concerned with symmetry of form and order.

Mathematics is a recreational study because it is used in many recreational pursuits and because people find pleasure and relaxation in delving into its content.

The teaching of mathematics is not restricted to any particular segment of the daily program, even though there must be provision for experiences that are specifically designed to call attention to and to develop proficiency with specific aspects of mathematical knowledge or technique.

The goal of this broad concept of mathematical experience is greater pupil competence — in the areas of both ideas and skills. But greater competence demands better teaching. "Mathematics, like democracy, must be born anew with each individual and instruction is the midwife."[1]

[1] Paraphrase of Dewey's statement concerning democracy.

1.3   NATURE of MATHEMATICAL LEARNING

There are some important ideas concerning the nature and functioning of the instructional process that need careful consideration:

1. Mathematical competence is a personal production. It is not a commodity that can be transplanted directly from one mind to another. Hence, instruction must stimulate the learner to undertake that production and then guide him in his productive endeavor.

2. Mathematical behavior is best activated by experiencing problem situations that pique interested, discriminative responses on the part of the participant. The IQ (signifying "inner quest") of the pupil is a major factor in establishing the dynamics of behavior. By presenting challeng-

Measuring to find out.

ing problems in a functionally ordered series of experiences and by then making available the necessary equipment for sensing and interpreting the properties of the problems, instruction serves its "midwife" function.

3. Mathematical development involves inferential reasoning. Initial experience is intrinsically concrete. Through subsequent experiencing, ideas normally become released from their initial concrete reference.

Their applicability to other things becomes apparent, and ideas of general properties are created. Instruction should lead pupils first to conceive valid ideas and pertinent adaptive responses regarding particular situations and then to seek out (infer) generalized or abstract concepts or procedures having broader application.

4. Mathematical competence includes communication. It involves not only the ability to express one's ideas efficiently in overt behavior but also the ability to utilize effectively appropriate conventional or technical language forms for such expression. This includes both the expression of one's own ideas and the understanding of comparable expressions produced by others. Mathematical language forms constitute an important part of mathematical subject-matter.

In the basic ideas of mathematics there is great simplicity, utility, and beauty. Teachers have the opportunity to open doors of understanding for themselves and their pupils. What is required is a stimulation and direction of the behavioral activities of students so they conceive the ideas and acquire the skills and techniques. This is the essence of mathematical instruction.

1.4   A BRIEF PREVIEW of COVERAGE of BOOK

Since mathematical behavior is concerned with *quantities and with relationships among quantities,* the basic processes of identification and of quantification are presented in Chapter 2. More specific treatment follows: *sets,* as identification and groupings of things (Chapter 3), *number* as a scale for quantifying measurement (Chapter 4), and general properties and relations of *number systems* (Chapter 5). The general *language patterns* used in communicating number ideas are highlighted in Chapter 6, followed by a discussion of a special phase of mathematical language, *numerical computation* in Chapter 7. *Decimal and common fractions and denominate numbers* are presented as systems of numeration with special types of referents (Chapters 8, 9, and 10, respectively). Higher levels of mathematical thought are introduced in discussions of generalized arithmetic (*algebra,* Chapter 11) and measurement of space (*geometry,* Chapter 12). Discussions of *problem solving* (Chapter 13), the *nature and treatment of computational errors* (Chapter 14), and *Beyond the Obvious Lies the Truth* (Chapter 15) conclude the book.

1.5   NEW TOPICS in the MATHEMATICS PROGRAM

Modern ideas for teaching mathematics in the elementary school center around:

(1) interpretation of the psychology of the learning process

(2) new topics that are incorporated into the curriculum

(3) interpretation of mathematics to include not only numerical computation but also pertinent concepts of position, size, order, amount, and relationships of function

(4) ideas concerning the placement within the curriculum of various topics of mathematics

(5) a change in emphasis given to certain topics

Some of the newer topics are: (a) ideas of sets (collections or groupings), (b) algebra or generalized arithmetic, (c) space measurement (geometry), (d) the principles underlying number systems, and (e) the orthography (correct writing and spelling) and language of mathematics.

1.6 PURPOSE of ILLUSTRATIVE LESSONS

Included within most of the chapters are reports of lessons or lesson plans used by teachers to stimulate their students to sense and interpret certain mathematical ideas. To facilitate the reader's understanding, various irrelevant statements have been deleted and misuse of words has been corrected; otherwise, most of the lessons are accurate reports of actual classroom activities.

In all of the illustrative material presented, the grade level or the age level of the children is mentioned. This does not indicate a recommendation for teaching the material at the given age or grade level of the group reported. The learner's understanding of mathematical relationships is not the product merely of chronological age or grade level. Mathematical understanding is the product of discriminative thinking with regard for quantitative relationships. For example, the adult is frequently less capable than the child in estimating quantity. Students in college who have not developed good standards of reference for estimation of size, distance, or amount may be less capable than young children. As one college girl said, "I never thought about how to estimate. I just learned the tables the teacher asked us to know. After seeing the children develop standards for reference, I know how to improve in my estimating of things."

The illustrative lessons include examples from the nursery school level through grade eight; however, not all levels are represented in a single chapter. The given concepts are important at all grade levels. If the concepts presented in the given lessons have not been well developed by the time pupils reach higher grade levels, including college level, they should be taught at the higher level. It is futile to attempt to build superstructures when a firm foundation is not present. The

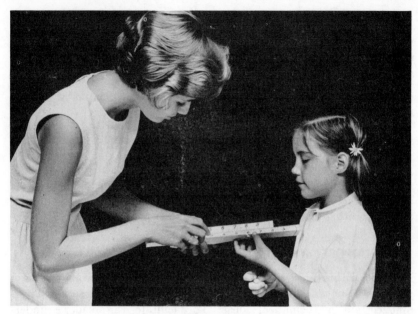

Using a teacher-made slide rule.

Making forms using pegboards.

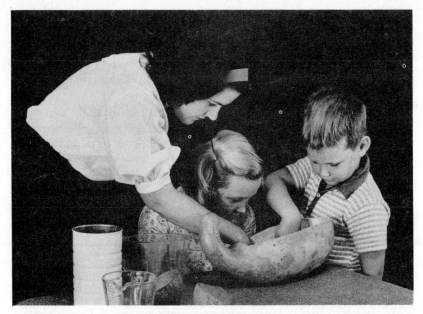

How much does it hold?

What is a cupful?

same lessons that were developed in primary grades have been developed in a similar way with older children, college students, and experienced teachers. The challenge of evolving the ideas can come through the use of a more discriminative vocabulary and a higher-pitched, faster-moving procedure.

In many of the illustrative lessons, there were very few errors with number facts and with the language of comparison. This is true because the children had achieved precision in the initial stages of learning, and because the material was meaningful to them.

The teacher who understands mathematical relationships, and interprets their emergence in the learner's behavior, can challenge the learner to refine the ideas in a way that is dynamic in pupil behavior. In many of the lessons presented in this book, very young children, undirected by the teacher, show evidence of discriminative thinking and of readiness to move ahead with ideas of mathematical relationships. In most instances, the teacher sensed the learner's readiness and led him to higher levels of interpreting ideas concerning quantitative relationships.

Discussion Questions

1. What is implied by the caption, "Mathematics: concealed or revealed"?
2. In a National Council of Teachers of Mathematics (NCTM) publication, it has been stated that the term mathematics should be interpreted as a "transitive, active verb." What are some illustrations of common types of mathematical behavior?
3. What evidence can you give that mathematics is a "social study," a "language arts" study, a "science study"?
4. What is implied by the statement, "Mathematics, like democracy, must be born anew with each individual, and instruction is the midwife"?
5. What is meant by the statement "Mathematical competence is a personal production"?
6. How does the idea of IQ as signifying "inner quest" relate to a learner's receptiveness for instruction?
7. What is meant by the term "inferential reasoning"? Illustrate instances in which you have performed that procedure.

Suggested Readings

An Analysis of New Mathematics Programs, National Council of Teachers of Mathematics, 1963. 68 pp.

Bergamini, David, and Editors of Life, Life Science Library, *Mathematics*. New York: Time, Inc., Book Division, 1963.

Brownell, William A., "Arithmetic in 1970," *The National Elementary Principal*, vol. 39 (October 1959), pp. 42–45.

Brownell, William A., "Revolution in Arithmetic," *The Arithmetic Teacher*, vol. 1 (February 1954), pp. 1–5.

Buswell, Guy T., "The Psychology of Learning in Relation to the Teaching of Arithmetic," National Society for the Study of Education, Fiftieth Yearbook, Part II, *The Teaching of Arithmetic*. Chicago, Ill.: University of Chicago Press, 1951, pp. 143–154.

Carroll, L. Grace, "A Mathematics Classroom Becomes a Laboratory," *Multi-Sensory Aids in the Teaching of Mathematics*, National Council of Teachers of Mathematics, Eighteenth Yearbook. Washington, D.C.: The Council, 1945, pp. 16–29.

Deans, Edwina, *Elementary School Mathematics — New Directions*. Washington, D.C.: Government Printing Office, 1963. 116 pp.

Fehr, Howard F., "Teaching for Appreciation of Mathematics," *School Science and Mathematics*, vol. 52 (January 1952), pp. 19–24.

Goals for School Mathematics: The Report of the Cambridge Conference on School Mathematics. Boston, Mass.: Houghton Mifflin Company, 1963.

Grossnickle, Foster E., and Leo J. Brueckner, *Discovering Meanings in Elementary School Mathematics*. New York: Holt, Rinehart and Winston, Inc., 1963, Chap. 3.

Hardgrove, Clarence E., Mildred Cole, and Anne Gustafson, *Thinking in the Language of Mathematics*. Illinois Curriculum Program, 1959.

Hartung, Maurice L., "Mathematics in the Total School Program," *The Mathematics Teacher*, vol. 51 (May 1958), pp. 336–343.

Howard, Charles F., and Enoch Dumas, *Basic Procedures in Teaching Arithmetic*. Boston, Mass.: D. C. Heath and Company, 1963.

Mansfield, Ralph, "Basic Mathematics — A Key to Democracy," *The Mathematics Teacher*, 37 (October 1944), pp. 248–253.

Meserve, Bruce E., "A Teacher's View of Mathematics," *School Science and Mathematics*, vol. 56 (December 1956), pp. 716–718.

Morton, Robert Lee, *Teaching Children Arithmetic*. Morristown, N. J.: Silver Burdett Company, 1953, Chap. 1.

Pieters, Mary Ballard, "Utilizing the Strategic Moment in Teaching Arithmetic," *The Arithmetic Teacher*, vol. 5 (December 1958), pp. 311–314.

Reed, Calvin H., "Developing Creative Thinking in Arithmetic," *The Arithmetic Teacher*, vol. 4 (February 1957), pp. 10–12.

Risden, Gladys, "Meaning Is the Key," *The Arithmetic Teacher*, vol. 3 (November 1956), pp. 183–186.

The Revolution in School Mathematics. Washington, D.C.: The National Council of Teachers of Mathematics, 1961. (A Report of Regional Orientation Conferences in Mathematics.)

Van Engen, H., "Twentieth Century Mathematics for the Elementary Grades," *The Arithmetic Teacher*, vol. 6 (March 1959), pp. 71–76.

Weaver, J. Fred, "Misconceptions about Rationalization in Arithmetic," *The Mathematics Teacher*, vol. 44 (October 1951), pp. 377–381.

2

Mathematics: Systems of Concepts
of Quantity

2.1 MATHEMATICAL BEHAVIOR in REGARD to QUANTITY

In the *Eighteenth Yearbook* of the National Council of Teachers of Mathematics, we find the statement, "... if students are going to 'mathematick,' we must give them something to 'mathematick' about."[1] There is no dearth of things in the environment to provoke mathematical behavior. We are surrounded by things that we need to identify and to comprehend. Fulfilling this need is the very essence of mathematical behavior.

Anything that exists, exists in some form at some time, in some place, and in some amount. Identifying the things of concern and determining their amounts and their relationships with other things are activities that constantly demand our attention. To aid in those processes, we devise instruments and procedures. Often these are adopted by a group or by a society in general, and thus become conventionalized.

Among such conventionalized tools are number systems and devices for measuring form, size, position (location), and amount. Special languages are developed to express and communicate ideas and to describe practices concerning them. The tools and languages constitute a valuable social endowment which can be inherited only by the personal experience of each heir.

The basic ideas of mathematical behavior are initially quite simple and intuitive, but as they are developed and implemented they tend to lose those characteristics. Hence, it is important that we recognize

[1] National Council of Teachers of Mathematics, Eighteenth Yearbook, *Multi-Sensory Aids in the Teaching of Mathematics*. New York: Bureau of Publications, Teachers College, Columbia University, 1945, p. 2.

and utilize the simple behavior forms as a basis for the explanation of the complex mathematical practices. Any and all of the activities concerned with measurement may be termed "mathematicking" or "doing mathematics."

2.2   MATHEMATICAL PROCEDURES

Initially, mathematical behavior consists of observing things to identify them and to note their specific characteristics. When the process of identification is refined, procedures for extending and organizing this knowledge are evolved. As discussed in the sections that follow, identification, comparison, and measurement are the basic processes of mathematical behavior.

IDENTIFICATION

Once the observer senses that there is *some thing* to be concerned about, he will identify it only if it can be structured so that the part may be differentiated from the situation as a whole and thus identified in its own right. This can be done by observing differences between the thing as compared with the remainder of the situation.

For example, as one views a cloudless sky without an earth horizon or anything else to break the continuity of the sky, nothing stands out. The vista is unstructured by contrasts. There is homogeneity throughout. Now an airplane, a cloud, a bird, or some other object appears and alters the scene. Immediately a contrast is evident. A figure-ground relationship is experienced. The sameness of the sky is in contrast with the sensing of the object and by this means the object is sensed more clearly and identified.

COMPARISON

Having structured the situation so that both the part and the situation as a whole are identified, the learner proceeds to amplify and increase that awareness by discerning characteristics such as form, position, and amount. These processes, like the process of determining identity, involve a procedure of comparing, that is, of observing likeness and difference between things.

Referent-Relatum Technique

In making comparisons, the observer selects one object of concern as the basis for comparison. This is termed the *referent*. The thing which is compared with the referent is called the *relatum*. For example, the presence of something is compared with its absence; or, one thing is judged to be bigger or smaller, nearer or farther away, taller or shorter, and so forth, than is the referent thing with which it is compared. Comparative reference with modifiers expressing degrees of difference is used in such expressions as: "This is better than that," "John is taller than Jim," "A whale is not a fish," "Not all that glitters is gold." Taking care to observe references such as those in one's own expression and in the expression of others will disclose how commonly this referent-relatum technique is used.

While each person will select and use for this purpose things that have special pertinency for *him*, there is need to establish some standard referents for the measurement of such things as time, weight, and distance, which will be acceptable to, and utilized by, all persons within a particular society. This is of such importance that nations have established Bureaus of Standards to seek out proper referents and determine how they shall be used. The establishment of standard measure illustrates how a simple, native behavior process is developed, refined, and implemented so that it becomes a very complex but essential factor in one's personal and social behavior. Leading pupils in their development from highly personalized use of the referent-relatum technique to the skillful use of standard referents of their society is a responsibility of the teacher.

MEASUREMENT: a process of quantifying

Measurement is essentially a process of making comparisons. If the referent and relatum are judged to be equal, each may be used as the measure of the other. However, if they are unequal, the relatum may be structured into parts that are judged to be comparable to the referent, and the number of such parts may be noted. This is comparatively easy to do, when the relatum is easily structured, as for example, a set of books in which each book is visible, or a pile of blocks wherein the blocks are easily separable. All that is necessary for this type of measurement is to establish one-to-one correspondence with the referent (a single book or block) and note the recurrence of this matching.

The process is not so readily visualized when the relatum is a homogeneous unstructured object, as for example, a mass of water or a pile of sand. In such comparisons, amounts equivalent to the referent may be separated repeatedly from the relatum and compared as mentioned above, or measurement may be accomplished by a less direct procedure. For example, when we know how much space the relatum occupies and how much space the referent occupies, we may proceed to compare those space measurements and use that result as the measure of the relatum object expressed in the terms of the referent.

2.3   MATHEMATICAL FINDINGS

As noted in the preceding section, identification, comparison, and the refinement of comparison through measurement are the basic procedures of mathematical behavior. As we refine these procedures, we reach higher levels of mathematical thought: the analysis of constancy and variability, the study of the direction of the variation in quantity, and the interpretation of the relationships of function.

CONSTANCY AND VARIABILITY: basic comparative judgments

When the observer compares things, he senses that they are either alike or they are different. If the things compared are the same or are equal to the same thing, the basis for the concept of *equality* is present. This type of judgment gives rise to the use of the equation which makes possible many mathematical calculations. It also suggests that the like things be grouped together and quantified as to *how many* of such things are experienced.

When the things differ (when they are unlike or variable), the observer is stimulated to identify and to describe the nature and degree of difference. Following through on this type of discrimination leads one to develop ways for determining *how much* difference there is. This idea is the basis for interpretation of *inequalities*. The sentences below illustrate ideas of inequalities:

5 is greater than $2 + 2$	$5 > 2 + 2$
7 is less than $5 + 5$	$7 < 5 + 5$
3 plus 2 does not equal 4	$3 + 2 \neq 4$

DIRECTION

Describing the nature and degrees of variation often involves the idea of direction, an important mathematical concept. This idea is conceived very early in human development and is used extensively throughout life. The infant turns his head toward a stimulus of sound or light. Positional direction in space is experienced by everyone using himself as a referent and directionally locating other things as being in front of, behind, to the side, or above or below him. Direction in time is identified by using "now" (the present) as a referent and "not now" as an opposed period that is structured into positions such as "before now" or "later on."

The determination of a reference point to serve as a point of origin is an important *mathematical* accomplishment. For example, time is conceived as a continuum that is unstructured except by events which occur in association with it. Once an event in time is established as a reference point, all other points may be expressed in terms of their directional relationship to it; that is, as simultaneous in occurrence, or as prior to or after. When noon is selected as the directional referent, all other events may be expressed as before noon or after noon. There are many other common examples of reference points in time, including lunchtime, bedtime, schooltime, summertime, and sunrise.

Elevational direction is likewise a continuum which is commonly structured in a like manner. A point of origin such as ground floor or sea level is selected, and other positions described as above or below that place. Another familiar continuum is the temperature scale, wherein directional variation is described as being hotter or colder than the referent temperature selected.

There are very many uses of the directional idea in human behavior. For example, we write from left to right, and positional cues depict sub-grouping values within numerals. We commonly refer to movements as being clockwise or counterclockwise in direction. Locations on the earth are identified in terms of direction and distance from standard referent sources: the equator, prime meridian, or related lines of latitude and longitude. Many positional references, such as before-behind, above-below, inside-outside, and under-over, imply directional relationships.

FUNCTION: relationships of dependency

The range of mathematical concern is broader than just identifying things and quantifying them in terms of amount. We are concerned also with the nature of other relationships among things; we observe if things merely coexist or if there is an interrelationship among them.

If two things are interdependent, an "If . . . then" procedure may be used to describe their relationship. Simple illustrations are quite common:

"If Mother will let me, then I will come."

"If the servings are enlarged, then more food will be needed."

"If the barometer 'falls,' then a storm is forecast."

Similarly, ideas of dependence are basic to many computational procedures. For example, if the multiplicand is constant, then the numerical value of the product of multiplication depends directly upon the numerical value of the multiplier. We reason as follows: If $2 \times 4 = 8$, then $.2 \times 4 = .8$. The multiplier (.2) of the relatum example

$$2 \times 4 = 8 \quad \text{referent example}$$
$$.2 \times 4 = .8 \quad \text{relatum example}$$

represents a value that is 10 times as small as the value the multiplier of the referent example expresses. Hence, the product in the relatum example must be 10 times as small as the product in the referent example. A great deal of mathematicking involves this type of reasoning.

2.4   QUANTIFICATION: a SCALING of AMOUNT

The basic procedures of identification, comparison, and measurement normally lead to the need for the development and use of many types of referent units and for scales based on them. Many of these types are merely suggestive, for example, "flavor to taste." Others are somewhat more specific: "a pinch of salt." Still others have a substantial degree of exactness, as "a level teaspoon of sugar."

The calibration of a series of related but variable measurements is likewise commonly experienced. Being happy, for example, is distinguished from being very happy. That state is in turn rated differently from being very, very happy. Ratings such as these are presented in grammar as the positive, comparative, and superlative degrees expressed by modifiers. Such degrees of variance, while not based upon precise measurements, do suggest the need for a type of systematic calibration that makes possible a more exact scaling of respective amounts.

Satisfying the need for careful measurement and for precise quantification of the results has been a challenging problem in many fields of study. The selection of the proper referent unit for measuring is a very important matter. The referent unit must be representative of the thing that is to be measured. Time is measurable with a referent time-unit. Weight is measured by means of a unit of weight. Distance is measured in linear units. By tracing the history of linear measurement from the time when some physical feature of a person, such as the length of the king's arm, was used as a referent unit through the attempts to relate linear measures to a particular arc of a selected great circle of the earth to the present-day use of the wavelength, under standard conditions, of Krypton 86, we can get an idea of the general and continuous concern that is given to the selection of suitable referent units.

Having established a satisfactory unit, we then need to devise a calibrated scale for its use. Normally the *primary* graduations of such a scale will be measures equivalent to the basic referent unit. However, in many measurements there is need for establishing a comparable *secondary* referent, which is related in a prescribed manner to the primary referent. For example, if a linear inch is chosen as the referent unit for distance measurement, a more suitable secondary unit might be a foot unit

(12 inches), a yard unit (36 inches), a mile unit, or even a "light-year" when the measurement by miles becomes cumbersome. Each of the secondary referent units needs to bear a definite relationship to the primary unit. This procedure of primary calibration and secondary organization within such calibration is used over and over in the development and application of scaling devices.

Perhaps the most common and best calibrated of our scales is the counting number scale. That scale has the advantage of being abstract, that is, its referent unit deals only with the idea of oneness (specific identities). The ones may be anything that is of concern, such as a man, a tree, an inch, a drop of liquid, or merely the idea of a single entity. Unlike the other quantifying scales which are usable only in relation to the specific measures for which they are designed, the counting number scale is commonly incorporated within other scaling devices. Hence, an understanding of it and of the languages that are used in connection with it is a matter of considerable importance. Chapter 4 is specifically devoted to a discussion of systems of number and of numeration. In other chapters, some of the devices that extend the number scale idea for use in measurement are discussed.

ILLUSTRATIVE LESSONS

The following illustrative lessons and lesson plans are presented in this chapter:

Lesson 1. Size

Lesson 2. Starting point in a circle

Lesson 3. Basic points of origin

Lesson 4. Concepts concerning dependency and standard measures

Lesson 5. Establishing and using known measurements as standards of reference

Lesson 6. Using known measurements as standards of reference for estimating other measurements

Lesson 7. Some procedures suggested for teaching concepts concerning size, shape, weight, position, time, temperature, space, and so forth

Lesson 8. Measuring temperature

Lesson 1 illustrates the nature of the young child's sensing, hypothesizing, and formulating concepts of size. Concepts of how much, how many, how big, how small, and how given things are alike and how they are different are used extensively in the conversation of young children. "He couldn't be the same size! What if he *had just one hair out*, he'd be different!" Such statements illustrate the child's interest in precision with small amounts.

Lessons 2 and 3 indicate children's concepts concerning zero as a point of origin. Many experiences of the type described occur in all subject areas. The concept of zero as a point of origin in measuring temperature, annual time, elevation, latitude, and longitude are a few of the many examples. In Lesson 2, the children discussed the starting point and the position of up and of down on a ball. It is evident that they sensed the need for agreement concerning points of origin. They were in a position to develop keen insight and appreciation concerning points of origin that lead to the type of understanding indicated in the statements from the class in Lesson 3.

Lesson 4 gives procedures through which the children evolved ideas concerning dependency and standard measures. Christina's statement expresses interpretation of the concept of dependency. "Big may be small or big may be big! It is big or small — whichever you want — by having a bigger or a smaller glass to use [for comparison]."

Lessons 5 and 6 indicate procedures through which children established and used known measurements as standards of reference. Developing familiar, known measurements such as the ones that these children developed is an important part of mathematics in the elementary school.

Lesson 7 is a list of procedures for teaching concepts with regard for quantity in various grades.

In Lesson 8, the teacher challenged the children to sense the need for establishing points of reference for measuring temperature.

Lesson 1
SIZE[2]
Nursery School Level

Adult: Are all Saint Bernards the same size?
Child: Yes. Well, they're big.
Adult: Very big!
Child: Yes! I guess this big. [Showed with arms.]
Adult: Is every Saint Bernard exactly that big?
Child: No! [Laughter.] They're somewhere about that big; it depends.
Adult: On what?
Child: If he's a baby, he's little. Or if he's a big Saint Bernard or not.
Comment from a five-year-old child standing nearby: Or if it's hot and he's had his hair all cut off.
[At this, there was excitement evident in the behavior of the first boy.]

---

[2] Mary B. Pieters, "A Study of Early Childhood Behavior Evidencing Awareness of Quantity," an unpublished study.

Child: He couldn't be the same size! What if he *had just one hair out*, he'd be different!

Lesson 2
STARTING POINT IN A CIRCLE
Grade Two Class

A group of children had formed a ring to play a game in which they needed to number off. There was need for identifying which person should be number one.

Teacher: Who is at the beginning of the circle?

Sarah: What a question! You're teasing us!

Jimmie: We are all at the beginning.

Keith: No one is at the beginning.

Jimmie: No one is last.

Teacher: If we agree to let Dick be first, who would be last?

Marie: I would! I'm next to first. That's funny. Last is usually last and not next to first!

[Teacher had a ball ready for the circle game.]

Martin marked "U" for "up" on the ball.

Teacher: Where is up on this ball?

Martin: Here. [He pointed to the side that faced toward the ceiling.]

Teacher: Here is a piece of chalk. Mark a letter U for up. [Martin marked U for up.]

Teacher: If this is up, where is down?

Robert: It would be right under up. I'll mark it. [Robert marked a D for down.]

[Teacher threw the ball to Jimmie.]

Jerry: It didn't land the right way. Now U isn't up and D isn't down.

Teacher: Do you think that there is any up or any down on the ball unless we agree where we want up and down to be on it?

Sarah: No. It is just like our circle. No one is first unless we agree to agree.

Lesson 3
BASIC POINTS OF ORIGIN
Grade Six Class

The children in Mr. B's room had discussed ideas concerning using points of origin to serve as reference points for naming and measuring things. They had keen insight and appreciation for man's agreement concerning points of origin. After the discussion, a problem-solving activity followed in which the children illustrated and described examples in which they sensed that agreement concerning a point of origin existed. The children worked out their ideas independently. In many cases, they kept the things that they were doing a surprise until the period for presentation. The ideas were shared and discussed at a later period. Then the children arranged a bulletin board for their classroom in which the materials were exhibited. The following are some of the ideas that were illustrated and developed for the bulletin board:

(1) Sea level as a point of origin for measuring altitude
(2) Middle C on the piano for measuring to the right and to the left of the keyboard
(3) Zero for decimal notation — negative and positive values
(4) Home as a point of origin for measuring "here" to "there" (school, for instance)
(5) Our city as "here" to measure distances to other places
(6) Football field
(7) Exponential notation
(8) "Off" on the scale to measure heat on the dial of an electric stove
(9) Zero degrees latitude and zero degrees longitude
(10) Units' position to measure other positions
(11) Birth of Christ for measuring time — A.D. and B.C.
(12) Twelve o'clock midnight for measuring days (24-hour clock)
(13) Twelve o'clock noon to measure A.M. and P.M.

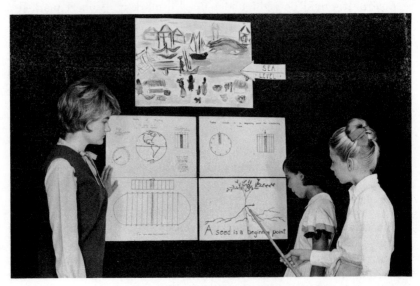

There are many points of origin.

Middle C is a beginning point on the piano keyboard.

Lesson 4
CONCEPTS CONCERNING DEPENDENCY
AND STANDARD MEASURES
Grade One Class

This was a lesson on concepts with regard to size (large, medium, small), estimation of amount, and procedures for measuring.

Lesson Procedure

The group had been discussing what they meant by a large glass, a small glass, and a medium-sized glass. They had brought many glasses and cups to show what they meant by a "glassful" and a "cupful." The teacher selected 3 of their glasses that were of 3 different sizes.

Teacher: When we talk about these 3 glasses, how would you tell about their sizes? What would you call this one? [Teacher held up largest of the 3 glasses.]

Class: The large one.

Teacher: What would you call this one? [Teacher held up smallest glass.]

Class: The small one.

Teacher: What would you call this one? [Teacher held up medium-sized glass.]

Class: The middle-sized one. [Possibly from the story of *The Three Bears.*]

[Teacher selected a much larger glass to compare with the "large glass" of the former group of glasses.]

Teacher: Now which is the larger glass?

Class: [Pointing to the larger glass] That one.

Donald: When you get a larger one, the big one (meaning glass which was largest previously) gets little.

Paul: Yes, big becomes little. . . . May I get the glass I brought? [Paul got the glass that he had brought. His glass was much larger than the last one classified as "large."]

Paul: Now, your glass is small and mine is large.

Teacher: What makes a large glass "large"? And, what makes a small glass "small"?

Christina: Big may be small or big may be big! It is big or small — whichever you want — by having a bigger or a smaller glass to use.

Teacher: We have brought many cups to school. How do we know what people mean when they say a "cupful"?

Paul: It means the cup must be full to the top.

Richard: When my mother bakes cookies, she uses a measuring cup.

It has marks on it, and when it is full, Mother says that it is one cupful.

Jimmy: My mother has a measuring cup, too.

Class: [A general agreement that a measuring cup is used by Mother.]

Jimmy: When I have a cup of cocoa, we don't use a measuring cup. I say that I have a cupful of cocoa, but it's not a measuring cup full of cocoa.

Teacher: Why do you think that Mother uses a measuring cup when she cooks?

Jean: Because other cups are all different sizes, and measuring cups are all the same size.

Tommy: Do you think they are, Jean?

Jean: Yes, my mother said that a measuring "cupful" was a real "cupful," and I think that all measuring cups hold the same.

Teacher: How could we find out if Jean is right?

Norman: We could bring a measuring cup from home. If all of us bring a cup, then we could use water and see if all of the cups hold the same amount of water. I know that my mother will let me bring a measuring cup. She has 2 of them.

Christina: I know that I can bring a measuring cup. We have a big one that holds more than a "cupful." I'll show you.

Donald: I know that I can bring one, too.

Class: [General consensus of opinion was that measuring cups could be brought, and there was much interest in the activity!]

Teacher: Would you like to put your measuring cups on our table of things that we have to help us measure? I suggest that you have your mother put a piece of tape with your name on it on your cup so that you won't get your cup mixed up with other people's cups.

The following day a number of measuring cups (one-cup and two-cup sizes) were brought to school. Much measuring was done preceding generalizations concerning a standard cup.

Lesson 5
ESTABLISHING AND USING
KNOWN MEASUREMENTS AS STANDARDS
OF REFERENCE
Grade Three Class — Section of a Lesson from a Discussion Period

Purpose of lesson: To stimulate the children to establish and to use known measurements to estimate other measurements.

Background of children: The children had established many known measures as reference standards for estimation of other measurements.

They had evolved procedures for such comparisons and were excellent "estimators."

Lesson Procedure

[The children had completed a story about animals and were discussing the sizes of animals that they had read about.]

Mary: That was interesting about blue whales. They are surely immense.

Tim: I'll say! It said in our book that some blue whales are more than 100 feet long.

Teacher: How long is that?

Tim: It's very long — a lot longer than this room.

Helen: I bet it is as long as our school building.

Teacher: What could you measure that would help you picture 100 feet?

Terry: I suggest we measure our hall. It is more than 3 times the length of our room because there are 3 classrooms that go into the hall.

Mary: That's a good idea. We measured our room. It was about 25 feet long. I'll measure the hall at recess. Have you a steel tape measure that we can use?

Terry: I'll measure it, too. I'll help you, Mary.

[At recess time, the two girls measured the length of the hall and found that it was approximately 100 feet in length (96 feet), and the length of the hall became an established familiar measurement to use for comparison with unfamiliar measurements.]

The next example was about how tall the elephant in the story was.

James: That is very high. That is about as high as this room.

Tom: Yes. This room is about 11 feet high. We measured it and found that it was a little over 11 feet from the floor to the ceiling.

Lesson 6
USING KNOWN MEASUREMENTS AS STANDARDS
OF REFERENCE FOR ESTIMATING OTHER
MEASUREMENTS
Grade Four Class

This grade four class had measured many things in their environment. The following list tells some of the things that they had measured and used as standards of reference for estimation of other quantities.

Height of classroom door — 6' 8"
Width of classroom door — 3'
Height of classroom (floor to ceiling) — 11'

Length of classroom — 26′

Height of ledge near windows — 2′ 6″

Height of their teacher — 5′ 2″

Distance from school to main avenue — about 1 mile

Sizes of paper — 8½″ × 11″ (scratch paper for doing schoolwork)

18″ × 24″ and 12″ × 18″ (paper for art work)

6″ × 9″ (scratch paper for doing schoolwork)

Cards for making book reports — 5″ × 8″

3″ × 5″

Height of school building — 35′

Span — distance from end of thumb to end of little finger when hand is stretched out. Each child had measured his span, and knew about how many inches it was.

Lesson 7

SOME PROCEDURES SUGGESTED FOR TEACHING CONCEPTS CONCERNING SIZE, SHAPE, WEIGHT, POSITION, TIME, TEMPERATURE, SPACE

1. Lead the learner to formulate basic concepts that underlie measurement. Children should develop concepts concerning what to compare and how to compare. Ideas of how and what to compare lead to techniques for comparing, measuring, evaluating, expressing, and interpreting quantitative relationships. Experimentation and investigation of problems such as the following offer opportunities for developing concepts underlying measurement.

(a) How shall we measure these things? (Length of room, distance around a cylindrical can, distance from home to school, and so on)

(b) Do we need to agree on the device (measuring stick) that we use to do our measuring? Why?

(c) What units for measurement are used?

(d) Which measuring device shall we use to measure these things? (Temperature, length of hall)

(e) Do we need to decide upon a starting point to measure these things? (To run a race, to measure who is first in a circle game)

(f) How small is small? How big is big?

(g) Is there *small* without *large*? Is there *in* without *out*? Could there be *down* if there were no *up*?

(h) What is the direction of change? (Increase or decrease, up or down, north or south)

Using procedures for measuring, evolving concepts underlying measurement, and achieving intelligent interpretation of measurement

372.7 Sp3b

are very significant parts of mathematics in the elementary school.

2. Have the child measure with nonstandardized instruments — sticks, string, paper, boards, branches — so that he senses the need for, and appreciation of, standard measures.

When the child is handed yardsticks, foot rulers, and common devices for measuring and told to measure things, he may achieve skill in using them. However, mere skill in using measuring devices may not challenge the child to sense concepts underlying procedures for measuring and basic concepts of relationship. It is well to have the child use other than standard measures for several lessons. Through such lessons, the child will meet the problem of need for agreement concerning which measure is to be used for measuring a given thing, how to divide his measuring stick to express units of it, and so forth.

3. After the child has used nonstandardized things for measuring, lead him to use standard measuring devices. The child should have much experience in using yardsticks, foot rulers, cups, pints, quarts, scales, and the other standard measuring devices. These experiences should grow out of many of his activities throughout the day.

4. Have the learner develop given measurements with which he is familiar so that he can use them to compare and estimate the measurement of given things whose quantity he does not know. Developing familiar, known measurements such as the length of the classroom, the height of the classroom door, the distance of a mile, the width of one's hand, the distance from home to school, and the capacity of a quart jar are important references for estimation of quantities unfamiliar to the child. Many known measurements for estimating unknown quantities should be developed and used by each group of children studying mathematics in the elementary school.

5. Lead the learner to sense, understand, and appreciate man's ingenuity in measuring through development of a brief, simple historical treatment of some familiar measures. Development can evolve through having the child sense the problems that faced his forefathers and challenging him to recommend procedures for dealing with *what* and *how* to measure. The following illustrations are examples:

(a) If you lived alone on an island and had no watch, no clock, and no radio, how could you tell time?
(b) Could you use a log of wood and a piece of charcoal to help you tell time?
(c) If you had no thermometer, how could you judge hot and cold?
(d) Do you think that man did a good job in developing our number system? Why?
(e) Do you think that man could have improved anything in making our decimal system of notation? How?

6. Have the child estimate measurements of given things and then check his estimate through actual measurement. Good estimating of quantitative value is the product of many experiences of comparing known quantitative values with quantitative values that are unknown and of evaluating one's estimate through actual measurement. With skill in teaching, children become astute in estimation. As college students who observe children often note: "How are children able to do such fine estimating? We adults are older, but the children are better estimators than we are."

7. Have the child measure to determine basic quantitative relationships such as the following:

> foot-yard relationship
> pint-quart-gallon relationship
> diameter-circumference relationship
> side-perimeter relationship of a square
> length-width-perimeter relationship of
>   a rectangle (other than a square)
> time-speed-distance relationship
> size-capacity relationship (for example,
>   width, length, and height of container
>   as related to its capacity)
> unit of measure-area relationship

The teacher who challenges the child to sense, to discover, to understand, and to interpret such relationships releases the child to achieve a high level of competency in mathematics. Procedures such as these are the foundation of the thrill of learning and the thrill of teaching mathematics.

Lesson 8
MEASURING TEMPERATURE
Grade Three Class — Section of a Lesson on Measurement

Purpose of lesson: To stimulate the children to think about the nature of measurement and procedures for measurement, and to appreciate man's ingenuity in measuring his universe.

Background of children: The children had been stimulated to interpret many concepts with regard for measurement, and this section of the lesson was part of their study of measurement.

Lesson Procedure

Teacher: We have been studying about measuring things. If you had been born long ago, and if man had not invented ways to measure, what do you think you would have known about measurement?

Tommy: Not as much as we know now. We know much more than early man.

Teacher: What things do we measure in this room that you wouldn't have been able to measure as we do?

Susanna: Time. We use a clock.

Tommy: Temperature. We have a thermometer.

Marjorie: Maps. Early man didn't know about the world.

Elizabeth: Light. We use electric lights, and we measure electricity. [Many things were named, and the teacher directed the discussion toward specific things that had been named.]

Teacher: How would you have measured temperature?

Billy: By hot and cold and lukewarm.

Marian: By the way you liked your food — warm or cold.

Denny: If you lived where it was cold in winter, you might have called ice very cold.

Billy: Fire is very hot.

Jerry: So are hot peppers. Some of them are very hot — too hot for me.

Teacher: What are some things that man had to agree upon to measure temperature?

Keith: He had to decide what was hot and what was cold.

Denny: Ice is cold. It is a good way to measure cold.

Teacher: That is a very good point. What do you think would be a good way to measure hot?

Kenneth: Fire. Fire is hot.

Denny: That would be hard to measure. Sometimes fire is very, very hot. When we have a fire in our fireplace, at first it isn't very hot. After the wood has burned and there are coals, they are really hot.

Teacher: Can you suggest a way to use water to measure hot?

Keith: When the water boils.

Class: That is a good way to tell hot water.

Teacher: Man had to decide upon some substance to use to measure temperature. He observed changes in water — water frozen to ice, ice melting, water boiling — and he decided to use water to measure changes in temperature. The freezing point and the boiling point of water were used.

Frances: But how did he decide to use a thermometer?

Teacher: He didn't invent a thermometer until he had experimented with many things.

Denny: Could we experiment with hot and cold and measure temperature?

Teacher: Would you like to study about measuring temperature and construct a thermometer? We can do it in your science class.

Class: Yes, I want to find out how a thermometer works.

[The study of temperature was continued in the science period.]

Discussion Questions

1. What is implied by the statement we must give students something to "mathematics about?"

2. List and describe briefly some comparisons that you make that do not require the use of specific number.

3. To what do the terms "referent" and "relatum" refer? Cite instances of your use of referents in your everyday behavior.

4. What are some "standard referents" which you commonly use? How would our society function without the use of accepted referents?

5. List some referents for making comparisons that are not "standard" referents.

6. What is the work of our Federal Bureau of Standards? What agencies of your local government are directly concerned with referent standards and their application?

7. What would life be like if one experienced no inequalities?

8. How do you distinguish between measurements of "how many" as compared with measurements of "how much?"

9. The idea of direction has many applications in human behavior. Cite some uses that you make of it. Be on the lookout for other uses.

10. The idea of causal relationship, that is, dependence, needs careful consideration. Give instances where you have used it effectively in your behavior. What does "independence" imply?

11. Explain why the selection of a referent unit for measurement is important. How does the system of scaling affect the usability of a system of measurement?

Suggested Readings

Adler, Irving, *The New Mathematics.* New York: The John Day Company, Inc., 1958.

Baumgartner, Margery, "The Littlest Mathematician, An Approach Applicable at All Levels," *The Arithmetic Teacher,* vol. 5 (April 1958), pp. 131–136.

Breslich, E. R., "Teaching Mathematics as a System of Understandings," *The Mathematics Teacher,* vol. 42 (January 1949), pp. 61–66.

Brown, Kenneth E., Walter H. Carnahan, Rolland R. Smith, Veryl Schult, and Daniel W. Snader, "Promoting the Continuous Growth of Mathematical Concepts," *The Growth of Mathematical Ideas, Grades K–12,* National Council of Teachers of Mathematics, Twenty-fourth Yearbook. Washington, D.C.: The Council, 1959, pp. 431–498.

Brownell, William A., and G. Hendricksen, "How Children Learn Information, Concepts and Generalizations," *Learning and Instruction,* National Society for the Study of Education, Forty-ninth Yearbook, Part I. Chicago, Ill.: University of Chicago Press, 1950, pp. 92–128.

Court, S. R. A., "Numbers, Time and Space in the First Five Years of the Child's Life," *Pedagogical Seminary,* vol. 27 (March 1920), pp. 71–89.

Deans, Edwina, "Arithmetic in the Primary Grades," *The National Elementary Principal,* vol. 39 (October 1959), pp. 22–28.

Douglas, Harl, and Herbert F. Spitzer, "The Importance of Teaching for Understanding," *The Measurement of Understanding,* National Society for the Study of Education, Forty-fifth Yearbook. Chicago, Ill.: University of Chicago Press, 1946, pp. 7–25.

Eads, Laura K., "Teaching Mathematics in the Kindergarten," *Grade Teacher*, vol. 26 (October 1958), pp. 134–135.

Enrichment Mathematics for the Grades, The National Council of Teachers of Mathematics, Twenty-seventh Yearbook. Washington, D.C.: The Council, 1963, 368 pp.

Fehr, Howard F., "A Philosophy of Arithmetic Instruction," *The Arithmetic Teacher*, vol. 2 (April 1955), pp. 27–32.

Gibb, E. Glenadine, "Some Approaches to Mathematics Concepts in the Elementary School," *Journal of the National Education Association*, vol. 48 (November 1959), pp. 65–66.

Harrison, M. Lucille, "Nature and Development of Concepts of Time among Young Children," *Elementary School Journal*, vol. 34 (March 1934), pp. 507–514.

Hartung, Maurice L., "Distinguishing between Basic and Superficial Ideas in Arithmetic Instruction," *The Arithmetic Teacher*, vol. 6 (March 1959), pp. 65–70.

Hogben, Lancelot, "The Grammar of Size, Order, and Number or Translating Number Language," *Mathematics for the Million*. New York: W. W. Norton & Company, Inc., 1950, Chap. 3.

Johnson, Donovan, and H. C. Trimble, "Evaluation of Mathematical Meanings and Understandings," *Emerging Practices in Mathematical Education*, The National Council of Teachers of Mathematics, Twenty-second Yearbook. Washington, D.C.: The Council, 1954, pp. 343–355.

Junge, Charlotte W., "Depth Learning in Arithmetic — What Is It?" *The Arithmetic Teacher*, vol. 7 (November 1960), pp. 341–346.

Lovell, K., *The Growth of Basic Mathematical and Scientific Concepts in Children*. London: University of London Press, 1961.

Maier, Norman R. F., "Reasoning in Children," *Journal of Comparative Psychology*, vol. 21 (June 1936), pp. 357–366.

Mother Constance Dooley, "The Relationship between Arithmetic Research and the Content of Arithmetic Textbooks," *The Arithmetic Teacher*, vol. 7 (April 1960), p. 179.

Piaget, Jean, *The Child's Conception of Number*. New York: The Humanities Press, 1952.

Piaget, Jean, *Judgment and Reasoning in the Child*. Translated by Marjorie Warden. New York: Harcourt, Brace & World, Inc., 1928.

Polya, G., *How To Solve It*. New York: Doubleday Anchor Books, 1957.

Risden, G., "Knowing Is More Than Saying," *Instructor*, vol. 58 (October 1949), pp. 25ff.

Russell, Ned M., "Arithmetic Concepts of Children," *Journal of Educational Research*, vol. 29 (May 1936), pp. 647–663.

Swenson, Esther J., "Arithmetic for Preschool and Primary Grade Children," *The Teaching of Arithmetic*, National Society for the Study of Education, Fiftieth Yearbook, Part II. Chicago, Ill.: University of Chicago Press, 1951, pp. 53–75.

Syer, Henry W., "Sensory Learning Applied to Mathematics," *The Learning of Mathematics, Its Theory and Practice*, The National Council of Teachers of Mathematics, Twenty-first Yearbook. Washington, D.C.: The Council, 1953, pp. 99–155.

Thiele, C. L., "Arithmetic in the Middle Grades," *The Teaching of Arithmetic*, National Society for the Study of Education, Fiftieth Yearbook, Part II. Chicago, Ill.: University of Chicago Press, 1951, pp. 76–102.

Van Engen, Henry, "The Formation of Concepts," The National Council of Teachers of Mathematics, Twenty-first Yearbook. Washington, D.C.: The Council, 1953, pp. 69–98.

Worchester, D. A., "Memory by Visual and by Auditory Presentation," *Journal of Educational Psychology*, vol. 16 (1925), pp. 18–27.

3
Sets: Relationships among Collections

3.1 INTRODUCTION

"While it is conceivable that an adequate mathematical text could be written without using the word 'set,' it could not be written without using the concept."[1]

Recent discussion of the teaching of mathematics has given much attention to ideas of sets. The term *set* is used to designate "any collection of numbers, objects, or ideas so well-described that we can tell readily whether or not any item is a member of the set."[2]

As defined, the idea of sets is characteristic of much of human behavior. Differentiating between what a thing *is* and what it *is not* is essential to the process of identification and classification. The grouping of things into sets on the basis of selective criteria is a common activity. Many terms in our language such as *bunch, flock, covey, class, company, herd, gang, group, team, club,* and *bevy,* have connotations that are similar to that of the term *set*. It is common practice to establish a set of rules for conduct, to compile and examine a set of facts before forming conclusions, to assemble a set of tools needed in the performance of a task, or to group things into sets or categories according to some definite pattern.

The idea of sets and of relationships among sets is not new. What is new, however, is a precise and rigorous method of representing ideas concerning sets. This point is brought out very well in a recent publication from the Office for Scientific and Technical Personnel as may be noted in the following quotation:

[1] Advisory Committee, *The "Strands" Report of the Advisory Committee on Mathematics to the State Curriculum Commission*, California, March 8, 1962, p. 16.

[2] Edith J. Woodward and Roderick C. McLennan, *Elementary Concepts of Sets.* New York: Holt, Rinehart and Winston, Inc., 1959, p. 1.

"It is to be observed that the theory of sets sharpens many concepts of mathematics that are under consideration in these early years, and can best be used in the formulation of mathematical theories. For example, at the elementary level, the set of numerals, the set of integers,

Jim matched children and pebbles.

the set of even numbers, the set of fractions between 3 and 4, the set of numbers greater than 13. Set 'vocabulary' can be used even at an early stage in geometry where we speak of the set of points of a line, the set of points within a circle, the set of right triangles, the set of lines perpendicular to a given line either in a plane or in space.

"From the very beginning of instruction in mathematics, the teacher should see to it that students acquire, by their own effort, an understanding of the concept of 'set,' building largely upon examples that they have encountered in their social life, their experiences at school and in the world about them. In this manner, students will be taken into the confidence of the teacher, and will become active participants in an adventure in the learning of concepts for which the field of application transcends the boundaries of mathematics."[3]

There is need for teachers to become familiar with what is being proposed concerning the teaching of ideas of sets. In order to discuss some of the ideas of sets, it is necessary to identify the things and symbols that are being considered.

[3] Organization for European Economic Co-Operation, *Synopses for Modern Secondary School Mathematics*. Office for Scientific and Technical Personnel, Paris, 1961, p. 15.

3.2   SOME SYMBOLS and DEFINITIONS USED to EXPRESS IDEAS of SETS

Special sets of symbols have been devised to express succinctly and clearly the ideas of sets and relationships among sets. In Table 3.1, some of the simple and necessary definitions are given and illustrated. In the column at the far left, the term is presented in common language; in the second column is a definition of the term. Examples of the idea are given in the third column; the idea is expressed in language of sets in the fourth column; and comments concerning the symbols are given in the last column.

The table was designed for reference and to facilitate the reader's interpretation of the terms commonly used to discuss the topic of sets. The sections of the chapter following Table 3.1 bring out the meanings that are summarized therein.

3.3   SET DIAGRAMS

DIAGRAMMATIC TECHNIQUES

Diagrams or pictograms are often used to present ideas concerning sets. These are usually referred to as *Venn diagrams* in which a rectangle is used to depict the universal set that is being considered, and circles are used to represent the given sets within the universal set. The relative size of the circles and rectangles does not indicate the size or number of elements of the sets.

Another diagrammatic technique is that of shading the portion that is under special consideration. For example, Fig. 3.1 shows a

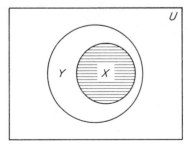

Fig. 3.1

universal set with Set Y a subset, and with Set X a subset first of Set Y and secondly of Set U. In the figure, $U = 50$ states of the United States; $Y =$ New England states; and $X =$ the state of Maine. X is identified by means of shading.

TABLE 3.1 SETS AND RELATIONSHIPS AMONG SETS

TERM	DEFINITION	EXAMPLE	LANGUAGE OF SETS	COMMENTS ON SET LANGUAGE
1. SET	The term *set* refers to a collection, group, or class of things so well defined that one may readily determine what things are included as well as what things are excluded from its membership.	The digits that we use to write whole numbers. The voters who cast ballots in a given precinct.	$A = \{0, 1, 2, 3, 4, 5, 6, 7, 8, 9\}$ $B = \{$persons who voted in a specified precinct$\}$	Sets are commonly designated by capital letters. What the set includes is enclosed within braces.
2. ELEMENTS OR MEMBERS	The members or elements of a set consist of the things that are included within it.			
(a) Identified by Rule	The members or elements of a set may be identified by a general description of them.	The set of digits used in the decimal system.	$A = \{$digits used for decimal numeration$\}$	The set is described when its members are identified by the rule procedure.
(b) Identified by Roster or Naming	The members or elements of a set may be named individually.	The digits for decimal numeration are 0, 1, 2, 3, 4, 5, 6, 7, 8, and 9.	$A = \{0, 1, 2, 3, 4, 5, 6, 7, 8, 9\}$	When the roster or naming procedure is used, individual members of the set are listed.
(c) Element Membership	An element may be identified as belonging to a given set.	9 is a member of Set A when Set A consists of the digits used for decimal notation.	$9 \in A$	The symbol $\in$ is used to indicate that a particular member belongs to a given set.

TABLE 3.1   SETS AND RELATIONSHIPS AMONG SETS (Continued)

TERM	DEFINITION	EXAMPLE	LANGUAGE OF SETS	COMMENTS ON SET LANGUAGE
3. KINDS OF SETS	Sets are classified in many ways.			
(a) Equal or Identical Sets	Two or more sets having the same membership. The order in which the members are listed does not matter.	One set contains the numerals 10, 25, and 50. The other set contains the numerals 50, 25, and 10.	$A = \{10, 25, 50\}$ $B = \{50, 25, 10\}$ $A = B$	$A = B$ indicates that Set A has exactly the same elements as Set B.
(b) Equivalent Sets	Two or more sets that have a one-to-one correspondence in terms of number of members. The sets are *numerically* equivalent.	The members of Set A are a ball, a doll, and a book. Set B contains a pen, a car, and a truck.	$A = \{$doll, ball, book$\}$ $\updownarrow\ \ \ \updownarrow\ \ \ \updownarrow$ $B = \{$pen, car, truck$\}$ $C \sim B$ or $A \leftrightarrow B$	Each element of Set A is matched with an element in Set B. An arrow indicates the matching of elements. $A \leftrightarrow B$ or $A \sim B$ are two ways of indicating that Set A is numerically equivalent to Set B.
(c) Nonequivalent Sets	Sets that are not matched in one-to-one correspondence in terms of the number of members.	The members of Set C are a cat and a dog. The members of set D are a horse, a dog, and a wolf.	$C = \{$dog, cat$\}$ $D = \{$horse, dog, wolf$\}$	Set C and Set D are nonequivalent sets. They cannot be matched in one-to-one correspondence.
(d) Null or Empty Set	Any of many situations expressed by the number idea of "not any."	The countries of Europe that border the Pacific Ocean.	$C = \{\ \}$ or ϕ	The symbol, ϕ, is used to indicate the empty or null set. Braces without anything enclosed are another way to indicate the empty set.

TABLE 3.1 SETS AND RELATIONSHIPS AMONG SETS (Continued)

TERM	DEFINITION	EXAMPLE	LANGUAGE OF SETS	COMMENTS ON SET LANGUAGE
(e) Unit Set	A set consisting of a single item.	The earth's natural satellite.	B = {Earth's moon}	The earth has only one natural satellite, the moon.
(f) Finite Set	A set having a limited number of elements.	The set of states of the United States that borders on the Pacific Ocean.	A = {Alaska, Hawaii, Washington, Oregon, California}	The states of the United States that border the Pacific Ocean may be identified by describing them or by naming them as indicated in the column at the left.
(g) Infinite Set	A set having unlimited or an indeterminate number of elements.	The points on a line	A = {points on a line}	Set A is termed infinite set because there is an infinite number of points in a line.
(h) Universal Set	The specific collections or class of things being considered is referred to as the *universal set*. The universal set varies from problem to problem depending on what one wishes to have it include.	The 50 states composing the United States of America.	U = {50 states of the United States}	The capital letter U is used to indicate the universal set.
(i) Complementary Set	A complementary set contains all of the elements in the universal set other than those in the given set or sets.	The univeral set is all four-legged animals. Set A is all dogs. The complementary set consists of all four-legged animals other than dogs.	U = {all four-legged animals} A = {all dogs} A' = {all four-legged animals other than dogs}	U stands for the universal set. A stands for the given set. A' stands for the complementary set.

TABLE 3.1 SETS AND RELATIONSHIPS AMONG SETS (Continued)

TERM	DEFINITION	EXAMPLE	LANGUAGE OF SETS	COMMENTS ON SET LANGUAGE
(j) Disjoint Sets	Disjoint sets are two or more sets that have no elements in common.	Set A consists of the 12 boys in the class. Set B consists of the 15 girls in the class.	$A = \{12 \text{ boys}\}$ $B = \{15 \text{ girls}\}$	Sets A and B have no elements in common. They are called disjoint sets. See p. 39 for illustrating disjoint sets with diagrams.
(k) Intersecting or Overlapping Sets	The intersecting or overlapping of two sets is the set of all elements that are common to the two sets.	Set A contains the letters a, s, and k. Set B contains the letters a, r, and m. The letter a is common to both sets.	Set $A = \{a, s, k\}$ Set $B = \{a, r, m\}$ $A \cap B = \{a\}$	The symbol for the intersection of two sets is $\cap$. It is sometimes referred to as a "cap."
(l) Subset	A subset consists of a collection of elements all of which are members of the given universal set. When all of the elements of the universal set are considered, it, too, is considered a subset.	Set A consists of a dime, a nickel, and a penny. A dime is a subset of Set A. A nickel is a subset of Set A, and so forth.	$A = \{$a dime, a nickel, a penny$\}$ $B = \{$a dime$\}$ $C = \{$a nickel$\}$ $D = \{$a penny$\}$	Subgroupings of all or some of the elements within a given set are called subsets of that given set. All of the possible subsets of Set A are listed below under "proper subsets" and "improper subsets."

TABLE 3.1 SETS AND RELATIONSHIPS AMONG SETS (Concluded)

TERM	DEFINITION	EXAMPLE	LANGUAGE OF SETS	COMMENTS ON SET LANGUAGE
(1) Improper subsets	By convention, the set that includes all members of a given set is considered an improper subset of that set. Similarly, the null set is considered an improper subset of every nonempty set.	The set of coins consisted of a dime, a nickel, and a penny. Jill had a dime, a penny, and a nickel. Jill had a full or complete set of coins. Bill did not have a nickel, a penny, or a dime. He had an empty set of these coins.	$A = \{$a dime, a penny, a nickel$\}$ The improper subsets for Set A are: $B = \{$a dime, a penny, a nickel$\}$ $C = \phi$	The original set is counted as an improper subset. The null set is an improper subset.
(2) Proper subsets	A proper subset is a subset that is less than the set itself.	The set of coins consisted of a dime, a nickel, and a penny. The following combinations of coins that are proper subsets may be made: a nickel; a penny; a dime; a nickel and a penny; a nickel and a dime; a penny and a dime	Given: The set consists of a dime, a penny, a nickel $D = \{$a dime$\}$ $E = \{$a penny$\}$ $F = \{$a nickel$\}$ $G = \{$a dime, a penny$\}$ $H = \{$a dime, a nickel$\}$ $I = \{$a penny, a nickel$\}$	The symbol, $\subset$ is used to indicate "is a proper subset of." The open part of the symbol faces toward the larger set. $G \subset A$ means G is a proper subset of A. $B \not\subset A$ means B is not a proper subset of A.

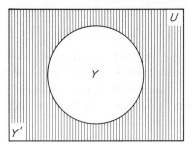

Fig. 3.2

In Fig. 3.2 the *complementary set* is shaded. Here U = the set of counting numbers; Y = the set of even numbers; and Y' = the set of all decimal integers with the exception of the set of even numbers. The complement of Set Y is shown as Y'. It is a set relative to the universal set and includes all of the elements of the universal set except those in Set Y. Thus, it includes all counting numbers that are considered odd numbers.

TYPES OF RELATIONSHIPS

Three main types of relationships among sets are diagramed in Figs. 3.3, 3.4, and 3.5.

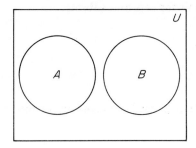

Fig. 3.3 Disjoint sets.

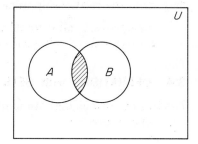

Fig. 3.4 Overlapping sets.

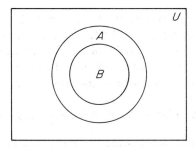

Fig. 3.5 B is a subset of A.

1. Disjoint Sets

When two sets have no elements in common, they are termed *disjoint sets*. In Fig. 3.3, the universal set $U = \{$all states of the United States$\}$; $A = \{$Pacific Coast states$\}$; and $B = \{$Atlantic Coast states$\}$. Sets A and B have no states in common. The sets are disjoint sets; therefore the circles do not touch each other.

2. Overlapping or Intersecting Sets

If two or more sets have elements in common, the set of such common elements is termed the intersecting or overlapping set. The part that is shaded in Fig. 3.4 indicates the intersection set of water animals and land animals which is the set of amphibious animals.[4] Here $U = \{$all animals$\}$; $A = \{$water animals$\}$; and $B = \{$land animals$\}$.

3. One Set May Be a Subset (or Part) of Another Set

When a subset is completely contained within another set, we may show the relationship as illustrated in Fig. 3.5: $U = \{$all quadrilaterals$\}$; $A = \{$all rectangles$\}$; and $B = \{$all squares$\}$. The subset of all squares is a subset of all rectangles, and all rectangles are quadrilaterals. We may write the relationship using symbols for sets and subsets:

> all squares $\subset$ all rectangles
> all rectangles $\subset$ all quadrilaterals

3.4   OPERATIONS with SETS

The two operations that are most commonly used with sets are termed *union* and *intersection*.

UNION

The union of two or more sets creates a new set that contains all of the elements of the respective sets. In the union of two or more sets, any given element is considered only once even though it may occur in more than one set. The union of sets may be shown through the use of Venn diagrams. The shaded area of the sets in Fig. 3.6 shows the union of the sets A and B.

The operation of union may be indicated using the symbol $\cup$. The

---

[4] *amphi* (double) $+$ *bios* (life) $=$ double life, that is, capable of living on land or in water.

shaded areas represent the result of the operation. For example, consider the following problem:

U = {all animals} A = {dog, horse, cat} B = {pig, dog, cat}
$A \cup B$ = {dog, horse, cat, pig}

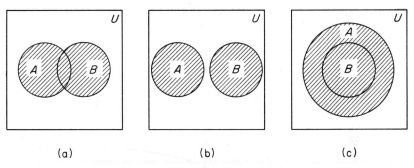

(a)   (b)   (c)

Fig. 3.6 Intersecting sets are shown in (a); disjoint sets in (b); and B is a subset of A in diagram (c).

INTERSECTION

The intersection of two or more sets may be a new set which contains all of the elements that are common to all of the sets being considered. The intersection of sets may be shown using Venn diagrams. The shaded area of the sets in Fig. 3.7 shows the intersection of Set E and

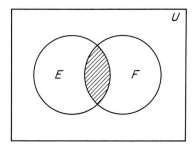

Fig. 3.7

Set F. In the figure, U = {Coastal states of the United States}; E = {Atlantic Coast states}; and F = {Gulf Coast states}. The intersection of E and F = states that are both Atlantic Coast and Gulf Coast states.

The operation of intersection may be indicated by using the symbol for intersection, $\cap$. The symbol is sometimes called a "cap." Intersection may occur with the three types of sets: disjoint, intersecting, and sets in which one set is a subset of another set. Consider the problem

$A \cap B$. The intersection is diagramed in Fig. 3.8 where $U = \{0, 1, 2, 3, \cdots\}$; $A = \{0, 2, 4, 6, \cdots\}$; and $B = \{3, 6, 9, 12, \cdots\}$. The three dots indicate "and so on in the same way."

$$A \cap B = \{0, 2, 4, 6, \cdots\} \cap \{3, 6, 9, 12, \cdots\} = \{6, 12, 18, \cdots\}$$

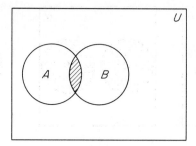

Fig. 3.8 Intersecting sets in $A \cap B$.

In Fig. 3.9 showing disjoint sets, $U = \{\text{geometric figures}\}$; $A = \{\text{triangles}\}$; and $B = \{\text{circles}\}$. Sets A and B are disjoint sets. They have no elements in common. Thus, $A \cap B = \phi$.

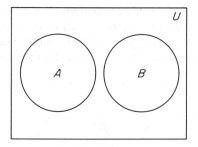

Fig. 3.9 Disjoint sets in $A \cap B$.

In the diagram of B is a subset of A (Fig. 3.10), $U = \{\text{all living things}\}$; $A = \{\text{all living plants}\}$; and $B = \{\text{all living rosebushes}\}$.

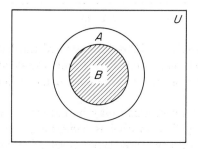

Fig. 3.10 B is a subset of A.

$A \cap B = B$. Figure 3.10 indicates that all members of Set B are also members of Set A, that is, all living rosebushes are members of the set of living plants.

BINARY OPERATIONS

Union and intersection are binary operations. This means that in the process of an operation only two sets are considered at a time. If the union of three sets is considered, the union of two sets is made and the answer determined. The answer to the union of the two sets is then considered to form the union with the third set. For example, the union of Set X, Set Y, and Set Z may be determined by taking $(X \cup Y)$ and the result from the union may be considered with Set Z. The order of finding the union does not affect the answer. Parentheses are used to indicate the order of working an example: $(X \cup Y) \cup Z$ indicates that the union of X and Y is determined first and then considered with Z. The set $X \cup (Y \cup Z)$ indicates that the union of Y and Z is first determined and then considered with X. If more than three sets are considered, a similar procedure is used.

Similarly, intersection is a binary operation. To find the intersection of Set A, Set B, and Set C, only two sets are considered at a time. To solve the problem $(A \cap B) \cap C$, consider $A \cap B$ first; the answer to that operation is then considered with Set C. For $A \cap (B \cap C)$, consider $(B \cap C)$ first; the answer to that step of the problem is then considered with Set A.

3.5   SOME PROPERTIES of OPERATION with SETS

We have discussed ideas of sets and of operations with sets. Let us make some statements concerning given sets and the operations of union and intersection. The statements that we may make concerning the sets and their operations are called *properties, axioms,* or *postulates.* We shall use the word *properties,* since it is the term used most frequently for elementary school consideration. The teacher should have an understanding of the concepts and the properties of sets, of whole numbers, of fraction numbers, and so forth. The teacher's understanding and his ability to teach should lead him to challenge his learners to arrive *intuitively* at the understanding of the properties. The ideas become powerful in pupil behavior not only in terms of the specific work that is being considered, but for growth in applying the procedures for creating and interpreting new systems.

CLOSURE PROPERTY

Closure implies that, if an operation is performed with any two elements within the universal set, the result from the operation will be a member of the universal set.

Union

The problem $A \cup B$ is diagramed in Fig. 3.11 where universe = {all states of the United States}; A = {West Coast states}; and B = {East Coast states}. Then

$$A \cup B = \{\text{West Coast states}\} \cup \{\text{East Coast states}\}$$
$$= \{\text{East Coast states and West Coast states}\}$$

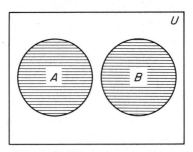

Fig. 3.11

The solution of the problem $A \cup B$ gives an answer that is a member of the set described in the universal set. We may say that the set is closed with respect to union.

Closure Property of Intersection

In Fig. 3.12 the problem $A \cap B$ is diagramed. Here universe = {all

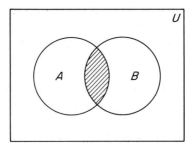

Fig. 3.12

states of the United States}; $A = \{$California, Oregon, Washington$\}$; and $B = \{$Oregon, Montana, Nevada$\}$.

$A \cap B = \{$California, Oregon, Washington$\}$
$\cap \{$Oregon, Montana, Nevada$\} = \{$Oregon$\}$

The solution to the problem $A \cap B$ produces an answer that is a member of the universal set, that is, a member of All States of the United States.

With any set that we select, we may show intersection of its subsets, and the answer will be an element of the universal set. This characteristic is called the closure property for intersection.

COMMUTATIVE PROPERTY

Union

The order in which the union of two sets is made does not affect the answer. For example, consider the sets:

universe $= \{$all plant life$\}$
Set $A = \{$all trees$\}$
Set $B = \{$all rosebushes$\}$

If $A \cup B = \{$all trees and all rosebushes$\}$ and $B \cup A = \{$all rosebushes and all trees$\}$, then $A \cup B = B \cup A$.

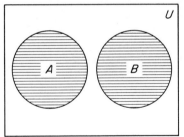 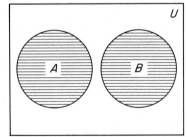

Fig. 3.13 $A \cup B = B \cup A$.

As shown in Fig. 3.13, it does not make any difference which set is the referent or beginning set.

Intersection

The order in which the intersection of two sets is made does not affect the answer. For example, consider the problem:

universe $= \{$all animals$\}$
Set $A = \{$all land animals$\}$
Set $B = \{$all water animals$\}$

The set $A \cap B$ = the set of all amphibious animals. The order in which the intersection is made does not affect the answer: $A \cap B = B \cap A$. See Fig. 3.14.

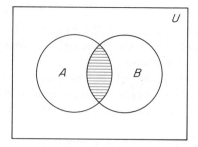

Fig. 3.14 $A \cap B = B \cap A$.

ASSOCIATIVE PROPERTY

The union or intersection of three or more sets does not depend upon

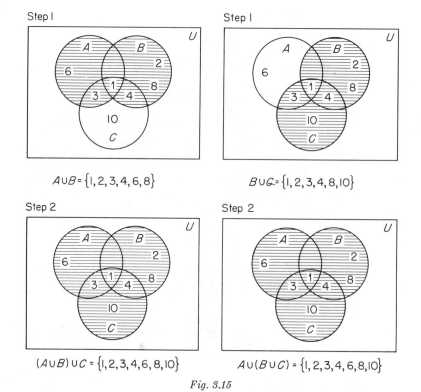

Step I

$A \cup B = \{1, 2, 3, 4, 6, 8\}$

Step I

$B \cup C = \{1, 2, 3, 4, 8, 10\}$

Step 2

$(A \cup B) \cup C = \{1, 2, 3, 4, 6, 8, 10\}$

Step 2

$A \cup (B \cup C) = \{1, 2, 3, 4, 6, 8, 10\}$

Fig. 3.15

the order in which they are grouped. We operate with only two sets at a time.

Union

Consider the following problem:

$$\text{universe} = \{\text{all whole numbers}\}$$
$$\text{Set } A = \{1, 3, 6\}$$
$$\text{Set } B = \{1, 2, 4, 8\}$$
$$\text{Set } C = \{1, 3, 4, 10\}$$

When the union of sets A, B, C is to be found in a stated order, we may use either of these two ways: $(A \cup B) \cup C$ or $A \cup (B \cup C)$. See Fig. 3.15. Shaded areas represent the result of operations, $(A \cup B) \cup C = A \cup (B \cup C)$. The union of three or more sets does not depend upon the order in which their union is made.

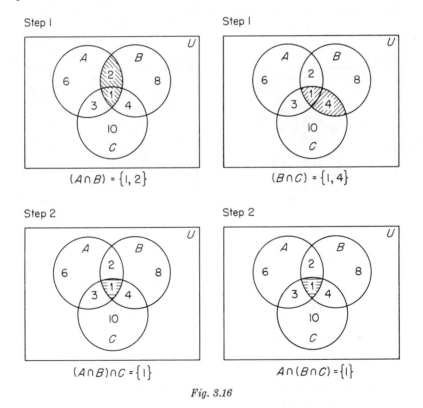

Fig. 3.16

Intersection

Consider the following problem, which is diagramed in Fig. 3.16:

universe = {all whole numbers}

Set A = {1, 2, 3, 6}
Set B = {1, 2, 4, 8}
Set C = {1, 3, 4, 10}

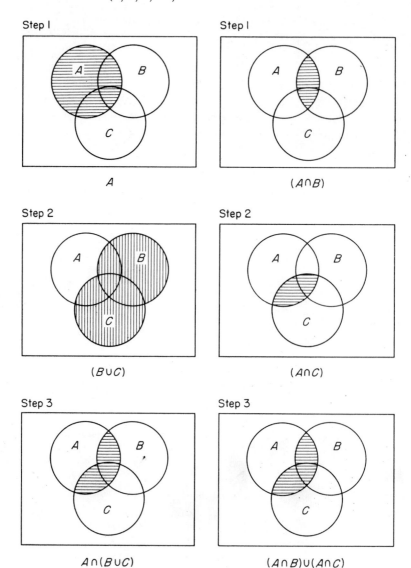

Fig. 3.17

Does $(A \cap B) \cap C = A \cap (B \cap C)$? The order in which the intersection of three or more sets is performed does not affect the answer.

DISTRIBUTIVE PROPERTY

Can *union* and *intersection* change places in the example, $A \cap (B \cup C)$? Does $A \cap (B \cup C) = (A \cap B) \cup (A \cap C)$? The relation $(A \cap B) \cup (A \cap C)$ indicates the set consisting of elements in A and B or in A and C. Figure 3.17 shows two ways of finding the same subset in the

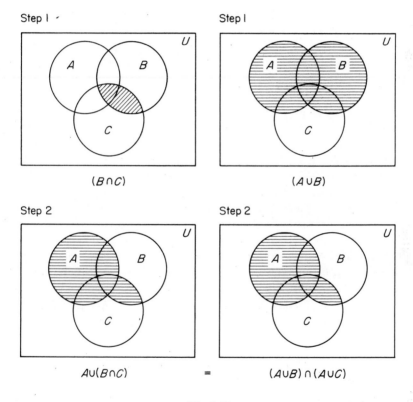

Step I

$(B \cap C)$

Step I

$(A \cup B)$

Step 2

$A \cup (B \cap C)$

Step 2

$=$

$(A \cup B) \cap (A \cup C)$

Fig. 3.18

three given sets. It may be said that intersection is distributive with respect to union.

Are there two ways of finding the same subset for the problem: $A \cup (B \cap C)$? Does $A \cup (B \cap C) = (A \cup B) \cap (A \cup C)$?

There are two ways of finding the same subset in the problem illustrated in Fig. 3.18. It may be said that union is distributive with respect to intersection.

3.6 AN INTERESTING APPLICATION

An interesting application of the idea of special groupings or sets for serving a human need is that of "direct distance dialing" (DDD) now incorporated into our telephone systems. In order to facilitate DDD, a numeral-like labeling system was devised. This makes feasible "all-number calling" (ANC). The "all-numeral" numbers consist of 10 digits arranged in subgroupings as follows: 3 digits at the left designate a particular geographic code area. The 3 digits toward the right of the code area label a subregion within the code area. And, the 4 digits at the right identify the particular telephone within the subregion of the code area.

Figure 3.19 shows the universal set which consists of continental United States (except for Alaska) and Canada. More than 100 subsets or code areas are designated and given a numeral-like label. When calling from outside that area, this label is dialed first. For example, 212 is the area code number for New York City and 213 is the code call for Los Angeles.

Within the major code areas, there are further subgroupings which are similarly designated by numeral-like labels. When calling within the major code area, the code area label is not dialed, but the dialing begins with the minor code area numeral.

Finally, within each minor code area, the individual telephone constitutes a final subset. In the larger cities, this is likely to be a "unit set." It is given a numeral-like label consisting of 4 digits. Consequently, when one uses "direct distance dialing" and "all-number calling" from one code area to another, he dials a *10-digit* label using digits from the decimal alphabet, but these are not designed for spelling a decimal numeral value. See Fig. 3.20, where U is the coded area, the United States and Canada; A the code area, New York City; B the subarea of New York City; C, Holt exchange; and D, individual telephone extension.

The universal set consists of the coded area of the United States and Canada. The major subset, 212, is that of the New York City area designated by its "all-numeral" code number. The subset with the major code area is a regional district within the New York City exchange code area. The sub-subset within the regional district is that of the Holt, Rinehart and Winston, Inc., exchange. The final subset is the individual telephone extension from the company's exchange.

The discussion in this chapter has been designed to point out the importance of ideas concerning sets in reference to mathematical communication and behavior. Many of the ideas are not new, nor are they particularly involved or uncommon in human thinking. There

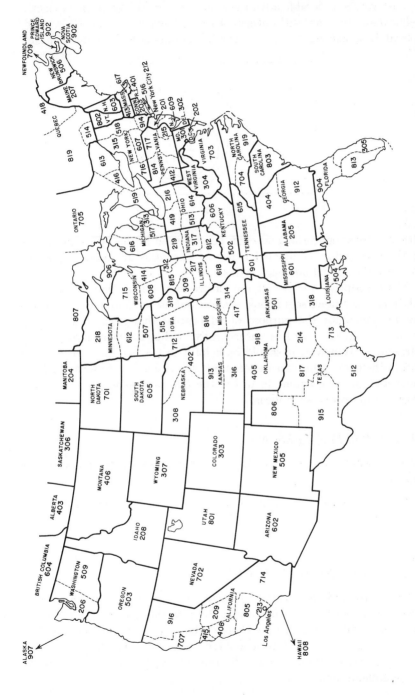

Fig. 3.19 Map showing telephone areas and area codes in the United States and Canada.

is, however, considerable advantage for teachers in having them clearly delineated. Just as with other phases of mathematical knowledge, special language forms are needed for mathematical communication,

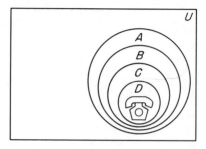

Fig. 3.20

although ideas concerning sets can be expressed in the terms and forms of the vernacular (common language). The *ideas* are more important than are the special language forms.

The descriptive analysis of the nature and composition of a set and relationships among sets is both timely and useful. This discussion was not presented for the purpose of advocating that such formal treatment of language forms be incorporated within the elementary school curriculum. However, it should be helpful to teachers in incorporating within their programs experiences that will lead pupils to formulate the ideas and to some extent to utilize the language expressions that are designed to express such ideas.

ILLUSTRATIVE LESSONS

The following illustrative lessons and lesson plans are presented in this chapter:

Lesson 1: Using sets to help us classify (report of a field trip)
Lesson 2: Limited or limitless

Lesson 1
USING SETS TO HELP US CLASSIFY

The sixth grade had taken a field trip to read directly a certain area and to gather specimens for study. Prior to the trip, they had agreed that each individual was to choose whatever specimen he found of interest and bring it back to school for study and discussion. Naturally, the result was a heterogeneous collection including rocks, plants, insects, bugs, animals, and so forth.

The class had discussed ideas of sets in connection with their mathematics program. Hence, they decided to use those ideas in relation to their field trip collection.

Tim pointed out that their universal set was composed of many different sorts of things, but that they belonged together because they were things collected while on the field trip.

Nan agreed, but she suggested that subsets composed of things which belonged together might be interesting to make. The others agreed, and they set about making subgroupings under the captions *plants, animals, others.*

Bill called attention to the elements of the subset of animals. He pointed out that there were animals with backbones and those without backbones. There were water animals and land animals, as well as those that lived in both places. There were bugs and insects. He said, "There are a lot of subgroups among the animal collection."

Jerry said, "Mike didn't collect anything. So, what he brought in makes a 'null set'."

Mike objected, pointing out that he had "collected a bee sting" and no one else had, so he really contributed a "unit set."

Peggy called attention to the two sets, one for animals and the other for plants. She wanted to know whether they would be called "disjoint sets." Tom doubted that they were truly "disjoint sets" because animals consume plants and plants eat animals. This caused a lively discussion.

Alice raised a question about the minnows. They live only in the water, so they would be water animals. Since there were animals that live only on land, she said the water animals and land animals make up "disjoint sets."

Mary agreed insofar as the animals lived *only* in one place or the other, but she pointed out that frogs live in both places. She said, "Frogs make up an intersecting set of the water animals and land animals."

The discussion went on at a lively pace. The children were enjoying the chance to use the ideas and language terms previously experienced only in their mathematics work. Bill rather clinched the discussion by remarking that "Everyone knows about those things, but they don't always say what they know in these words."

Lesson 2
LIMITED OR LIMITLESS

Background of children: The children had developed a background of interpretation of the decimal system of notation and of simple ideas of sets.

Purpose of lesson: To develop ideas concerning finite and infinite sets and to challenge critical thinking concerning some ideas of sets.

Lesson Procedure

Jim: We talked about how we use sets to fit whatever we are doing. I think it's easier to think about sets that don't have too many members.

Mr. Evans: What are some sets that have many members?

Jerry: The set of people in the United States. It is hard to keep track of that set because new babies are born every second and people die every second, so . . .

Julie: The stars in the sky. I can never count them. I wonder if anyone really knows how many there are?

Sam: The number of grains of sand on the beach. I could never count them, but maybe they could be counted by a computing machine.

Mr. Evans: Do you think that the grains of sand could be counted?

Bill: Not by any one man or even by many men counting, but I guess that there are only so many and not any more.

Mr. Evans: All of the things you have talked about are sets whose elements could be counted if one had time to count them.

Jim: Wouldn't you have to have nine lives like a cat?

Mr. Evans: I'm afraid that we can't answer that question for sure, Jim, but we can all think about it.

Mr. Evans: Are there sets that have an unlimited number of elements? In mathematics, we have talked about some things that may help you answer the question.

Mary: There are 26 letters in our alphabet, and you could write words forever and never come to the last word. We talked about this idea in spelling and in math. There would always be another word that you could write — but it might not be a word that is in the dictionary.

Mr. Evans: A set like that which has an unlimited number of elements is called an *infinite set*. Infinite means without limitation. If it's an infinite amount, it is an amount greater than any specific quantity we can assign to it. Mary named an infinite set when she mentioned the set of words that we can make using the 26 letters of the English alphabet. Mary included words that may be make-believe words. Are there other infinite sets? We have been discussing number systems. What can you say about them?

Dick: That is easy! We use 10 digits to write all decimal values, but there is no last number. You can always add 1 more and have a larger number.

Jan: On the chart we made, we used 3 dots to show that the numerals go on and on and on and on. Beyond decillions, there are decillions of decillions, and . . .

Dick: Yes, but we wrote 3 dots going in the direction of decrease, too. We'd never come to the end either way. We can keep writing decimal fractions forever and never come to the smallest numeral.

Jan: We also made a chart using negative and positive. There would be no end to that way of writing either, but I can't read the numerals when there are too many of them.

Bill: All of this is true for the system we made using base five. We have a set that can go on forever. We just use the same digits over and over again.

Johnny: We could do the same with any base. We talked about a base using only 2 digits — 0 and 1. It would work the same way.

The discussion continued with the development of infinite sets. The following were considered: set of common fraction numerals, set of decimal fraction numerals, set of minutes that could be measured by clock time, and so forth. The discussion led to the children's designing and arranging a bulletin board that showed examples of finite and infinite sets.

Discussion Questions

1. Develop some ideas of sets as they apply to music. For example, a measure of music is a subset of a musical composition, and the individual notes are subsets of the measures. The union of the individual notes in a measure produces the measure. Orchestration, harmony, and many aspects of music offer a fine opportunity for the intepretation of sets.

2. Develop ideas of sets in the field of biological science. Species, genera, families, classifications, and so forth, offer unlimited possibilities for developing set ideas.

3. Discuss the idea of sets as it may apply to the study of "in-group" and "out-group" relationships in the field of sociology. Develop ideas using set notation and diagrams.

4. Select the topic of art or another subject field and develop set ideas using the methods suggested in the preceding questions.

5. Select some specific ideas for sets A, B, and C. Use Venn diagrams and test the following principles:

(a) The commutative principle:
Does $A \cup B = B \cup A$? Does $A \cap B = B \cap A$?

(b) The associative principle:
Does $(A \cup B) \cup C = A \cup (B \cup C)$?
Does $(A \cap B) \cap C = A \cap (B \cap C)$?

(c) The distributive property applied to sets:
Does $A \cup (B \cap C) = (A \cup B) \cap (A \cup C)$?
Does $A \cap (B \cup C) = (A \cap B) \cup (A \cap C)$?

Suggested Readings

Botts, Truman, "Numbers, Sets, and Counting," *The Arithmetic Teacher*, vol. 8 (October 1961), pp. 281–286.

Brumfiel, Charles F., Robert E. Eicholz, and Merrill E. Shanks, *Fundamental Concepts of Elementary Mathematics*. Reading, Mass.: Addison-Wesley Publishing Company, Inc., 1962, Chap. 16, 18.

Johnson, Donovan A., and William H. Glenn, *Sets, Sentences, and Operations*. St. Louis, Mo.: Webster Publishing Company, 1961.

Kemeny, John G., J. Laurie Snell, and Gerald L. Thompson, *Introduction to Finite Mathematics*. Englewood Cliffs, N. J.: Prentice-Hall, Inc., 1957, Part II.

Lerner, Norbert, and Max A. Sobel, "Sets and Elementary School Mathematics," *The Arithmetic Teacher*, vol. 5 (November 1958), pp. 239–246.

Meserve, Bruce E., and Max A. Sobel, *Introduction to Mathematics*. Englewood Cliffs, N. J.: Prentice-Hall, Inc., 1964, Chap. 4.

Mueller, Francis J., *Arithmetic, Its Structure and Concepts*, 2d ed. Englewood Cliffs, N. J.: Prentice-Hall, Inc., 1964, Unit 5.

Osborn, Roger, M. Vere De Vault, Claude C. Boyd, and W. Robert Houston, *Extending Mathematics Understanding*. Columbus, Ohio: Charles E. Merrill Books, Inc., 1961, Chap. 7.

Peterson, John A., and Joseph Hashisaki, *Theory of Arithmetic*. New York: John Wiley & Sons, Inc., 1963, Chap. 2.

Sets (Booklet Number 1), The National Council of Teachers of Mathematics. Washington, D.C.: The Council, 1964, 47 pp.

Suppes, Patrick, and Blair A. McKnight, "Sets and Numbers in Grade One, 1959-60," *The Arithmetic Teacher*, vol. 8 (October 1961), pp. 287–290.

Van Engen, Henry, and Kenneth O. May, "Relations and Functions," *The Growth of Mathematical Ideas, Grades K–12*, National Council of Teachers of Mathematics, Twenty-fourth Yearbook. Washington, D.C.: The Council, 1959.

Wilcox, Marie S., and John E. Yarnelle, *Mathematics, A Modern Approach*. Reading, Mass.: Addison-Wesley Publishing Company, Inc., 1963, Chap. 3.

Woodward, Edith J., and Roderick C. McLennan, *Elementary Concepts of Sets*. New York: Holt, Rinehart and Winston, Inc., 1959.

4

Concepts of Number
and Numeration

4.1 USES of NUMBER

When the term "mathematics" is mentioned, ideas of number are commonly suggested. The fact that a considerable portion of mathematical knowledge and behavior is not concerned with number is frequently overlooked.

Number ideas and the special languages for their expression are important mathematical developments. But, they are not separate or disparate bodies of subject-matter. They are, in reality, merely refinements of ideas and of techniques of communication that prevail generally throughout behavior.

The *cardinal* use of number is that of scaling quantitative amounts. The question of "How many?" gives rise to the development of scales for expressing quantitative measurements. Such expressions as "a few," "several," and so on, are obviously less specific than are "2," "50," and comparable numerical references.

The *ordinal* use of number, on the other hand, is not concerned with quantitative amounts. Its purpose is to indicate position within an ordered series. For example, "Independence Day occurs early in July," is stated more specifically in ordinal number terms as "Independence Day is the fourth day of July."

Not all references to number are concerned with quantifying or with ordinal position, however. Sometimes number symbols are used as *labels*, for example, the numerals on the uniforms of athletes, or the so-called telephone "numbers." Expressions such as "I have his number" are likely to be more socio-psychological in reference than they are mathematical.

The cardinal use of number is of greatest concern for elementary school consideration. Hence, major attention will be directed to it in the discussion that follows.

4.2   NUMBER and NUMERAL

Some of the recent programs for mathematical instruction make a sharp distinction between the connotations of the terms *number* and *numeral*. The term *number* is restricted to refer only to the *idea* of a specific quantitative amount. The term *numeral* is comparably restricted to refer merely to the *symbols* used to represent a number idea.

The distinction between ideas and their symbols is in accord with the teachings of semantics. There is educational merit in recognizing that "words are not ideas." However, since the terms number and numeral are commonly used as synonyms in general conversation and are so identified in current standard dictionaries,[1] the educational value of rigorously differentiating between them is questionable. Until there is convincing evidence that such practices make substantial contributions to mathematical understanding and to educational development, they should be used sparingly or not at all. Clearly distinguishing between a number idea and the symbols referring to it is important. But, pedantic stressing of arbitrary distinctions between equally representative symbols leads only to confusion and frustration.

4.3   BASIC IDEAS of NUMBER

The awareness of things as identities inevitably leads to further experiences with regard to them. For example, having experienced the presence of a thing or things, one may then experience their absence. And, being able to identify individual things enables one actually to collect them into groups. At least, he can perceptively make such groupings. Simple intuitive experiences of that type can be extended, refined, and developed so that they produce generalized ideas that have great personal and social importance.

Consider the simple experience of picking flowers a stem at a time. The picker must have an awareness of the identity of the individual stems. He starts with the experience of "not any." He plucks a stem. That constitutes his total collection at that time. He is aware of the dif-

---

[1] *Webster's New International Dictionary*, 2d ed. "number *n*, a character or symbol, as a figure or word, or a group of figures or words representing graphically an arithmetic sum—"; "numeral *n*, (see number) a word expressing a number"; "figure *n*, a written or printed character representing a number; a numeral; a digit; as 1,2,3, etc."

ference between his having a stem as contrasted with the state of being without one. This is the basis of an important idea, that is, the quantitative distinction between "not any" and "some." "Not any" is an absolute amount. "Some," on the other hand, is a variable. In amount, "some" refers to a single identity or to any conceivable collection of identities. Hence, "some" is an idea that needs further consideration.

As the picker picks each stem, he increases the membership of the set of stems in his collection. He originally has a *null* set (not any). When he plucks the first stem, he then has a *unit* set. As each subsequent stem is plucked, a new set is formed of which the previous sets constitute subsets.

This simple, everyday type of experience provides a concrete basis for the idea of a graduated scale for measuring "how many." The scale is actually initiated when the identity (unit) is selected. If the identity is present, the single item is the simplest amount that can be conceived. If the identity is not present, the idea of "not any" (the null set) is suggested. Each perceived group contains *one member more* than the grouping that precedes it in the series. Or, by changing the referent, each set contains *one member less* than the set that follows it in the series. These are merely different ways of expressing the same observation of relationship, but together they tend to emphasize the idea that the series of sets created in such a collecting process is actually a *scaled series* each member of which varies by a single item from the member preceding or following it in the series. Progressing along the series in one direction, we find that each grouping contains one more member than the group preceding it. When we progress along the series in the opposite direction, each set except zero contains one less member than the set preceding it. In other words, the scaled series has a directional characteristic.

Each set within the series is identifiable in its own right and may be used as a referent for a comparative operation with other identified sets. This may be done by noting a one-to-one correspondence between the elements composing the respective sets. Expressions such as "as many as I have hands," "one for each person," "there are more in this grouping than in that one," and "as countless as the stars" illustrate such reference to one-to-one correspondence. They refer to number ideas without the use of specific labels.

The recurrence of concrete experiences of one-to-one comparisons normally suggests that the "how manyness" characteristic is not related to the nature of the elements composing the respective groupings. For example, "one chair for each person" does not express a function or property of either "chairness" or "person." The "how many" aspect of such comparisons is not related to the kinds of things being considered. Therefore, we conclude that "manyness" is an idea which is abstracted from concrete experiences, but that it is not a property which is restricted to such experiences.

Having arrived at the generalization that the measurement of how many is not concerned with the nature of the individual members of the set, we are able to carry that abstraction a bit further. We can construct an artificial or schematic representation of such a scaled series. This can then be used as a referent for any measurement of "manyness."

One of the best and most commonly experienced examples of such a device is that used with dominoes (Fig. 4.1). Each member of the re-

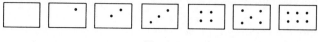

Fig. 4.1

spective sets is depicted by a dot. Since the null set has no member, that symbol has no dot.

The domino representation of the unit scale has proven to be very helpful in assisting beginners to perceive the general nature of a unit scale. It does, however, have a possible disadvantage. It presents no direct suggestion that sets preceding a particular set on the scale are included as subsets within the particular set. That is an important characteristic of the unit scale. The respective sets, as one follows the scale in the direction of increasing amounts, include the members of the preceding sets and add one more member thereto. This may be indicated in a number of ways. For example, a device such as that shown in Fig. 4.2 depicts the recurrence of individual membership in the successive groupings.

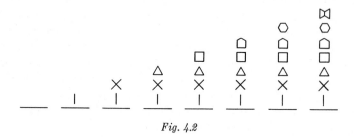

Fig. 4.2

Once the idea of the unit scale has been conceived, awareness that such a scale may be continued indefinitely naturally follows. Whether or not the actual experience of collecting one more item is performed, the idea that such is possible should be obvious. Hence, a concept of infinity is initiated.

The idea that the measurement of "manyness" is based upon the ability to identify things both individually and as members of sets, and that it is not a specific property of the particular things is basic to the understanding of the counting number scale. The number measure of "manyness" does not vary with the nature of the items counted. It is concerned only with their identities. Since the specific groupings which compose the scale are to be used as referents in determining how many, they need to be given identifying labels. A language of number is an important aid in the use of number ideas.

Every major language contains verbal symbols for specific number ideas; for example, the words zero, one, two, three, and so forth, correspond to the respective sets of the counting number scale. They serve adequately for the identification of those number ideas in general communication. For example, determining how many members there would be in a group that is composed of 4 disjoint sets containing 28 members each is difficult to do when the terms are expressed only in verbal symbols, such as

twenty-eight
multiplied by four

There is evident need for a special number language that has symbols which are more adapted for computational usage. History reveals that man has experienced that need and has striven throughout the ages to satisfy it. The decimal numeral language has now become generally accepted in all of the major countries as a reasonably adequate device for symbolizing number ideas. The decimal numerals are well suited for computational operations. For example,

28
$\times$ 4

is no longer a difficult matter when the terms are expressed as decimal numerals.

It is important to note that these parallel language forms occur only in the written versions of the language. The oral-aural (spoken-heard) forms are the same whether the idea is symbolized as a verbal word or as a numeral expression.

The development of language forms which accurately and readily express mathematical ideas is second in importance only to the conceiving of the ideas. See Chapter 6 for a more thorough discussion of this important language aspect.

4.4 THE DECIMAL NUMERATION SYSTEM

The decimal numeration system is one of the truly great inventions of the human mind. Its genius lies not in the selection of ten as a pattern for subgrouping, but rather in the ideas that underlie the system. The ideas of a *primary* grouping and of a *secondary* grouping (subgrouping) lead logically to the creation of a numeration system to express those ideas. The unit one is the building block for interpreting all number values. As the accumulation of ones becomes cumbersome, consistent subgrouping of number values facilitates keeping an account of "how many." Even the earliest number and numeration systems utilize these ideas.

In the decimal system, the numerals symbolizing number ideas are written by means of a set of 10 digits:

$$A = \{0, 1, 2, 3, 4, 5, 6, 7, 8, 9\}$$

There is no apparent reason for either the figural form of these digits or for the order in which they are ranked. However, they have become fixed in both of these regards by social convention.

The main ideas that underlie the operation of the decimal numeration system follow.

IDEA OF A PRIMARY OR CONSTANT VALUE

Each digit of the 10 digits in Set A just discussed represents a *primary* or *constant* value which is determined by its place within the series of digits. For example, in any given position within a numeral, a four has a value that is always one more than three, one less than five, and so forth.

IDEA OF A POSITIONAL OR A SECONDARY VALUE

Each digit used in a numeral represents a *positional* (secondary) value based upon its place within the numeral. In the expression, 44, the 4 at the left represents a value of 4 tens while the 4 at the right stands for a value of 4 ones. Each position to the left of the ones' place represents a positional value of groupings of tens or of powers of 10.

Since 9 represents the largest value in the set of digits, it is the largest value that can be expressed in any given position in a decimal numeral.

ZERO TO INDICATE A NULL SET

Zero represents "not any" (the null set). The use of a symbol for zero (0) is unique to decimal and other modern numeration systems. Roman, Egyptian, and other earlier numeration systems did not use a symbol for zero.

ONES' POSITION AS A REFERENT POSITION

The ones' (units') position is the referent position in which groupings of less than 10 ones are expressed. Positions toward the left of the ones' position represent groupings 10 times as great as those represented to their immediate right. Positional (secondary) subgroupings are illustrated in Fig. 4.3.

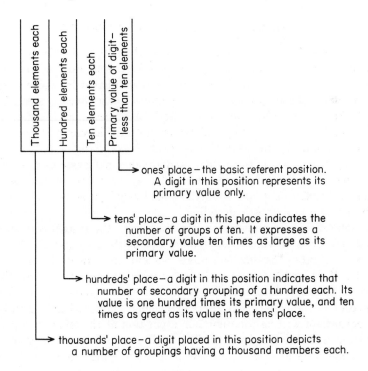

ones' place – the basic referent position. A digit in this position represents its primary value only.

tens' place – a digit in this place indicates the number of groups of ten. It expresses a secondary value ten times as large as its primary value.

hundreds' place – a digit in this position indicates that number of secondary grouping of a hundred each. Its value is one hundred times its primary value, and ten times as great as its value in the tens' place.

thousands' place – a digit placed in this position depicts a number of groupings having a thousand members each.

Fig. 4.3

ADDITION OF VALUES EXPRESSED BY DIGITS IN A NUMERAL

The value expressed by a numeral is the sum of all the values in the several positions. The numeral 243 represents two groups of 100 each, plus four groups of 10 each, plus a group of 3 ones: $243 = 200 + 40 + 3$.

DIGITS AS PLACEHOLDERS

Every digit, including zero, serves as a placeholder within a numeral. In 502, the 5 holds the place of the hundreds, 0 holds the place of the tens, and 2 is a placeholder for the ones' position.

4.5   OTHER NUMERATION SYSTEMS

The pattern of the decimal numeration system serves as a model for interpreting many other numeration systems that are isomorphic (similar in pattern).[2] Numeration systems using bases other than ten, and numeration systems for fractions and denominate numbers, will be mentioned in this section.

NUMERATION SYSTEMS USING BASES OTHER THAN TEN

With numeration systems using bases other than 10, just as is true with decimal numeration, the primary number values in each system are expressed by the digits that are selected as the alphabet for the system.[3] For example, the digits used for a *quinary* (base five) system are: 0, 1, 2, 3, 4. Similarly, 8 digits are used for an *octonary* (base eight) system: 0, 1, 2, 3, 4, 5, 6, 7; 2 digits are used for a binary (base two) system: 0, 1; and the duodecimal (base twelve) has 12 digits: 0, 1, 2, 3, 4, 5, 6, 7, 8, 9, χ, ϵ. Both the binary and duodecimal systems are used extensively. The use of the duodecimal may be noted in the use of dozens, inches to a foot, and so forth. The binary base is used with most computers and in linguistic decoding.

In each example of numeration systems above, the system consists of an ordered series in which each symbol except the first (which is zero) represents a group having one more element than does the set that precedes it. In order to express a value which is one more than that expressed by the last digit of the given numeration system, a technique of positional value like that used in decimal numeration is utilized. This consists of writing the digit 1 in a position at the left of the place used to express the ones' values. The digit 1 placed in the position to the left indicates a subgrouping (secondary grouping) equal to the set of elements in the given set of digits. For example, in decimal notation, a one placed to the left of the ones' place represents a grouping 1 larger than 9, that is, a group of 10. In base five systems, the one placed to the left of the ones' position represents a collection of 1 more than 4: a grouping of 1 five. In base twelve, the 1 represents one group of 12 ones, and so forth. The pattern for bases ten, five, eight, twelve, and two is given in Table 4.1.

---

[2] Isomorphic (ĭ′sō-môr′-fĭk). Having the same or like structure or form (*iso* meaning alike, equal, the same + *morphic* meaning form.)

[3] The word *decimal* comes from the Latin word, *decimus*, meaning 10. *Quinary* comes from the Latin *quinarius* meaning 5. *Octonary* comes from the Latin *octonarius* meaning 8. *Binary* comes from the Latin *binarius* meaning 2 at a time. *Duodecimal* comes from the Latin *duodecim* meaning 12.

TABLE 4.1

BASE TEN DECIMAL	BASE FIVE QUINARY	BASE EIGHT OCTONARY	BASE TWELVE DUODECIMAL	BASE TWO BINARY
0	0	0	0	0
1	1	1	1	1
2	2	2	2	10
3	3	3	3	11
4	4	4	4	100
5	10	5	5	101
6	11	6	6	110
7	12	7	7	111
8	13	10	8	1000
9	14	11	9	1001
10	20	12	χ	1010
11	21	13	ϵ	1011
12	22	14	10	1100
13	23	15	11	1101
14	24	16	12	1110
.	.	.	.	.
.	.	.	.	.
.	.	.	.	.

One of the easiest bases to work with is base five. New symbols and new number names can be created to work with base five as is illustrated in Lesson 2 at the end of this chapter. In the following discussion, however, the decimal symbols — 0, 1, 2, 3, 4 — are used. To express the decimal value five, a two-digit numeral is needed in base five. The symbol 10_{five} stands for one group of 5 ones and not any more. It is equal to the value expressed by 5 of decimal notation. The numeral 24_{five} stands for two groups of five and a group of 4 ones. The equivalent in base ten is 14, that is, a group of 10 and a group of 4. The two number lines below indicate the numerals used in bases ten and five, respectively, that represent the decimal values 0 through 13.

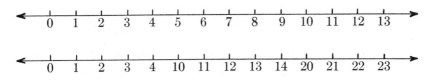

Each position to the left of the ones' position in a base five numeral represents a secondary or subgrouping of sets of fives or powers of five.

The pattern for the numeral 333 is:

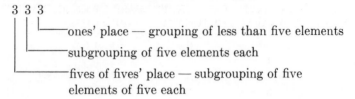

3 3 3

└───── ones' place — grouping of less than five elements

└───── subgrouping of five elements each

└───── fives of fives' place — subgrouping of five
elements of five each

TRANSLATING FROM NONDECIMAL BASES TO DECIMAL BASE

When numerals are written in a nondecimal base, their value is usually translated to the decimal base. A simple way to translate from a nondecimal base to a decimal base is shown below.

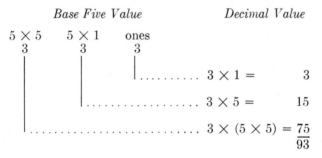

Base Five Value   *Decimal Value*

5×5 5×1 ones
3   3   3

.... $3 \times 1 = $ 3

.... $3 \times 5 = $ 15

.... $3 \times (5 \times 5) = $ 75
                                                        ——
                                                        93

Our language does not have symbols that correspond aptly with the numerals written in bases other than ten. It is incorrect expression to read the names of the numerals as one would read the numerals for decimal expression. For example, the *ty* of the names for decimal values indicates *tens*. The following ways are recommended for reading the numerals for:

33_{five} = three-three base five *or*
                3 fives and three

45_{eight} = four-five base eight *or*
                4 eights and five

321_{five} = three-two-one base five *or*
                3 five-fives, 2 fives, and one

TRANSLATING FROM DECIMAL BASE TO NONDECIMAL BASE

If we had a basket containing many pennies and we wished to count them, we probably would make sets of 10 pennies. If there were many sets of 10 pennies, we would group them into sets of 10 groups of 10 each (100), and so forth. Similarly, if we wished to group by eights, we would make sets of 8, and then sets of 8 groups of 8 each (64). For example, we have

125 pennies (decimal notation) in the basket, and we wish to arrange them in sets of 8, and of 64, and so forth. The solution of the problem may be approached in this manner:

Question 1. How many groups of 8 pennies each are there in 125 pennies?

$$
\begin{array}{r}
15 \\
8)\overline{125} \\
8 \\
\hline
45 \\
40 \\
\hline
5
\end{array}
$$

There are 15 groups of 8 pennies each and a group of 5 pennies. The 5 tells how many ones there are after the groups of 8 are used.

Question 2. How many sets of 8 groups of 8 each (64) are there in a set of 15 groups of 8 members each?

$$
\begin{array}{r}
1 \\
8)\overline{15} \\
8 \\
\hline
7
\end{array}
$$

There is 1 group of 8 eights (64), and there are 7 groups of 8.

A collection of 125 pennies may be grouped into 1 group of 8 eights (64), 7 groups of 8, and 1 group of 5.

eight eights	eights	ones
1	7	5

The numeral 175_{eight} may be used to record what we have done. The 1 of the numeral stands for 1 set of 8 eights (8^2 or 64). The 7 represents 7 groups of 8 (or 7×8^1) and the 5 stands for 5 ones. When we transpose these groupings into decimal notation, we have $64 + 56 + 5$ which equals 125.

The preceding steps are summarized as follows:

Division		*Remainder*
8) 125		
8) 15	sets of eights	5 ones left over
8) 1	set of 8 eights	7 eights left over
0	set of eight $\times$ eight $\times$ eight	1 set of 8 eights left over

The remainders written in the order that they occur from the bottom to the top are 175. This numeral expresses the value 175_{eight}.

NUMERATION SYSTEMS FOR COMMON AND
DECIMAL FRACTION NUMBERS, AND DENOMINATE NUMBERS

The basic unit for the fraction number scale, like the basic unit of the counting number scale, is *one*. However, the unit for the fraction scale is *one* of the equal parts into which a whole thing is structured. In order to be scaled numerically, the parts must be equal. Using eighths, for example, $\frac{1}{8}$ is the referent unit measure. Eights may be scaled in a way similar to the way whole numbers were scaled:

$$\frac{0}{8} \quad \frac{1}{8} \quad \frac{2}{8} \quad \frac{3}{8} \quad \frac{4}{8} \quad \frac{5}{8} \ldots$$

(See Chapter 9 for further development of this topic.)

The decimal fraction scale conforms to the pattern for scaling the decimal whole numbers; hence, they can be expressed as an extension of that pattern. Parts of the unit can be scaled as tenths, hundredths, thousandths, and so on. For example, tenths may be scaled as:

$$\longleftarrow \overset{0 \quad .1 \quad .2 \quad .3 \quad .4 \; \ldots}{\mid \;\; \mid \;\; \mid \;\; \mid \;\; \mid} \longrightarrow$$

(See Chapter 8 for development of decimal fractions.) Denominate numbers illustrate a similar use of a calibrated scale to measure "how many" of the specific units of measure for which each scale is adapted. (See Chapter 10.)

4.6 MODULAR ARITHMETIC

There is no perceptible limit to the extension of the counting number system. Conceivably one more thing can be added to any collection. A set that has no limit as to how many elements it may have, is termed an *infinite* set. However, there are phenomena that are limited in extent, for which suitable measurement needs to be provided. Because of their definite limitations, such phenomena are designated as *finite* and the systems of measurement designated for them are termed *finite systems*. There are many instances of such systems. While they have some characteristics that are similar to the familiar counting number scale, other characteristics are dissimilar. While the counting number scale is continuous, the finite systems are repetitive. This gives rise to some strange number combinations.

INFINITE VERSUS FINITE CONCEPTS OF TIME

Time is an infinite phenomenon. So far as we can discern, it has no beginning or ending. However, for our convenience, the continuum is structured into finite, definitely limited units, such as years, months, and days. The measurement of these finite units calls for a special type of scaling device.

By custom, a year is divided into 12 segments called months. The first month in the series is called January because, like the god Janus, it faces both the year that has just ended and the year that is just beginning. In other words, the scale of months has definite limitations. It begins and ends, but the ending of one series is the beginning of another. It is repetitious in application.

In like manner, the day as a unit of time has definite limitations. By custom it is scaled into 24 one-hour units. By custom, also, a day is measured directionally as 12-hour or half-day intervals preceding and following the zenith position of the sun. One day emerges from the day preceding and then merges into the day following. Daily time measurements are repetitive.

A standard unit of measurement is called a module. A system of measurement for using a module is, therefore, modular. It is commonly identified by the finite limits of the number of times the module is used, for example, the scale of a 12-hour clock is said to be modulus twelve (mod 12). The scale of a 24-hour clock would be modulus twenty-four (mod 24).

Modulus 12

The clock face at the left indicates that the time is 9 o'clock. What time should it show 6 hours after 9 o'clock? One way that we can find the answer is to start at 9 on the clock face and count clockwise 6 hour-units. If we count correctly, we shall be at 3. Another way we could solve the problem is to note that the clock is limited to a 12-hour scale of measurement. When one 12-hour span has passed, the scaling begins again. Hence, we may add $9 + 6 = 15$ and subtract 12 (the 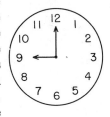 maximum measure in our scale) from 15 to determine at what place on the scale the hour hand should point, for example, 3.

The "clock arithmetic" pictured represents a system based upon the modulus 12. At whatever place we start on the clock face, we shall be at that same place 12 hours later. We can also describe additions or movements as follows: Start at 6 o'clock and count 8 hour-units around the face clockwise. From this adding of $6 + 8$, we come out at 2. We may show this idea as:

$$6 + 8 \equiv 2 \ (\text{mod } 12)$$

This is read, "$6 + 8$ *is congruent to* 2 in a modular system based on 12."

The mathematical symbol for spelling *is congruent to* is ≡. Sometimes
a wavy line is used: ≅.

If we start at 4 o'clock and wish to know the time on the face 16 hours
later, we may think:

$$4 + 16 \equiv 8 \,(\text{mod } 12).$$

We may add $4 + 16 = 20$ and think $20 - 12$ (the mod) $= 8$.

We may say that two numbers are congruent with respect to the
modulus (base of the system) if the two numbers have the same remainder when they are divided by the modulus. For example,

$$8 + 23 \,(\text{mod } 12) \equiv 7.$$

Then $8 + 23 = 31$ and $31 \div 12 = 2$ groups of 12 and *7* remainder.

Other examples of modular systems that may be noted are: modulus
7 — days of the week; modulus 12 — months of the year; and modulus
8 — the dial on some electric stoves.

Modulus 8

We may create a mathematical system using the dial illustrated and
making a set of elements and operations to use with the elements.

In our mathematical system, the alphabet of symbols
is: off (0) 1 2 3 4 5 6 7. We may define the operations
that we plan to perform as:

making turns to the right $\curvearrowright$

making turns to the left $\curvearrowleft$

If we start at *off* and turn 10 "clicks" to the right,
we shall be at 2.

$$\text{Off (0)} \curvearrowright 10 \equiv 2 \,(\text{mod } 8)$$

We may check this as follows: $10 \div 8 = 1$ group of 8 and *2* remainder.

Here is another example: Start at 4 and make 5 turns to the right:

$$4 \curvearrowright 5 \equiv 1 \,(\text{mod } 8)$$

In Chapter 5, properties and relations of whole numbers are discussed.
When reading that chapter you may wish to see if this modulus 8
mathematical system obeys the properties when the operations $\curvearrowright$ and
$\curvearrowleft$ are considered.

4.7   TEACHING CONCEPTS of NUMBER and NUMERATION SYSTEMS

COMPARISON OF NUMBER VALUES

As soon as a child reads numerals such as 21, he should sense that the 2 stands for 20 and the 1 stands for 1 more. This early awareness should be extended so that refinements of the idea and the language for their expression develop. The following steps indicate levels of refinement of comparisons that should evolve as the learner makes progress in his interpretation.

1. Simple awareness of the value represented by a two-digit numeral:

   2   2

   stands for a set of 2 ones

   stands for a set of 20 ones

2. Awareness that each digit in the tens' position stands for sets of 10s:

   2   2

   stands for 2 ones

   stands for 2 groups
   of 10 each or 20 ones

An abacus helps children to interpret numeration systems.

3. Awareness that each digit in the tens' position names the number of groups of 10 and that each digit in the hundreds' position names the number of groups of 100:

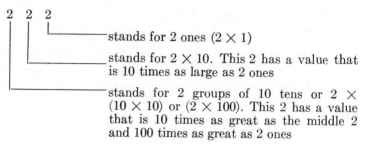

2 2 2

stands for 2 ones (2 × 1)

stands for 2 × 10. This 2 has a value that is 10 times as large as 2 ones

stands for 2 groups of 10 tens or 2 × (10 × 10) or (2 × 100). This 2 has a value that is 10 times as great as the middle 2 and 100 times as great as 2 ones

4. Making comparisons in the direction of increase and in the direction of decrease. The letters *a*, *b*, and *c* may be used to facilitate the making of comparisons:

Comparing in the Direction of Increase

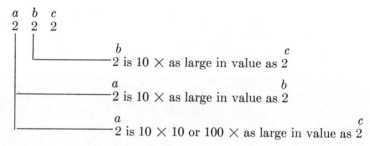

a *b* *c*
2   2   2

b   *c*
2 is 10 × as large in value as 2

a   *b*
2 is 10 × as large in value as 2

a   *c*
2 is 10 × 10 or 100 × as large in value as 2

Comparing in the Direction of Decrease

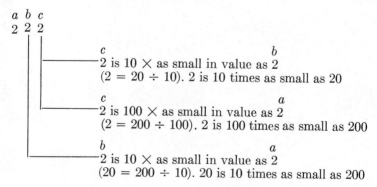

a *b* *c*
2 2 2

c   *b*
2 is 10 × as small in value as 2
(2 = 20 ÷ 10). 2 is 10 times as small as 20

c   *a*
2 is 100 × as small in value as 2
(2 = 200 ÷ 100). 2 is 100 times as small as 200

b   *a*
2 is 10 × as small in value as 2
(20 = 200 ÷ 10). 20 is 10 times as small as 200

By comparisons such as these, it becomes readily apparent that a given digit in the tens' position has a value *10 times as large* as if that digit were in the units' position. A given digit in the hundreds' position has a value 100 times as large as if it were in the units' position and 10 times as large as if it were in the tens' position. Conversely, a given digit in the units' position has a value *10 times as small* as if it were placed in the tens' position, and 100 times as small as if it were placed in the hundreds' position.

5. Refining the idea of positional value through sensing that each succeeding position to the left expresses a value 10 times that of the preceding position to the right.

Just as the units' position is the starting point for determining all values within a numeral, it is also the point of beginning for interpreting values in terms of how many 10s each position represents. The ones' position represents 1s only, and there are not any 10s shown in the position. Therefore, in terms of groupings of 10, the symbol 10^0 shows that there are not any groups of 10. The symbol 10^0 may be read as "ten to the zero power." The position that names the number of groups of 10 is symbolized as 10^1, and so forth.

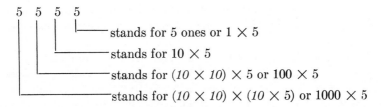

5   5   5   5

stands for 5 ones or 1×5

stands for 10×5

stands for $(10 \times 10) \times 5$ or 100×5

stands for $(10 \times 10) \times (10 \times 5)$ or 1000×5

The values may be shown as in Table 4.2.

TABLE 4.2

5	5	5	5
$(10 \times 10) \times 10$	(10×10)	$\times 10$	$\times 1$ (1s but not any 10s)
10^3	10^2	10^1	10^0

The use of exponents to express the idea above provides a kind of shorthand to record the number of times 10 is used as a factor. In the expression, 10^3, the 10 is called the *base* and the 3 is termed the *exponent*. The exponent tells how many times the base (ten) is used as a factor, that is, $10 \times 10 \times 10$. (See Chapter 11 for further development of this topic.)

IDEAS OF SIZE AND DIRECTIONAL RELATIONSHIP

An important idea of measurement is that of size. Size is relative. A thing may be classified as *large* or as *small* depending upon the referent used for comparison. A thing is considered large as compared with a referent that is considered small; a thing is classified as small when compared with a referent classified as large.

Another important idea that is basic in measuring is that of directional relationship. Contrasts in direction are made with many things, and our language indicates the significance of the idea as may be noted in innumerable expressions such as those indicated in Table 4.3.

TABLE 4.3

DIRECTIONAL RELATION

Direction			Referent		Direction	
largest	larger	large	normal size	small	smaller	smallest
coldest	colder	cold	normal temperature	hot	hotter	hottest
highest	higher	high	normal position	low	lower	lowest
$(10 \times 10) \times 10$	(10×10)	$\times 10$	units' position	$\div 10$	$\div (10 \times 10)$	$\div 10 \times 100$

Similarly, the idea may be noted in the directional relation of *up* and *down, over* and *under, add* and *subtract, increase* and *decrease*, and *multiply* and *divide*.

We extend this same idea to the comparing of number values. The expression, "times as large" and "times as small" helps to clarify the idea of *directional relation*. The expression, "times as small" is emphasized in this text, because it identifies the directional relationship and facilitates building concepts. In other places in the text, the language "one-tenth as large" is used, but for many of the comparisons "times as small" gives a sharper cue to the directional relation. The significance of the directional cues may be noted as one considers the interpretation of decimal fractions and common fractions.

USE OF AN ABACUS TO FACILITATE COMPARISON OF POSITIONAL VALUE [4,5]

The abacus was one of man's first counting machines. An open-end abacus can be used to interpret number systems. The number of sticks

---

[4] Using 10 or more counters in the units' position and then regrouping 10 units to 1 set of 10 facilitates understanding of the idea of grouping by tens. For accelerated learners, a more sophisticated interpretation may be developed. The sticks of the abacus may be adjusted in length so that the maximum number of counters that will fit on a single stick is 9. If another number base is used, the length of sticks may be adjusted to fit the base. For example, only 4 counters will fit on the stick for any given position when base five is used, 7 counters for base eight, and so forth. See p. 64–68 for interpretation of bases other than 10.

[5] Ben A. Sueltz, "Counting Devices and Their Uses," *The Arithmetic Teacher*, vol. 1 (February 1954) pp. 25–30.

used to represent positions may be varied to fit the level of readiness of a given group of learners. An open-end abacus with four sticks is shown below. Using decimal notation, the stick at the far right may be used to show groupings of ones, the next stick toward the left to show groupings of tens, the next stick to show groupings of tens of tens (hundreds), and the stick at the far left to show groupings of tens of hundreds (thousands). See Fig. 4.4.

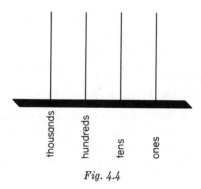

Fig. 4.4

As we use the abacus to show "how many," the idea of grouping by 10s may be developed. For example, in adding 7 + 7 on the abacus, we may put 7 counters on the ones' stick and then add 7 more counters on the ones' stick, making 14 counters on the ones' stick. But when we illustrate decimal numerals using the abacus, 9 is the largest value we express in any one position. Thus, when we have 10 or more than 10 counters in a position, we take 10 counters off the stick standing for the ones' position, and the *group of 10 ones* is regrouped as one set on the stick standing for the tens' position. The *one counter on the tens' stick stands for 1 group of 10 ones.* (Fig. 4.5).

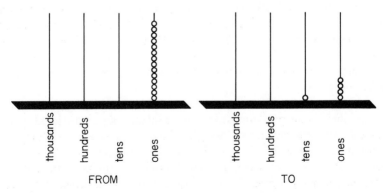

Fig. 4.5

Similarly, a group of 10 groups of 10 each can be regrouped as a single group of 100. The one counter on the hundreds' stick stands for a group of 100. And, 10 of the hundreds' groupings will be represented by one counter on the thousands' stick.

ILLUSTRATIVE LESSONS

The following illustrative lessons are presented in this chapter:

Lesson 1. Early experience using a number line
Lesson 2. Creating a base five numeration system
Lesson 3. Evolving concepts concerning the decimal system of notation
Lesson 4. Concepts concerning constant and positional value
Lesson 5. Continuation of Lesson 4
Lesson 6. Odometer and speedometer

There are many ways that a number line may be used to develop concepts concerning number systems. Lesson 1 is a simple idea that may lead the reader to develop many additional uses for a number line. The topic is given further consideration in the succeeding chapters of the text.

In Lesson 2, creating a base five numeration system, the children brought out some pertinent points concerning the symbols for a numeration system. The names of their second decade numerals are logical and facilitate working with the system.

In Lesson 3, the children evolved the story of how, in days long ago, shepherds kept an account of how many sheep they had. The children, through their activity of grouping pebbles, achieved considerable insight into the concept of constant and positional value for digits and into the idea of zero as a placeholder. They sensed that each digit holds a position in a column, and zero is the placeholder for the expression of "not any" in a column. These children had already carried in addition when they regrouped 10 units to 1 ten, 20 units to 2 tens, 10 tens to 1 hundred, and so on. The learners formulated the basic idea that underlies numerical computation. That idea is that *only terms having the same positional value can be grouped together:* units must be grouped with units, tens with tens, hundreds with hundreds, thousands with thousands, and so on.

Lessons 4 and 5 indicate the nature of thinking that children do in refining their concepts concerning the constant and positional value. The children reported in the lesson could have been led to refine their vocabulary. The word *digit* probably should have been developed. Readiness for the word was indicated through the ability of the children to use language with precision and to state ideas of mathematical relationships.

In Lesson 6, the children in the grade one class interpreted odometers. In their interpretation, they were aware of decimal fractions. Harry's statement concerning the digits at the extreme right of the odometer, "They go too fast to be a mile each time one numeral moves and another comes" indicates awareness of fraction numerical value. Refinement of the awareness is present in Kenneth's statement, "Then it takes 10 of the numerals way over at this side [extreme right] to show a mile." Odometers and other meters that utilize the principle of decimal notation are excellent interpretive devices to use at all grade levels.

Lesson 1
EARLY EXPERIENCE USING A NUMBER LINE

Background of children: The children had used counters and had developed skill with easy combinations. They had talked about positional value of digits in simple numerical expressions such as 25 and had developed ideas concerning 0 and 10 digits being used to write all (decimal) numerals.

Purpose of the lesson: To challenge the children to use a number line to develop directional counting (adding and subtracting) and to use zero as a point of origin on the scale.

Lesson Procedure

The teacher used a roll of adding machine paper and stretched it along the length of the board at the front of the room. There was much unrolled paper at either end of the board. The teacher asked the children what they thought concerning why she had the paper on the board with nothing written on it. The children gave their reasons:

"So we can write the names of the boys and girls in our class. We can can write them in A, B, C order."

"Maybe we are going to make up a story and write it on the paper."

The teacher suggested that the paper was for mathematics and that it could be used to write numerals. She asked for suggestions as to how it could be used to write the numerals. The children were not at a loss of suggesting ways:

Dick: We could start at one end and continue writing numerals. We could write on and on and . . .

Peter: We talked about zero as a starting point when we talked about how many numerals there are. We could start with zero and keep writing numerals to the end of the board.

Craig: And then we could unroll the roll and keep writing, and . . .

The teacher did not have the children pursue this idea since she wished to have them work on directional counting, that is, adding and subtracting on their number line. She appointed a small group of children to help write the numerals and make the number line so that it would be ready for the next day.

The line below shows the idea of their number line:

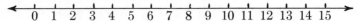

The teacher asked the children to tell how they could use their number line to add and subtract. Each step to the right shows adding one (unit) to the one preceding it. "Not any" $+ 1 = 1; 1 + 1 = 2; 2 + 1 = 3; 3 + 1 = 4$, and so forth. They worked out the ideas using chalk under the chart and showing "counting into" and "counting out from" as shown in Chapter 7. The teacher had left strips of paper of various colors near the chart, and the children suggested that the colored paper could be used to show adding and subtracting on the number line. They used strips of various lengths to stand for selected intervals — for example, a strip of 5 intervals, one of 3 intervals, one of 2 intervals, and so on. The children suggested that they could see how far they would be

The children made a number line.

on the number line if they used their strips and started at zero and added such as the following: $5 + 5 + 5; 3 + 3 + 3; 4 + 4 + 4.$ They talked about 3 fives, and so forth. Thus, on their number line, multiplication as a special case of addition developed. Similarly, they did such things as the following: start at 15, and see how many times the 5 strip can be used to reach 0. The ideas of division as successive subtractions developed. Some of the other activities included: start at 2 and make 3 steps and then move 1 more step. At what numeral will you be on the line?

Older Group of Primary Grade Level

A similar activity was used with an older group of primary grade level children. The children had visited the Institute of Oceanography in their study of tidepools and seashore. At the Institute, there were many exhibits of sea life that the teacher had planned for the children to see. However, the thing that captivated the interest of the children was a map which indicated the elevation of the nearby regions in terms of sea level, above sea level, and below sea level. The teacher led the children to sense that sea level would be a good beginning point to measure from to determine above and below sea level. One child said, "Oh, it's like me when I borrow money from my daddy. If I borrow 10 cents, I am 10 cents in the hole. I'm minus 10 cents. I have to pay the money back. My daddy doesn't let me forget it." The children were ready to extend the number line to a scale indicating directionally the negative and positive values.

The teacher had a group of children help her make a number line. The number line in this case had the 0 toward the center of the number line to challenge the extension of it.

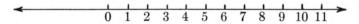

The next day when the children looked at their number line, they asked why the people who made it did not start at the far left.

Craig: I bet I know why. There could be numerals written to that side [pointed left] as well as to this side [pointed right]. I'd write 1, 2, 3, 4, 5, . . . going this way [pointed to the left].

Jim: But, that would look like the side we have made already.

Wendy: I know something. When we saw that map on our trip to the ocean, we saw places that were marked with a minus sign. We could use the minus sign to show below sea level.

Peter: That's a good idea; 0 would be sea level, and the numbers (numerals) on the right are for above sea level.

[A chart using a vertical line was also used.]

The teacher read the readiness of her learners and introduced the words "negative" and "positive." The following were some of the things that were discussed:

(a) *Borrowing money and "going into the hole."* The child had mentioned this idea during the visit to the Institute.

(b) *Below freezing.* However, the children did not go into ideas of Fahrenheit and Centigrade until later.

The children developed the following ideas concerning taking steps on the number line:

You can take one or more steps to the right or to the left of your starting point or you can stay at the place you started — that is, make no move. It is important to tell where you start and how many steps you are taking and in which direction you are taking them.

The children worked mathematical sentences through showing steps on the number line. They started with simple examples, as shown in Table 4.4.

TABLE 4.4

STARTING PLACE	NUMBER OF STEPS	DIRECTION OF MOVE	LANDING PLACE
2	7	right	9
5	3	left	2
6	6	left	0
5	7	left	−2
5	7	right	12

This activity led to making more than single moves and to charting the moves in a way that was adapted from studies by David Page[6] (see Table 4.5).

TABLE 4.5

STARTING PLACE	NUMBER OF STEPS	DIRECTION OF MOVE	LANDING PLACE
5	3	right	—
—	7	left	3
—	4	right	17
−3	4	right	—
−3	4	left	—
7	5	—	12
7	5	—	2

[6] David Page, "Number Lines for the Orbiting Atomic Teacher," reprinted from *The Grade Teacher.* Arithmetic Project, Urbana, Ill.

Lesson 2
CREATING A BASE-FIVE NUMERATION SYSTEM[7]

Purpose of lesson: to challenge the children to refine concepts of the decimal system through building a numeration system using a base other than ten.

Lesson Procedure

The children in Miss S's room had discussed number systems. They had a sharp understanding of the decimal system of notation, and they

What is $1 + 1 + 1 + 1 + 1$?

had worked with number systems using bases other than ten. The following ideas had been stated by the children:

"The idea of the decimal system is really great compared with the Roman system. You'd really have to work to do much dividing with Roman notation."

"I wish that man had made the spelling of words as easy as the spelling of numerals. It's easy to spell 948 when we write numerals."

"I don't see why man didn't make the names of the numbers as

---

[7] The children discussed some properties of their numeration system (page 83). The properties of whole numbers are developed in Chapter 5 of this text. This lesson, however, pertains primarily to the topic of concepts underlying number and numeration systems.

sensible as the numerals. Then we would not have names like *eleven, twelve, thirteen, . . .*"

[The children had discussed the idea that suffix *ty* represents tens in the words twen*ty* through nine*ty*.] Miss S challenged the children to think about the things that they would do if they invented a number system. The following ideas were listed by the children:

1. "The number names should help you see how the system works."

2. "The numerals should be easy to write. Our (decimal) numerals are easy to write, but when I was in second grade I used to mix up a 6 and a 9."

. . . "and I used to make my 7 go the wrong way at the top."
. . . "and I made 3's like E's. It's easy to mix up which way to go."
. . . "I wouldn't have to use many digits, and then I wouldn't need to learn so many number facts."

The children with their teacher's help invented a number system with a set of five elements. They decided to use the concepts, principles, and properties of decimal notation, but to develop their set of elements for the system and to make their own names for the numbers. However, they used the names *zero, one, two, three,* and *four* for the first five symbols of their system. The following set of elements were developed:

NAME IN COMMON LANGUAGE	NUMERAL TO EXPRESS THE VALUE
zero	0
one	1
two	∩
three	△
four	□

They decided to use the numerals *0* and *1* because they could not be reversed and are easy to write. The new numerals for *two, three,* and *four* were named *two, three,* and *four* to facilitate communication, and the names were as good as they thought they could make.

They then had to decide what to name the numeral 10_{five} which stood for one group of 5 ones. Since the system was a base five system, the name decided upon was *onefi*. Thus, *11* was *onefi one*, and *1* ∩ was *onefi two*, and *1* △ was *onefi three* and *1* □ was *onefi four*. The development of the system is shown in Table 4.6.

TABLE 4.6

NUMERAL LANGUAGE BASE FIVE	COMMON LANGUAGE BASE FIVE	EQUIVALENT DECIMAL VALUE
0	zero	0
1	one	1
∩	two	2
△	three	3
☐	four	4
1 0	onefi	5
1 1	onefi one	6
1 ∩	onefi two	7
1 △	onefi three	8
1 ☐	onefi four	9
∩ 0	twofi	10
∩ 1	twofi one	11
∩ ∩	twofi two	12
∩ △	twofi three	13
∩ ☐	twofi four	14
Etc.	through	
☐ ☐	fourfi four	24

In their numeration system 100_{five} has an equivalent value of 25 in base ten. They called 100_{five} *onefifi*. ($1 \times 5 \times 5$ decimal base.)

The following were among the ways the children used their numeration system.

1. They made a chart showing the primary combinations for addition, subtraction, multiplication, and division.

2. They added, subtracted, multiplied, and divided, using simple examples such as:

$$\cap + \cap = \square \qquad \cap 0 - 10 = 10$$
$$\triangle + \triangle = 11 \qquad \cap \times \cap = \square$$
$$11 + 11 = \cap\cap \qquad \frac{\square}{\cap} = \cap$$

3. They experimented to see if their system obeyed some of the properties and principles of decimal notation: Do addition and multiplication obey the commutative principle? For addition:

$$\cap + \square = \square + \cap$$
$$11 = 11$$

For multiplication:

$$\triangle \times \square = \square \times \triangle$$
$$\cap\cap = \cap\cap$$

Do addition and multiplication obey the associative principle? For addition:

$$(\square + \cap) + \triangle = \square + (\cap + \triangle)$$
$$11 + \triangle = \square + 10$$
$$1\,\square = 1\,\square$$

For multiplication:

$$(\triangle \times \cap) \times \square = \triangle \times (\cap \times \square)$$
$$11 \times \square = \triangle \times 1\,\triangle$$
$$\square\square = \square\square$$

Similarly, they tested to see if other principles and properties of decimal notation held true for their base five system (Fig. 4.6).

ADDITION

Top Addend

	O	1	∩	△	□
O	O	1	∩	△	□
1	1	∩	△	□	10
∩	∩	△	□	10	11
△	△	□	10	11	1∩
□	□	10	11	1∩	1△

Fig. 4.6

Lesson 3
EVOLVING CONCEPTS UNDERLYING THE DECIMAL
SYSTEM OF NOTATION
Grade Two Class (Early in School Year)

The following report is of a group of children in grade two who worked with the concept of zero as a placeholder. The children had discovered many things about the decimal system. They had heard the story of how the shepherds in early days kept track of their sheep by using a pebble to stand for each sheep. Using one pebble for each sheep, a pictorial account of number of sheep was simple — just a long line of pebbles was needed to depict how many. As the line of pebbles grew very long, ten pebbles were taken out of the original line and one pebble was placed in a line at the left. The one pebble in the position at the left stood for one ten. This procedure can be repeated as long as there are ten pebbles left in the original position. The procedure was extended to form groupings of hundreds and tens of hundreds. The children wanted to act out the story of the shepherds who in days long ago used counters to keep an account of how many sheep they had. A supply of pebbles was found on the playground. The children made their long line of pebbles and proceeded to regroup them into tens and units. One child had 13 pebbles in one line which he regrouped as indicated in the following table.

ORIGINAL GROUPING	REGROUPED
*	* *
*	*
*	*
*	
*	
*	
*	
*	
*	
*	
*	
*	
*	

He took 10 pebbles out of the original line and used 1 of the 10 pebbles to represent 10 by placing it in the column to the left. One child discovered that it took only 8 pebbles to represent 1 2 5. Another child used 8 pebbles to represent 5 2 1.

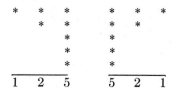

*	*	*	*	*	*
	*	*	*	*	
		*	*		
		*	*		
		*	*		
1	2	5	5	2	1

However, the children had not done very much regrouping of columns until the need of a "not any" placeholder arose. One child had 20 pebbles, and he counted out 2 tens and selected 2 of the 20 pebbles to stand for 20. As soon as he placed the two pebbles in a column to the left, the original column was empty. He said, "Now my 20 says only 2. What should I do?" Other children were called upon to help solve the problem that had arisen. The children said that something was needed to show that there weren't any "ones." These children — not unlike the usual group of learners — didn't lack ingenuity. One suggestion was to mark the column by drawing strong lines in the sand. When the column was "bare," it meant that there were not any for that column. Other ideas followed. Using the materials that were close at hand, the children suggested that a piece of chalk, a ball of string, a foot ruler, a stick, or another available object could stand for "not any." These children sensed a need that made zero truly significant in terms of a placeholder. In such instances the expression "not any" is much better than "none." "Not any" expresses an absence of quantity and carries meaning that is different from the concept of nonexistence connoted by "none." With the numeral 1 0, the expressions "one ten" and "one ten and not any units" are desirable in the initial stages of discovery of positional value with the teens.

Lesson 4
CONCEPTS CONCERNING CONSTANT
AND POSITIONAL VALUE
Grade Two Class

This lesson was developed by a group of children in grade two. In this lesson, the word *digit* was not introduced. The word *numeral* was used until later in the school year. Consequently, the expression that there are only "10 numerals" was used instead of the expression "10 digits."

Purpose of the lesson: To develop concepts with regard to the decimal system of notation.

Lesson Procedure

Teacher: You have been using numerals for a long time. How many *different numerals* do you think there are in the number system that we use?

Jerry: There are many, many numerals.

Tommy: Oh, there are so many that we couldn't count them. There must be a million! That's very many.

Teacher: What is the very beginning numeral?

[Preceding this lesson, the children had talked about beginning points. They had discussed why they needed a starting point when they ran races, and so forth. Through such discussions, they had developed concepts of zero as a starting point. Hence, there was background for the question "What is the very beginning numeral?" and it was not surprising to find that many of the children offered the following answer.]

Richard: Zero. Zero is the very beginning numeral. It comes before one. [Teacher wrote "0" on the blackboard.]

Teacher: What is the next numeral?

Class: The next numeral is 1. Then 2. Then 3, 4, 5, 6, 7, 8, 9, 10, 11, 12, 13, 14, 15, 16, 17, 18, 19, 20 . . . .

[Teacher wrote 0, 1, 2, 3, 4, 5, 6, 7, 8, 9, 10, 11, 12, 13, 14, 15, and so forth, on the blackboard.]

Teacher: Do you notice how the symbol for ten shows that it *is* 10?

Dick: It isn't really a new numeral. It is made up of 1 and 0.

Teacher: But that isn't all there is to it. I'll write something that is made up of 1 and 0, but it isn't 10.

[Teacher wrote 0 1.]

Dick: That doesn't say ten. The one is in the wrong place. The one has to be in front of the zero.

Teacher: That is correct. It is because the one is written in front of the zero that makes the symbol mean ten. The symbol really means *one ten and not any more.* Is that true?

Sue: Yes, that's true. Zero means not any, and when it is used with 1 ten, it would mean 1 ten and not any more.

Jean: Eleven is 2 ones. It means 1 ten and 1 more.

Mary: And 12 is just a one and a two. It means 1 ten and 2 more.

Denny: And 13 is just a 1 and a 3, and 14 is just a 1 and a 4, and . . . .

Jim: And 15 is just a 1 and a 5, and . . . .

Teacher: How many different numerals do we have on the blackboard? [Children counted 0, 1, 2, 3, 4, 5, 6, 7, 8, 9. A general agreement of "ten" was the result.]

Teacher: Can we express numbers like 23 using only numerals that are among the 10 numerals — 0, 1, 2, 3, 4, 5, 6, 7, 8 and 9?

Marian: Yes. To write 23, all we need to use is a 2 and 3.

Edith: We can write the biggest numerals we know using those 10 numbers. I'll write one on the blackboard.

[Edith wrote a number on the blackboard that none of the group could read, and there was a general "Oh!" indicating that the numeral value written was a very large one.]

Meredith: I'd like to know the name of the very largest numeral in the whole world.

Class: What is the biggest numeral that you know, Teacher?

Teacher: The names to express large numbers will not mean much to you now, but we call them hundreds, thousands, millions, billions, trillions. We'll learn more about such names at another time.

Lesson 5
CONCEPTS CONCERNING THE CONSTANT
AND POSITIONAL VALUE OF NUMBER
Continuation of Lesson 2

This lesson followed the one in which the children discovered that there are 10 primary digits in the decimal system of notation.

Purpose of lesson: Continued development of concepts of the decimal system of notation.

Lesson Procedure

Teacher: Yesterday, we talked about *different* numerals we have. What did you discover about the numerals we use?

Dick: We discovered that there are really only 10 numerals.

Tommy: And the numerals are 0, 1, 2, 3, 4, 5, 6, 7, 8, 9.

Jean: Ten is just a 1 and a 0, but the one must be written in front of the zero to say 1 ten and not any more.

Tommy: And eleven is just 2 ones, and twelve is just a 1 and a 2, and 13 is just a 1 and a 3, and . . . .

Richard: You could go on and on like that, Tommy.

Teacher: I am going to write a numeral that tells about marbles. [Teacher wrote "22 marbles" on the blackboard.]

Teacher: Can you read what I have written on the blackboard? See if you can read as I point with this pointer.

[Teacher pointed slowly enough that the children read as follows:]

Class: Twenty-two marbles.

Teacher: There are two of the twos. If you could have the marbles that one of the twos stands for, is there one of the twos that you would want rather than the other one?

Denny: I should say so. It would make a lot of difference. I know which two I want.

Teacher: Would you like to go to the blackboard and point to the 2 that you would choose?

Denny: Yes.

[Denny went to the blackboard and selected the 2 to the left.]

Denny: I want this 2. It means 2 tens or 20 marbles, and I like marbles.

Teacher: Mary, you did not get a chance to choose. If we gave you the marbles that the other 2 stands for, how many marbles would you get?

Mary: Only two, but I'd rather have Denny's 2 if I could.

Teacher: Here is another example.

[Teacher wrote "55 pennies" on the blackboard.]

Marian: May I be the first to choose the 5 that I want? I know which one I want.

Teacher: All right, Marian.

[Marian went to the blackboard and pointed to the 5 at the left.]

Marian: That 5 says fifty. I'd rather have 50 pennies than just 5 pennies.

Jim: May I have the other 5? It isn't the 5 that I would choose, but I'd rather have it than not to have any at all.

Teacher: Jim's 5 stands for 5 pennies, and Marian's 5 stands for 50 pennies. How many of Jim's group of 5 pennies would it take to make Marian's 50 pennies? [Pause] . . . Who can suggest how we can find out?

Jim: It would take quite a few. [Pause] . . . We could count by fives to see how many it takes to make 50 .

Teacher: I'll write fives on the blackboard while you count by fives. Each time you count, I'll write a 5. Would that help you? [Teacher wrote on the blackboard as the children counted 5, 10, 15, 20, 25, 30, 35, 40, 45, 50.]

Class: Let's see how many fives it took.

[Class counted as the teacher pointed to the fives.]

Jim: It takes 10 fives to make 50 so Marian has 10 times as many pennies as I have.

Marian: And, you have 10 times as few as I have. I wouldn't want to trade with you.

Jerry: I bet that Jim would like to trade with you, Marian.

Teacher: We have found that 22 really means 2 tens and 2 more. 55 means 5 tens and 5 more. We discovered yesterday that each numeral shows its value through the *place* it is written or said. If we write the numerals like this, it may help to make our discovery clear.

[Teacher wrote the following on the blackboard:]

```
 0   1   2   3   4   5   6   7   8   9
10  11  12  13  14  15  16  17  18  19
20  21  22  23  24  25  26  27  28  29
```

Teacher: The top row is the 10 numerals that we use in writing number values. How is the second row different from the top row?

Jim: The second row has a one written in front of each of the numerals that were written in the top row.

Dick: Yes, and the ones mean 1 ten. You use the one to say ten.

Marian: And in the third row, you wrote a 2 in front of each of the numerals that are written in the top row. The two shows 2 tens or 20. But, every row has the 10 numerals we use to write all numerals.

Teacher: That is true. What you have discovered about the way number values are shown will be very useful to you. Before tomorrow, try to discover what is the highest number value that you can write using only 2 digits.

Lesson 6
ODOMETER AND SPEEDOMETER

Purpose of lesson: To challenge observation, to refine concepts with regard to how distance is measured, and to develop concepts of decimal fractions through discussion of an odometer.

Teacher: When you have been riding in a car, how many of you have watched the instrument on the dashboard that measures how far you have gone?

Paul: I have. When you go fast in your car, the numerals surely move fast. When my daddy goes too fast, the numbers go very fast. My mother tells my daddy to drive slower.

Mildred: I have watched. The numerals over at this side [she pointed to the right] go to nine, and then they start at zero again and go to nine, and then back to zero.

Teacher: Have you noticed the numerals that go the fastest? Where are they on the instrument?

Jean: The numerals that go the very fastest are way over to this side. [Jean pointed to the right.] The ones to this side don't move very often. [She pointed to the left.]

Harry: My daddy says "how many miles" when he talks about a

An odometer is used to measure distance.

trip that we are going to take, but the numerals way over to this side
[to the right] aren't alike. They go too fast to be a mile each time one
numeral moves and another numeral comes.

[This group of children had discussed that their school is about a mile
from the main intersection of a large highway. Through that discussion
and other ideas of a mile that had arisen, the children had a fairly good
idea of a mile.]

Teacher: How many times do the numerals to the right change in
going a mile?

Stephen: I don't know for sure, but I think that it goes 0, 1, 2, 3, 4,
5, 6, 7, 8, 9, and then the numeral next to the fastest numerals turns.
Is that right?

Bruce: Yes, I think that is right. That is the way it works with our
car.

Kenneth: Then it takes 10 of the numerals way over at this side
[to the right] to show a mile.

Teacher: That is right, but I suggest that each of you watch while
you are in a car and see the miles being measured. Maybe you can
discover some other things about measuring how far you go. I have
an instrument from an old car. Do you know what the instrument is
called?

Verna: The one that measures speed is called a speedometer, isn't
it? We talked about that one day.

Teacher: That is right. Do any of you know what the one that measures
distance is called? [Children did not know.] It is called an *odometer.*
I shall write the word on the blackboard. [Teacher wrote *"odometer"*
on the blackboard.] I am going to leave this instrument in our room, and
you may experiment with it. See how many things you can discover
about how it works, and we'll talk about the things that you find out.

Note: The group of children had been led to observe the speedometers
and odometers of cars. Discussion of speed and of the speedometer had
taken place previous to this lesson. Having an odometer and a speedometer from an old car so that the children can manipulate them is
very helpful. "Seeing and working" them adds interest and stimulates
mathematicking.

The refinement of language should evolve with the refinement of
concepts. The words "odometer," for an instrument to measure distances traveled, and "speedometer," for an instrument to measure
speed, and the expressions "to the right" and "to the left" can be
developed in the primary grades. With the given group of children, the
words "to the right" and "to the left" were developed in a lesson that
was taught soon after the lesson reported above.

Discussion Questions

1. Write an equivalent decimal numeral for each of the following: 125_{eight} 436_{twelve}; 144_{five}; 1111_{two}.

2. The numeral 54 stands for 5 groups of 10 each and 4 ones when we use base ten. Express the equivalent value when you use: base five; base twelve; and base eight.

3. Write your chronological age in the following bases: base ten; base five; base twelve; and base two.

4. Use the structure of the decimal system, and select another number base and make a number system. You may use decimal digits or you may make new symbols and new names for the digits. With your number system,

   (a) Write the names for the primary digits that you selected.
   (b) Write the 2-digit numerals and their names for the second decade values.
   (c) Using your number base, write some addition examples and solve them.
   (d) Using your number system, write some examples for subtraction and solve them.

5. What is meant by stating that number ideas and number languages are not "disparate bodies of subject-matter"?

6. Why is counting considered to be the cardinal use of number?

7. Is it possible to have a graduated scale having a referent unit other than one?

8. What advantages would there be in a 24-hour clock scale as compared with a 12-hour scale?

9. The expression, "10 times as large" in number value does not have the same meaning as "10 times larger than." Use the numerical expression, 55, to explain and illustrate the difference in the two meanings.

10. How would you make clear the important difference between the statement, "Zero means *no thing*" and the statement, "Zero means *nothing?*"

11. The Science News Letter for July 14, 1962, p. 22, states, "A neutrino is so small that one billion trillion trillion trillion neutrinos could fit into *a square inch of space.*" What other striking illustrations of micro-measurement can you find?

12. What advantages are there in a duodecimal number system, that is, one based on subgroupings of twelves rather than subgroupings of tens?

13. You plan to teach some ideas of "clock arithmetic." Suggest some modular systems that you think children have observed which are good illustrations of systems.

14. Give instances in your experience of the use of the one-to-one correspondence techniques.

15. A numerical symbol for zero (the null set) was introduced into the numeral pattern long after symbols for the other symbols were established. Does this suggest that 0 is not an important symbol? What are the distinctive things that one needs to know regarding the uses of the symbol 0?

Suggested Readings

Banks, J. Houston, *Learning and Teaching Arithmetic*, 2d ed. Boston, Mass.: Allyn and Bacon, Inc., 1964, Chap. 2.

Brumfiel, Charles F., Robert E. Eicholz, and Merrill E. Shanks, *Fundamental Concepts of Elementary Mathematics.* Reading, Mass.: Addison-Wesley Publishing Company, Inc., 1962, Chaps. 3, 4.

Deery, Ruth T., "Linda Learns the Hexal System," *The Arithmetic Teacher,* vol. 5 (November 1958), pp. 251–255.

Douglass, Harl R., "The Development of Number Concept in Children of Pre-School and Kindergarten Ages," *Journal of Experimental Psychology,* vol. 8 (December 1925), pp. 443–470.

The Duodecimal Bulletin. The Duodecimal Society of America, Staten Island, N. Y.

Gibb, E. Glenadine, Phillip S. Jones, and Charlotte W. Junge, "Number and Operation," *The Growth of Mathematical Ideas, Grades K–12,* National Council of Teachers of Mathematics, Twenty-fourth Yearbook. Washington, D.C.: The Council, 1959, pp. 7–64.

Johnson, Donovan A., and William H. Glenn, *Understanding Numeration Systems.* St. Louis, Mo.: Webster Publishing Company, 1961.

Lovell, K., *The Growth of Basic Mathematical and Scientific Concepts in Children.* London: University of London Press, Ltd., 1961.

McSwain, E. T., "Discovering Meanings in Arithmetic," *Childhood Education,* vol. 8 (February 1950), pp. 267–271.

Meserve, Bruce E., and Max A. Sobel, *Introduction to Mathematics.* Englewood Cliffs, N.J.: Prentice-Hall, Inc., 1964, Chap. 2.

Mueller, Francis J., *Arithmetic, Its Structure and Concepts,* 2d ed. Englewood Cliffs, N.J.: Prentice Hall, Inc., 1964, Units 1,2,3,4.

Osborn, Roger, M. Vere De Vault, Claude C. Boyd, and W. Robert Houston, *Extending Mathematics Understanding.* Columbus, Ohio: Charles E. Merrill Books, Inc., 1961, Chaps. 1, 2, and 10.

Peters, Ann C., "The Number System and the Teacher," *The Arithmetic Teacher,* vol. 4 (October 1957), pp. 155–160.

Peterson, John A., and Joseph Hashisaki, *Theory of Arithmetic.* New York: John Wiley & Sons, Inc., 1963, Chap. 1.

Rappaport, David, "Understanding Meanings in Arithmetic," *The Arithmetic Teacher,* vol. 5, (March 1958), pp. 96–99.

Riess, Anita P., "Pre-First Grade Arithmetic," *The Arithmetic Teacher,* vol. 4 (March 1957), pp. 50–54.

Sanford, Vera, "Hindu-Arabic Numerals," *The Arithmetic Teacher,* vol. 2 (December 1955), p. 157.

Smith, David Eugene, and Jekuthiel Ginsburg, *Numbers and Numerals.* New York: Bureau of Publications, Teachers College, Columbia University, 1937.

Sueltz, Ben A., "Counting Devices and Their Uses," *The Arithmetic Teacher,* vol. 1 (February 1954), pp. 25–30.

Swenson, Esther J., *Teaching Arithmetic to Children.* New York: The Macmillan Company, 1964, Chaps. 3,4.

Tingley, E. M., "Base Eight Arithmetic and Money," *School Science and Mathematics,* vol. 40 (June 1940), pp. 503–508.

Van Engen, H., "An Analysis of Meaning in Arithmetic," *The Elementary School Journal,* vol. 49 (February, March, 1949), pp. 321–329; 395–400.

Weaver, J. F., "Our Number System and the Use of Manipulative Materials in Arithmetic," *Journal of Education,* vol. 136 (October 1953), pp. 8–10.

Wilcox, Marie S., and John E. Yarnelle, *Mathematics, A Modern Approach.* Reading, Mass.: Addison-Wesley Publishing Company, Inc., 1963, Chaps. 1,2.

Willerding, Margaret F., "Take a Number and Build a Number System," *The Arithmetic Teacher,* vol. 7 (January 1960), pp. 35–37.

5

Properties and Relations
of Whole Numbers

5.1 INTRODUCTION

There are basic concepts of mathematics that occur and recur in many different settings. The interpretation of the patterns of these concepts serves as a foundation for the growth of mathematical ideas.

An important consideration is the learner's discovery and development of the patterns that operate in mathematical systems. In a very simple way,[1] a mathematical system may be considered as consisting of the following:

(a) a set of elements

(b) one or more operations using the elements of the set

(c) properties (axioms or postulates) concerning the set of elements and its operations

(d) one or more relations, such as equivalence $(5 + 5 = 10)$

The properties (axioms or postulates) are assumptions; they are ideas that are accepted as truths concerning how the system works.

One of the first mathematical systems with which a child works is the decimal whole number system, which serves as a pattern for other systems. In this chapter, we shall consider some of the main properties and relations with decimal notation. These serve as a model for interpreting common and decimal fraction numbers, other number bases,

---

[1] A more profound interpretation of a mathematical system should be developed as the learner progresses in his study of mathematics.

and so forth. There are mathematical systems for which the properties and relations of decimal notation do not operate, but these are usually studied after one has a considerable background in understanding the decimal system.

5.2   DECIMAL NOTATION: its elements and operations

SET OF ELEMENTS

The set of digits used for writing the symbols for decimal whole numbers is:

$$\{0, 1, 2, 3, 4, 5, 6, 7, 8, 9\}$$

The set of decimal whole numerals is created from the set of ten digits. As discussed in Chap. 3, the collection of decimal whole numbers is an infinite set. There is no last number. We may indicate the idea using numerals.

$$\{0, 1, 2, 3, 4, 5, 6, 7, 8, 9, 10, 11, 12, 13, \cdots\}$$

OPERATIONS

The operations that we shall discuss in the first part of this chapter are addition and multiplication. These are called *binary operations*, because only two terms at a time are involved in their operation. For example, addition is a *binary operation:* only two numbers are added at a time. If there are three addends in a given example, we may add any two of the addends and then combine that sum with the other addend. For example, $(5 + 3) + 2$. We may add $5 + 3 = 8$. We then add $8 + 2 = 10$. If there are more than three addends, a similar procedure is used. We add pairs of numbers.

Similarly, multiplication is a *binary operation*. We multiply only two numbers at a time: $(5 \times 6) \times 2$. We may multiply $5 \times 6 = 30$, and then multiply $30 \times 2 = 60$. We multiply pairs of numbers. Hence, we say that addition and multiplication are *binary operations*.

5.3   PROPERTIES of ADDITION and MULTIPLICATION

The following properties are those axioms or postulates that students can discover readily. They should be evolved by the student a considerable length of time before their vocabulary and formal development occur.

CLOSURE PROPERTY

If an operation on the members of a set yields another member of that set, the set is said to be closed with respect to that operation.

Of Addition

Since each member in the number scale represents a grouping of ones, it follows that adding two or more such groupings or sets of ones will produce another grouping of ones, that is, another number on the scale.

$$3 + 4 = 7 \qquad 5 + 5 = 10 \qquad 16 + 16 = 32$$

With any whole number that we select, we may add another whole number to it, and the sum will be a member of the set of whole numbers. If a and b are members of the set of whole numbers, than $a + b$ will be an element of that set. This characteristic is called the *closure property of addition*. We may say that the set of whole numbers is closed with respect to addition.

Of Multiplication

Initially, the process of multiplication is one of finding the sum of a series of addends consisting of repetitions of the same numerical value. It is evident that the result will be another grouping of ones. Therefore, the answer lies within the number scale.

$$5 \times 6 = 30 \qquad 7 \times 9 = 63 \qquad 100 \times 100 = 10,000$$

If a and b are elements of the set of whole numbers, then $a \times b$ will be an element of the set. Hence, we may say that the set of whole numbers is closed with respect to multiplication.[2]

IDENTITY ELEMENTS

If there is any element of the set of numbers that can be multiplied by or added to the other elements of the set leaving those elements unchanged, that element is called an identity element for the particular operation.

---

[2] It is interesting to note that the case of subtraction is not so readily settled. When the set of whole numbers is restricted to positive integers, the closure property does not apply. However, when the set is inclusive of both the positive and negative scales of directional numbers, the closure property is applicable for subtraction.

The operation of division with whole numbers may, and often does, result in a number value that is not a member of the set of whole numbers, that is, $2\overline{)\,7}$. Hence, the property of closure does not apply for the operation of division with whole numbers.

Zero—the Identity Element for Addition

$$5 + 0 = 5 \qquad 25 + 0 = 25 \qquad 0 + 2 = 2$$

$N + 0 = N$ The sum of any whole number and zero is that number.

$0 + N = N$ The sum of zero and any whole number is that number.

Since the sum of any whole number and zero is that whole number holds true for the set of whole numbers, we say that 0 is the identity element for addition.

One—the Identity Element for Multiplication

$$9 \times 1 = 9 \qquad 1 \times 6 = 6 \qquad 25 \times 1 = 25$$

$N \times 1 = N$ The product of any whole number and one is that whole number.

$1 \times N = N$ The product of one and any whole number is that whole number.

Since the product of any whole number and one is that whole number holds true for the set of whole numbers, we say that 1 is the identity element for multiplication.

COMMUTATIVE PROPERTY (INTERCHANGEABLE ORDER)

The order in which two numbers are added or multiplied does not affect the sum or product.

Of Addition

$$3 + 4 = 4 + 3 \qquad 25 + 15 = 15 + 25$$
$$7 = 7 \qquad\qquad 40 = 40$$

The sum of any two numbers does not depend upon the order in which they are added. This property is called the *commutative property of addition*. The idea may be generalized that $a + b = b + a$ when a and b are members of our set of positive whole numbers.

Of Multiplication

$$3 \times 5 = 5 \times 3 \qquad 25 \times 4 = 4 \times 25$$
$$15 = 15 \qquad\qquad 100 = 100$$

The product of any two numbers does not depend upon the order in which they are multiplied. The idea may be generalized that $a \times b = b \times a$ when a and b are members of our set of numbers. This property is called the *commutative property of multiplication*.

ASSOCIATIVE PROPERTY

Since addition and multiplication are binary operations, if more than two addends or factors are to be totaled, they will need to be selected in a serial order. The order in which the terms are selected and associated does not affect the value of the result. This property is called the *associative property*.

Of Addition

$$(3 + 4) + 5$$

As pointed out earlier, we add pairs of numbers at a time. We get the same final sum no matter how the numbers are associated or paired. We may add $(3 + 4) + 5$ as $3 + 4 = 7$, and then add $7 + 5 = 12$. Or, we may add 3 to $(4 + 5)$ and have $3 + 9 = 12$. Either way the sum is 12.

$$(3 + 4) + 5 = 3 + (4 + 5)$$
$$7 + 5 = 3 + 9$$
$$12 = 12$$

This idea may be generalized letting a, b, and c represent whole numbers.

$$(a + b) + c = a + (b + c)$$

Of Multiplication

$$(6 \times 5) \times 3$$

We get the same product no matter how the numbers are associated or paired. We may multiply as indicated below:

$$(6 \times 5) \times 3 = 6 \times (5 \times 3)$$
$$30 \times 3 = 6 \times 15$$
$$90 = 90$$

This idea may be generalized letting a, b, and c represent whole numbers: The associative property applies to multiplication.

$$(a \times b) \times c = a \times (b \times c)$$

DISTRIBUTIVE PROPERTY OF MULTIPLICATION WITH RESPECT TO ADDITION

Every number in the counting number series is a sum of two or more numbers in the series. Suppose we wish to multiply any number value a specified number of times. A question arises as to whether the multiplication operation can be distributed and applied with the addends as well as to their sum without affecting the equality relationships. An answer to this question may be attempted as follows:

$3 + 2 = 5$. If we multiply each of the terms by 5, will the equivalence still prevail?

$$\text{Does } 5 \times (3 + 2) = (5 \times 3) + (5 \times 2)?$$
$$5 \times 5 = 15 + 10$$
$$25 = 25$$

We can see that the result is the same either way.

$4 + 3 + 3 = 10$. If we multiply each term by 7, will equivalence prevail?

$$\text{Does } [(7 \times 4) + (7 \times 3)] + (7 \times 3) = 7 \times [(4 + 3) + 3]?$$
$$(28 + 21) + 21 = 7 \times 10$$
$$49 + 21 = 70$$
$$70 = 70$$

This conforms with the generalization that the value of a sum is directly related to the value of its addends. Hence, making each of the addends a specified times as great or as small in value results in a corresponding increase or decrease, respectively, in the value of the product.

Consider the following example: $6 \times 656 = ?$ The value expressed by any decimal numeral is the sum of the values expressed in the several digit positions of the numeral — 656 may be rewritten as $600 + 50 + 6$. The multiplication of this expression by 6 may be distributed as follows:

$$6(600 + 50 + 6) = 3600 + 300 + 36 = 3936$$

or as

```
  656      or      656
 × 6             × 6
  36            3936
  30
  36
 3936
```

The fact that multiplication has a distributive property is the basis for the common procedure used in that operation.

The idea of distributing the multiplier over the terms of the other factor (the multiplicand) is called the *distributive property of multiplication with respect to addition*. This property makes it possible to perform the computations that we commonly use when we multiply, using examples that have more than one digit in the multiplicand. We use the common multiplier for each of the values of the digits in the multiplicand — that is, the common multiplier is used to find the product for the units, the tens, the hundreds, and so forth. We then add the separate products to find the sum.

The idea may also be illustrated when the common multiplier is distributed over two addends that may each represent unit values. For example, Bill bought 3 ice cream cones at 5 cents each on Monday and 4 ice cream cones at 5 cents each on Tuesday. What was the cost of Bill's ice cream cones for these two days? The problem may be solved as follows:

$$5 \times (3 + 4) = (5 \times 3) + (5 \times 4)$$
$$5 \times 7 = 15 + 20$$
$$35 = 35$$

The properties of whole numbers that have been developed in this section are summarized in Table 5.1, where a, b, and c stand for elements of Set A.

TABLE 5.1

set of elements $A = \{0, 1, 2, 3, 4, 5, 6, 7, 8, 9, 10, 11, 12, 13, \cdots\}$

OPERATIONS→	ADDITION	MULTIPLICATION
Properties		
Closure	$a + b$ is a member of Set A	$a \times b$ is a member of Set A
Identity elements	0 — identity element for addition	1 — identity element for multiplication
Commutative	$a + b = b + a$	$a \times b = b \times a$
Associative	$a + b + c =$ $(a + b) + c = a + (b + c)$	$a \times b \times c =$ $(a \times b) \times c = a \times (b \times c)$
Distributive	$a(b + c) = (a \times b) + (a \times c)$	

These properties should be intuitively sensed and then developed so that learners develop a mastery of them. After mastering the properties with decimal whole numbers, the properties should be developed with decimal and common fraction numbers and with systems using bases other than ten, and so forth.

5.4   RELATIONS

The language of mathematics is a language of comparison. We associate objects with other objects, and then may form ideas concerning their relationship. We talk about how the objects are related in terms of how they are alike and how they are different. Two things may be compared in innumerable ways. Their relations may express very simple ideas such as one thing "is heavier than" another, that the sun looks as though it "is the same shape as" the moon, John "can run faster than" Susan, and Mary "is the sister of" Sue. The language of comparison accounts for much of our language.

The following are some simple relations that young children interpret:

"IS INCLUDED IN" (inclusion relation)[3]

Mary belongs to our team. Sue belongs to the set of volleyball players at Chase School. Tom is a member of the science club. In the preceding chapter, the symbol ϵ was used to indicate "is a member of." The symbol is one of the many ways that are used to show the idea "is included in."

ONE-TO-ONE CORRESPONDENCE[4]

When two sets are matched in one-to-one correspondence, they are termed equivalent sets. The matching process is essentially what is done in any counting operation because one is comparing the members of the set under consideration with the set of points on the counting number scale to determine the equivalence of the two sets. Matching sets is a very natural experience of young children. Jill has one pencil for each person at her table. There are as many pencils as there are children. There are as many cartons of orange juice as there are children in the room. There is one carton for each child, and there are not any cartons of juice left over.

EQUIVALENCE RELATION

The idea of "is equal to" or "is the same as" is an equivalence relation. Three relations that are true for equivalence will be discussed briefly. When an example satisfies the three relations of reflexive, symmetric, and transitive, the equivalence relation holds true.

Reflexive Relation

If a thing is equal to itself, the relation is called reflexive. Six is six, the sky is as blue as itself, and $4 = 4$ illustrate the reflexive relation. The mathematical symbol that may be used to express the idea of the reflexive relation is $a = a$.

[3] See Chap. 3.
[4] See Chap. 3.

Symmetric Relation

If two things are equal to each other, the relation is termed symmetric. Mary weighs the same as John; then John weighs the same as Mary. Sue is a classmate of Tom; then Tom is a classmate of Sue. The sky is as blue as Mary's dress; then Mary's dress is as blue as the sky. Tom is Mary's brother is not a symmetric relation — Mary is not Tom's brother! The symmetric relation may be expressed as:

$$\text{If } a = b, \quad \text{then } b = a$$

Transitive Relation

When a given element is equal to a second element, and the second element is equal to a third element, then the third element is equal to the given element. This relation is termed transitive. John has 30 cents + 20 cents and Mary has 20 cents + 30 cents. John and Mary have the same number of cents. Sue has the same number of cents as Mary. Therefore, John and Sue have the same number of cents. The relation "is next to" is not a transitive relation. Reading in the direction of increase on the counting number scale, 3 is next to 4 and 4 is next to 5, but 5 is not next to 3.

The transitive relation may be expressed as:

$$\text{If } a = b \text{ and } b = c, \text{ then } a = c$$

To satisfy the relation "equal to" as used in mathematical sentences, all three relations — reflexive, symmetric, and transitive — must hold true.

Reflexive $a = a$ The number is equal to itself: $2 = 2$

Symmetric   If $a = b$, then $b = a$. If $4 \times 5 = 20$, then $20 = 4 \times 5$.

Transitive   If $a = b$ and $b = c$, then $a = c$. If $3 + 9 = 12$, and $10 + 2 = 12$, then $3 + 9 = 10 + 2$

INEQUALITIES

As brought out in Chapter 2, when two things are compared, we select one as the referent and compare the other (the relatum) with it. The compared things are either alike or they are different. For example, we may consider the value of two integers, 5 (the referent) and 8 (the relatum). The relatum is greater in number value than the referent.

When any two integers, a and b, are compared, one of the three following conditions must be true:

$a = b$ a is equal to b, or

$a > b$ a is greater than b, or

$a < b$ a is less than b

Only one of these conditions can be true for any given pair of integers.

The equal sign with a line through it, $\neq$, is the mathematical symbol for "not equal."

In comparing integer values, the relation "greater than" is not reflexive, and it is not symmetric, but it is transitive. For example, $6 + 4 > 4 + 3$ and $4 + 3 > 3 + 2$. Then $6 + 4 > 3 + 2$. The relation "is less than," "is richer than," "is heavier than," are examples of transitive relations that are neither reflexive nor symmetric.

5.5 FUNCTIONS

A function is defined as "Any quality, trait, or fact so related to another that it is dependent upon and varies with that other."[5] As developed in Chapter 2, common awareness of this relationship is indicated by expressions such as "that depends upon, . . ." Some simple illustrations may be noted:

The distance traveled by an airplane is produced by, and therefore is a function of, time and speed of travel.

The amount of postage for sending a package by first class mail depends upon the weight of the package.

The force of attraction or of repulsion between two magnets is a function of the distance between them.

PROPORTION

A proportion is a common type of functional relationship that expresses equality between two ratios. A ratio is used to compare two quantities. We may say that the ratio of two numbers is the quotient of the first number divided by the second number. One of the forms used most frequently to indicate a ratio is that of common fractions. For example, $\frac{1}{4}$ indicates the ratio of 1 to 4. This may be read in the ratio form $1 : 4$ (see Chapter 9).

$$3/4 = 6/8 \quad \text{or} \quad 3 : 4 :: 6 : 8$$

[5] Webster's New Collegiate Dictionary.

A proportion is illustrated in the equality between these two ratios.

Two main types of proportions that are significant in mathematics are (1) direct proportion, and (2) inverse proportion.

Direct Proportion

When the proportion indicates equality between two ratios, the proportion is direct proportion. There are many examples of direct proportion that children interpret. For example, when one factor is held constant and the other factor is changed, there will be a directly proportional change in the product.

Example A $3 \times 4 = 12$

Example B $6 \times 4 = 24$

The second factor in the examples is held constant. In Example B, the first factor is two times as large as the first factor in Example A, and the product of Example B is two times as great as the product of Example A.

When the divisor is constant, the quotient and dividend are in direct proportion:

Example A   *Example B*

$$2 \overline{)\ 2}^{\ \ 1} \qquad\qquad 2 \overline{)\ 20}^{\ \ 10}$$

The divisors of the two examples are the same. The dividend in Example B is 10 times as large as the dividend in Example A, and its quotient is 10 times as large as the quotient of Example A.

Inverse Proportion

Inverse means opposite in order. Inverse proportion moves in the opposite direction of change from that of direct proportion. As one element *increases*, the other element correspondingly *decreases*. There are many examples of inverse proportion that are important for interpretation of topics in mathematics. For example, when the dividend is constant, the divisor and quotient vary in inverse proportion:

Example A   *Example B*

$$10 \overline{)\ 100}^{\ \ 10} \qquad\qquad 1 \overline{)\ 100}^{\ \ 100}$$

In the two examples above, the dividends are the same. The divisor of Example B is *ten times as small* as the divisor of Example A, and its quotient is *ten times as large*. A decrease in the value of the divisor produces an inversely proportional increase in the value of the quotient when the dividend is constant.

ILLUSTRATIVE LESSONS

The following illustrative lessons are presented in this chapter:

Lesson 1. What's in a name?
Lesson 2. A bed of roses

The lessons in this chapter indicate ways that children may develop the properties of whole numbers. The topics offer ideas for child-created bulletin boards.

Lesson 1
WHAT'S IN A NAME?[6]

The children in Miss Bell's room discussed the idea of the commutative principle of addition and of multiplication. They had worked with specific numerals and had stated the ideas using examples such as $4 + 5 = 5 + 4$ and $6 \times 3 = 3 \times 6$. They generalized the idea for addition by having A stand for any specific numeral (positive integer) and B stand for another specific numeral (positive integer). $A + B = B + A$.

They developed the idea of A as one action and B as another, and found sets of actions that obeyed the commutative principle.

"Joe: A represents dirt; B represents water. $A + B$ is equal to $B + A$. It's mud!"

"Martha: A is putting silverware on the table; B is putting dishes on the table. Either way the table is set."

Sets of actions that do not obey the commutative principle were found.

[6] Marguerite Brydegaard, "What's in a Name?" *The Instructor*, vol. 70 (November 1960), p. 10.

"*Bill:* A is getting undressed; B is taking a bath. $A + B$ = clean boy; $B + A$ = angry mother."

"*Sally:* A is washing hands; B is wiping hands on towel. $A + B$ = clean hands and clean towel; $B + A$ = clean hands (maybe) and dirty towel."

"As the children's ideas expanded, so did their terminology." The children read old meanings and new meanings into the name.

"Teachers and pupils who use terms correctly facilitate their interpretation and communication of ideas. It is desirable for the teacher to refine his terminology and to create learning situations through which clarity of language begets clarity of thought."

Lesson 2
A BED OF ROSES[7]

[Susan drew a picture to show the bed of rosebushes she had planted.]

Miss North asked the children to name different ways that they could tell how many rosebushes Susan had planted. Some of the replies were:

"You could count the bushes one by one if you didn't know a better way."

"I counted 6 across and 5 down and thought $6 \times 5 = 30$."

[7] Marguerite Brydegaard, "A Bed of Roses," *The Instructor*, vol. 70 (May 1961), p. 10.

"I counted 5 one way and 6 the other and thought 5 × 6 = 30."
"I saw 6 across and took three 6s for the ones in the upper bed.

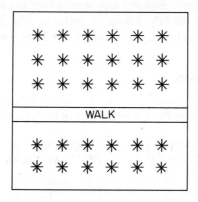

Then I took two 6s for the lower bed. You get the same answer that way: (6 × 3) + (6 × 2) = 30."

[Miss North asked the children to write the different ways that they had named.]

Susan: "My way was 5 × 6 = 30. Bill's way was like mine except that he wrote 6 × 5 = 30. 6 × 5 = 5 × 6. I'll write both of them on the board."

Sue: "I'll have to write 30 ones to tell my way. That's a lot!" (She wrote 1 + 1 + 1 + 1 + 1··· = 30.)

Jim: "This is the way I worked mine: (6 × 3) + (6 × 2) = 18 + 12 = 30."

Miss North: "There is another way we can write your problem, Jim. I'll write it on the board. [She wrote 6 × (3 + 2) = (6 × 3) + (6 × 2) = 18 + 12 = 30.] I put the 3 + 2 in parentheses because 3 + 2 is to be considered together. 3 + 2 is another name for 5."

Jim: "I see. (6 × 3) + (6 × 2) gives the same answer as 6 × 5. You can add the 3 and 2 and then multiply by the common multiplier."

Mary: "That's the same idea I use when I don't know a multiplication fact. Sometimes I forget 7 × 6, so I think (7 × 3) + (7 × 3) = 21 + 21 = 42."

William: "That's like when I multiply 5 × 55. I think (5 × 50) + (5 × 5) = 250 + 25 = 275."

Miss North realized that the children sensed the following ideas in the rosebush problem.

Commutative law — 6 × 5 = 5 × 6

Distributive law — 6 × (3 + 2) = (6 × 3) + (6 × 2) = 18 + 12
= 30

Miss North realizes that teaching can be a "bed of roses." She often utilizes situations such as the one above to challenge excellent mathematicking in her class. But she also senses how far to go in developing the ideas with her specific group of learners. She knows the level of readiness and the point of good return for time and energy invested.

Discussion Questions

1. In Illustrative Lesson 2 of Chapter 4, the children created a base five numeration system using the symbols shown in the following table:

NUMERAL BASE FIVE	EQUIVALENT DECIMAL VALUE
0	0
1	1
∩	2
△	3
□	4

Using the set of elements given, illustrate the following properties of addition and multiplication: closure, commutative, associative, and identity elements. Show the distributive property of multiplication with respect to addition.

2. List some relationships that may be classified as transitive but that do not fit the reflexive and symmetric relations.

3. The sketch of the dial at the left represents a modular five system. Consider the following operations: clockwise turns–operation C; and counter-clockwise turns–operation $\circlearrowleft$. Test the modular system for the commutative, associative, and closure properties.

4. Create a number system using a base of your choice. Create symbols that you recommend because their orthography is simple and frees the user to concentrate on ideas of operations, problem solving, and so forth. Use the simple ideas of a mathematical system discussed in Chapter 4 and develop a system using your symbols and number base.

Suggested Readings

Banks, J. Houston, *Elements of Mathematics*. Boston, Mass.: Allyn and Bacon, Inc., 1956, Chap. 3.

Fujii, John N., *An Introduction to the Elements of Mathematics*. New York: John Wiley & Sons, Inc., 1961.

Gibb, E. Glenadine, Phillip S. Jones, and Charlotte W. Junge, "Number and Operation," *The Growth of Mathematical Ideas, Grades K–12*, National Council of Teachers of Mathematics, Twenty-fourth Yearbook. Washington, D.C.: The Council, 1959, pp. 7–64.

May, Kenneth O., and Henry Van Engen, "Relations and Functions," *The Growth of Mathematical Ideas, Grades K–12*, National Council of Teachers of

Mathematics, Twenty-fourth Yearbook. Washington, D.C.: The Council, 1959, pp. 65–110.

Osborn, Roger, M. Vere De Vault, Claude C. Boyd, and W. Robert Houston, *Extending Mathematics Understanding.* Columbus, Ohio: Charles E. Merrill Books, Inc., 1961, Chap. 3.

Terry, George S., *The Dozen System.* New York: Longmans Green & Company, Ltd., 1941.

Meserve, Bruce E., and Max A. Sobel, *Introduction to Mathematics.* Englewood Cliffs, N.J.: Prentice-Hall, Inc., 1964, Chap. 3.

Peterson, John A., and Joseph Hashisaki, *Theory of Arithmetic.* New York: John Wiley & Sons, Inc., 1963, Chap. 3.

The Whole Numbers (Booklet Number 2) and *Algorithms for Operations with Whole Numbers* (Booklet Number 4), The National Council of Teachers of Mathematics. Washington, D.C.: The Council, 1964. 55 pp. and 34 pp.

6

Languages and Mathematical Communication

6.1 MATHEMATICAL COMMUNICATION: an INTEGRAL PART of LANGUAGE ARTS

"Mathematics is undoubtedly one of man's greatest intellectual achievements. In addition to the knowledge which the subject offers, its language, processes, and theories give science its organization and power."[1]

"Mathematics as a creative discipline operates in 3 fundamental steps: (1) A problem situation is experienced and a pattern is discovered in it; (2) A symbolism is designed to express this pattern; (3) This symbolism is organized into a systematic language. This language is a piece of mathematics."[2]

The importance of the languages of mathematics should not be overlooked. Language functions in the development of mathematical knowledge as well as in its communication. The process of refining one's ideas and of testing them to determine their validity normally leads to a more exacting and careful use of language, which in turn often causes one to re-examine and sharpen his perception. Thus a sharper use of language tends to assist both in the refinement of ideas and in their effective communication to others.

6.2 COMMON LANGUAGE USAGE: EXPRESSION of MATHEMATICAL IDEAS

The expression of mathematical ideas via language symbols is intended to map out a course of perceiving on the part of the learner. Such map-

[1] Morris Kline, "The Meaning of Mathematics," *The Saturday Evening Post,* vol. 223, no. 10, September 3, 1960, p. 20.

[2] *The Greater Cleveland Mathematics Program.* Pamphlet published February 1962, p. 2.

ping needs to be precise, concise, and accurate in its identification of the idea of concern and in its cuing of the perception process, for both creating the idea and recalling it to mind. A truly functional mathematical expression must "say what it means" and "mean what it says." Because much of human behavior involves mathematical ideas which are general in nature, these are often adequately expressed in common language usage.

LABELING: a distinctive language function

In Chapter 2, identification is discussed as a basic mathematical process. Identification is normally associated with a language process of naming (labeling). This consists in "voluntarily produced symbols" adapted for that purpose. Actually, each language symbol is a label for a mathematical idea. As the process of perceptual comparison is used, the mathematical discrimination of referent-relatum relationship is operative. Language forms signifying the use of that relationship are many and varied, that is, "this" as contrasted with "that," "here" as opposed to "there," "some" as related to "all," "now and then," "inanimate vs. animate," and so forth.

SENTENCE STRUCTURE: a mathematical pattern

Language symbols individually connote mathematical ideas, and their arrangements in sequence for the expression of other ideas is governed by mathematical patterns. A sentence must have a subject. It must likewise have a verb. These elements must be explictly symbolized or implicitly identified. The sequential order in which the sentence elements are presented is an integral aspect of the technique of language communication, for example, "John was there" expresses a different idea than does "Was John there?", or the word arrangement, "There was John." The fact that an ordered arrangement of words is important for facile communication may be illustrated by the following scrambled grouping: moon The over the jumped cow. Relatively simple but very basic mathematical ideas are essential guides for the effective compositional structuring of language expressions.

VERBS: mathematical time references

The so-called tense (time) connotation of verbs has reference to the mathematical concept of a time scale consisting of three segments: the present (the referent) and directionally related segments, the past, and the future. The time aspect of a verb symbol is an important part of the message expressed by a sentence. The verb form differs according to the time reference symbolized. The selection of the proper form of the symbol for use in expressing a specific message entails a clear mathematical idea concerning the time aspect and a knowledge of the language forms and of the principles of the grammar affecting their use.

MODIFIERS: expressions of mathematical variance

Modifications of symbols for the purpose of indicating a degree relationship are a familiar example of the expression of observed variation. What has been termed a "positive" degree is used as a referent. The related states, "comparative" and "superlative," are given both a directional and quantitative connotation:

$$\underline{\text{decrease}\text{(Referent)}\text{increase}}$$

superlative   comparative   positive   comparative   superlative

The idea of scaled variance as well as its directional expression are experienced again and again in different language forms.

The distinction between definite and indefinite identification as indicated by the articles *the* and *an*, respectively, is another instance of mathematical discrimination.

PHONIC LANGUAGE EXPRESSION: mathematical scaling of sound

A considerable portion of language expression utilizes a phonic or sound medium. Mathematical analysis of that medium provides a basis for many of the language forms. Space does not permit an exhaustive discussion of this aspect of mathematical language usage, but calling it to attention is important.

Typographical techniques are used to attract special attention to certain symbols or groups of symbols; for example, italics, underlining, and capitalization are examples of such practices. Punctuational characters also illustrate certain aspects of mathematical patterning. However, the written music language is probably the best illustration of the symbolizing of mathematical ideas regarding patterns of sound. Music is a phonic phenomenon.

For purposes of written musical expression, the sound medium is structured in terms of a pertinent referent unit, tone. Tone is defined as "a sound having such regularity of vibration as to impress the ear with its individual character, especially as regards pitch, and to enter into harmonious relations."[3]

---

[3] *Webster's New International Dictionary.*

The mathematical analysis involved in identifying and utilizing aspects of tonal expression is worthy of careful consideration. The identification of a music expression as a patterned arrangement of tonal units having the characteristics of pitch, duration, sequence, and harmonious blending and then devising a simple system of symbols for mapping all of the many aspects involved is a great mathematical and linguistic accomplishment.

HOW MANY: a mathematical query common to all languages

The vernacular terms from five major languages symbolizing the initial values of the counting scale are given in Table 6.1.

TABLE 6.1
Verbal Symbols Representing Counting Number Ideas

ENGLISH	JAPANESE	GERMAN	FRENCH	SPANISH	RUSSIAN
zero	rei	null	zero	cero	нуль
one	ichi	eins	un	uno	один
two	ni	zwei	deux	dos	два
three	san	drei	trois	tres	три
four	shi	vier	quatre	cuatro	четы́ре
five	go	fünf	cinq	cinco	пять
six	roku	sechs	six	seis	шесть
seven	shichi	sieben	sept	siete	семь
eight	hachi	acht	huit	ocho	во́семь
nine	kū	neun	neuf	nueve	де́вять
ten	jū	zehn	dix	diez	де́сять
eleven	jūichi	elf	onze	once	одиннадцать
twelve	jūni	zwölf	douze	doce	двена́дцать
thirteen	jūsan	dreizehn	treize	trece	трина́дцать
fourteen	jūshi	vierzehn	quatorze	catorce	четы́рнадцать
fifteen	jūgo	fünfzehn	quinze	quince	пятна́дцать
sixteen	jūroku	sechzehn	seize	dieciseis	шестна́дцать
seventeen	jūshichi	siebzehn	dix-sept	diecisiete	семна́дцать
eighteen	jūhachi	achtzehn	dix-huit	dieciocho	восемна́дцать
nineteen	jūkū	neunzehn	dix-neuf	diecinueve	девятна́дцать
twenty	nijū	zwanzig	vingt	veinte	два́дцать
twenty-one	nijū ichi	ein und zwanzig	vingt et un	veintiuno	два́дцать один
...	...	...	...	...	...
thirty	sanjū	dreizig	trente	treinta	три́дцать
thirty-one	sanjū ichi	ein und dreizig	trente et un	trentiuno	три́дцать один

From the point of view of mathematical concepts, it is of interest to note that the same idea of a counting number scale is expressed by the symbols of each of the languages. This suggests that counting as a way of quantifying "how many" is universally practiced. However, there are other characteristics displayed by the symbols of each of the languages that have even greater pertinence for this discussion. Within each of the respective series of symbols, the first ten members have no intrinsic cues depicting their sequential order. Both their form and the order of occurrence appear to be arbitrarily established. But, beginning with or at some place within the second decade of each series, intrinsic cues depicting their sequential order appear. In every instance, these cues refer to a grouping of 10. Thereafter, beginning with the third decade every language makes use of a systematic pattern which indicates that the primary grouping by ones, which is characteristic throughout the scaling, has been supplemented by a secondary or subgrouping by tens. The Japanese language beautifully illustrates this pattern beginning with jū (ten) and followed by nijū (2 tens), sanjū (3 tens), shijū (4 tens), gojū (5 tens). The English language, in contrast, uses a confusing pattern in the second decade and abandons it with the beginning of the third decade. Not until the seventh decade (60) does the customary aural symbol for the primary numbers come into use as a cue to the sequential order of the groupings of 10. Experience has revealed that learners have considerable difficulty with the translating of the aural symbols of the second decade into their written visual forms. Since the transforming from one language form to another is a prominent part of mathematical communication, such sources of difficulty need to be carefully studied and, if possible, alleviated.

6.3   PARALLEL LANGUAGE FORMS: ORAL-AURAL, WRITTEN-VISUAL

There is need to recognize that sight as well as hearing is a basic medium for communication. Four parallel forms of language are in common use. Two of them are expressive, speech and writing. And, two are impressive, hearing and seeing. Normally, the primary expressive form is speech. Written language forms are normally designed to re-present the spoken symbols. Likewise, normally, the primary impressive form of language is heard, that is, the orally expressed symbol is aurally received. Hence, the phonic and phonetic aspects of language forms need careful attention.

Written symbols similarly relate to the primary spoken counterparts. Hence, they need to be constructed so that they clearly map the sound patterns of the spoken symbols and in such a manner that the symbol may be easily sensed visually and readily transposed perceptually. The functional interrelationships of such parallel language forms is a matter for serious consideration. It is a problem that has troubled man throughout the ages.

6.4   ORTHOGRAPHY: the CORRECT SPELLING and WRITING of SYMBOLS

Orthography, "the representation of the sounds of a language by written or printed symbols," has many mathematical implications. We mentioned previously the matter of indicating the sequential order of a series of symbols and the related problem of making clear the respective positions of each individual reference within such a series. Any symbol consisting of two or more elements which are arranged to map an ordered series presents those problems for practical solution. Mathematical ideas have suggested some pertinent solutions. One such suggestion is derived from the idea of one-to-one correspondence. Its application consists in analyzing the composition of the thing to be symbolized to determine its elemental structure, and then assigning a distinctive label to each of the identified elements. When the respective labels are assembled in a proper pattern, they present a description or map of the composition. Such a series of primary labels is called an *alphabet*. Hence, an alphabet is an important orthographic tool.

MUSICAL ORTHOGRAPHY: pattern with a single element alphabet

A musical expression is an extremely complex phonic (sound) composition. As mentioned previously, it consists of tones, pitch, duration, sequence, blending, stressing, and many other aspects. In spite of this evident complexity, the orthographic pattern for written musical expression is amazingly simple. The basic alphabet symbol or phonetic element is **O**, representing a note as a symbol of tonal duration, that is, the note symbol is basically a time referent.

The primary note symbol is modified by "stems," "flags," or by shading to indicate calibrated divisions of the basic time unit. Each such modifier divides by two the time value of the preceding symbol in an ordered scale, as follows:

This is an extremely significant instance of the application of the idea of fractioning and of the relation of fraction values for symbolizing a scale measure.

Pitch refers to the position of the tone within an ordered scale ranging from "low" to "high" as determined by the vibration frequency that produces the sound. Pitch is symbolized in musical writing by a positional cue. The scale for depicting the range of pitch quality consists of a "staff" composed of five horizontal lines together with the four uniform space intervals between them, as shown in the figure. This device presents a calibrated scale having nine sections identified as "lines" or "spaces." The pitch desired for tonal expression is indicated by its position in this scale.

Music expression has a sequential characteristic. This is mapped positionally from left to right along the staff. The sequential process is scaled in the form of "measures," which are marked off on the staff by means of vertical lines that cross it. Each measure is quantified as to the kind and number of note values it may contain. This quantifying symbol is called a "time signature." It indicates the kind of note symbol which is the unit of reference and the number of such units which equals the time assigned to each measure, for example, $\frac{3}{4}$ indicates that the quarter note is the unit and that the equivalent of three of them constitutes the quantity for the measure. The portion of a familiar musical expression in Fig. 6.1 illustrates the use of the basic features of the orthographic pattern.

Fig. 6.1

VERNACULAR ORTHOGRAPHY: use of a multiple letter alphabet

As long as only the oral-aural (spoken-heard) forms of language communication are used, orthography is not a problem. However, when written-visual languages are used as counterparts of the spoken and heard forms, the spelling and writing of symbols becomes necessary. The sharp identification of the sound units and of their sequence and blendings in the phonic languages is basic to the construction of techniques for aural-to-visual transposition. Naturally, a transitive relation prevails in the matter of transposing from the visual to the oral language forms. This transposition process is essential for the efficient use of the parallel language forms.

The English language customarily uses an alphabet of 26 letter characters with which to construct its written word symbols. The patterned arrangement of these letters within the symbol follows a left-to-right sequence to indicate directionally the occurrence of the arrangement of the sound elements in the spoken expression. Hence, the letters functioning as cues for respective sounds are given positional status by which to depict the respective sounds and their sequential order of occurrence in the spoken symbol. For example, consider the different arrangements of the letters *r-t-a* in the following symbols. When the letters are arranged in the sequence *r-a-t*, they map the sounds of a word referring to an animal. When they occur as *t-a-r*, they form a different mapping which refers to a sticky substance. When they are written in the order *a-r-t*, they name the counterpart of an aural word designating a skill or the product of a skillful production. Each arrangement produces a distinct word symbol. This is possible because each character of the alphabet represents a certain sound element and because the positional order indicates the sequence of the occurrence of the sound elements in the spoken word. The fact that all of the written words of a language can be spelled with such an alphabetic procedure is evidence of the value of such an orthographic technique. Its mathematical bases should not be overlooked.

NUMERICAL ORTHOGRAPHY: writing number symbols

The system of symbols for number ideas as expressed in the letter alphabets of the common languages is reasonably adequate for some forms of mathematical usage, but it is not adapted for other important forms. Hence, a special type of symbol pattern is needed which transforms the respective symbols of the vernacular into a special type of number symbol which is better adapted for those particular needs, especially computation. Since this involves written language forms, it constitutes an orthographic problem.

Having already contacted that type of problem with the construction of the written symbols of the vernacular language, and for the written language of music, we can readily foresee some of the steps that are likely to be involved. (1) A set of simple alphabetical characters is needed to represent the elements being considered, and (2) a pattern for arranging the alphabetical symbols so that they map a serial order must be provided. In the English-language orthographic pattern, 26 such alphabetical characters are used to depict some 40 or more elemental sounds. This leads to confusion in the spelling of the symbols.

In dealing with the scaling to determine *how many*, one (an individual identity) is the basic referent. Hence, there is need for only two alphabetical characters, one that represents the presence of an identity and another that indicates its absence. The simple characters 0 and 1 could serve this purpose easily. Actually such an alphabetical basis is used in our binary system, but its symbols are cumbersome for general usage. A less cumbersome pattern can be devised by using more members in the alphabet, but selecting a larger alphabet entails setting up a criterion for their selection. A logical reference is to the initial groupings of ones on the scale. Then the question arises, what and how many of such groupings should be included? The decision can be an arbitrary one.

As pointed out previously, each of the six major languages has used an orthographic technique that involves a process of supplemental subgrouping by groups of 10 throughout its series. Such a universal patterning must have a basis in a common human experience. It is generally explained as being derived from the intuitive tendency to tally collections of identities by a one-to-one association with the fingers. Since there are normally 10 digits on the two hands, when 10 has been counted, that constitutes a special group. Regardless of the explanation, the fact is clear that the common language symbol structure has a characteristic pattern of regrouping by tens. This needs to be incorporated in the special number symbol pattern designed to parallel such a series. Hence it serves as the criterion for choosing the number of characters in the numeral alphabet.

Decimal Orthography—a Universal Special Number Pattern

The decimal alphabet consists of simple characters that represent the first ten number groupings on the counting-number scale: $0, 1, 2, 3, 4, 5, 6, 7, 8, 9$. That serial order is basic. As pointed out previously, it depicts an initial contrast between *not any* and *some*. "Not any" is absolute, but "some" needs to be quantified or scaled into groupings of how many. The orthography of these initial number symbols is simply a matter of how they are formed. But a different orthographic problem is encountered when one must arrange those alphabetic characters so as to "spell-out" the idea of subgroupings by 10. Positional cues are used in other symbolizations, and they are applicable for use in this connection. However, direction becomes a factor in positional symbolism. Direction was arbitrarily decided. Increasing values by groupings of tens are depicted by placing the alphabet character to the left of its basal position. Each position to the left represents 10 times the value represented in the position to its right. This pattern has been discussed at some length in other sections of this book. At this time, our concern is merely with the orthographic principles that are involved. Once the pattern has been conceived, its extension is readily foreseen.

The pattern for decimal numeral symbols was developed for use with ideas of whole numbers, but when the idea of directional cues for changes in the values that the digits represented was incorporated, it made the same system feasible for representing fraction numbers as well. All that is necessary is a device to indicate which position in the numeral depicts the primary value of the alphabet character. And then values less than those can be represented to the right in the same manner that greater values are expressed to the left. Directional placement is the cue to value.

Just as the counting-number scale is used as the basis for many other types of numeral scaling, so also, the decimal written numeral system is used with other types of numeral scales.

Fraction Orthography: a Way of Depicting the Scaling of Parts

The basic referent for the counting-number scale is *one*. Since the nature of the identity is not specifically indicated, the reference is general or abstract. No particular one is implied. When a particularized identity is indicated, the abstract reference is no longer used. For example, one, two, three, . . . , suggests a scale that can be used in general, but 1 horse, 2 horses, 3 horses, . . . refers only to horses. Any designated thing-type of identity performs correspondingly to change the scaling from the abstract to a concrete reference.

Very often in quantifying, one's concern is with particularized things such as trees, foot measures, pint measures, degrees of temperature, etc. When the reference of concern shifts from a *whole* to a *part*, some way of designating that idea needs to be devised.

In musical orthography, as discussed previously, this is accomplished by altering the basic note symbol so that as modified it serves as a label for a specified part of what the whole note symbol represents. The basic note reference was divided into specified fractional units, and each such unit then became a referent in its own right, but always with its meaning derived from its relationship to the whole note.

A similar technique of "fracturing" any referent can be used to produce fractional units of it. A fragment is merely a part of something. But, if the fracturing has produced *equal* fragments, they may be scaled as equivalent identities. In mathematical language, equal divisions are termed *fractions*. The vernacular labels for fractions name the number of equal parts into which a whole has been fractured, such as half, third, fourth, ... Then, as each is used as a referent, its label is modified numerically to indicate how many of such referents is being considered: one half, two thirds, three fourths, . . .

The numeral orthography differs from the vernacular by specifically symbolizing the division basis for the fraction identity, and by specifying by number how many equal segments are being considered. In this manner, full use is made of the basic counting number scale. As a matter of fact, it may be considered as a fraction scale for which the part being scaled is the whole identity.

$$\frac{0}{1}, \quad \frac{1}{1}, \quad \frac{2}{1}, \quad \frac{3}{1} \cdots$$

Each fraction unit then initiates a comparable scale

$$\frac{0}{2}, \quad \frac{1}{2}, \quad \frac{2}{2}, \quad \frac{3}{2} \cdots \quad \text{or} \quad \frac{0}{3}, \quad \frac{1}{3}, \quad \frac{2}{3}, \quad \frac{3}{3} \cdots$$

There are as many fraction scales as there are possibilities for equal division of a whole thing. Every fraction indicates division.

Orthography of Denominate Numbers: Scaling Named Measures

A denominate number makes specific reference to a particular unit of measure, that is, it is a number symbol that names its referent unit. Most of the number references that one experiences in ordinary communication are denominate, since it is important to know to what the number idea refers, for example, five people, six flags, three fourths, three men and a car, two feet six inches, and so forth.

Customarily, the term denominate number is applied to expressions concerning systems of weights and measures. Commonly, such systems are scaled according to a primary referent unit with subdivisions representing secondary referent units which bear a definite relationship to the primary unit. In many cases these relationships vary; for instance, 12 inches are regrouped as 1 foot, but only 3 feet are included in the subgrouping of yards, and $5\frac{1}{2}$ yards are grouped as 1 rod. The irregularity of the scaling is a source of difficulty.

Actually the pattern for writing denominate numerals is very similar to the pattern for writing decimal numerals. The decimal use of systematic positional cues for subgroupings makes unnecessary the labeling of its subdivisions. One hundred twenty-three as a number label is not very different in form from one yard, two feet, three inches.

ORTHOGRAPHY OF OPERATIONS AND RELATIONS

The preceding discussion has been mainly concerned with the spelling of the nouns of mathematical communication. However, communication involves more than mere labeling. Ideas of relationship are of importance; symbols for their representation are needed.

Verb Symbols

The verb symbols ("operators") of elementary number language are as follows:

$+$	signifies addition
$-$	subtraction
$\times$, $\cdot$,	or in the case of some expressions mere adjacent position indicates multiplication

$\div$, :, $)\underline{\quad}$, $\overline{)}$, $/$, $-$, all are used to indicate division.

Relational Symbols

Relational symbols are of many forms:

$=$	stands for equality
$\neq$	signifies lacking equality
$\cong$ or $\equiv$	represent the idea of equivalence
$\ncong$ or $\not\equiv$	imply lacking in equivalence

Inequality has a directional characteristic depending upon which of the compared terms is used as the referent. The symbols for the idea of inequality are $>$ and $<$. The pointed end is directed toward the smaller of the two quantities. The widely spread side is in the direction of the larger value, $2 < 3$ and $5 > 4$.

Directional Numbers

Directional numbers are depicted by the same numerals; hence, there is need for a modifier sign to designate which directional scale is being considered. The positive sign $(+)$ and the negative sign $(-)$ are used for this purpose. They are commonly written a bit higher in relation to the position of the numeral when used as adjectives than when used as verbs; for example, $^{+}5$ and $^{-}5$ are equal in number value but opposite in their directional reference.

Pronumerals

When a number idea of a general nature (without specific quantitative reference) is being symbolized, a type of "pronumeral" symbol is commonly used. Just as a pronoun stands for a noun in our common language, a pronumeral represents the idea of a numeral in the special number language. For example, the idea that the rate of travel multiplied by the time of travel identifies a product that is equivalent to the distance traveled can be expressed as $RT = D$, when R stands for the rate of travel, T for the time of travel, and D for the distance.

Mathematical Sentences

Translation from one language form to another is an important aspect of communication. Since the unit of thought in the vernacular language is the sentence, a comparable unit is needed in the special number language. Every idea that can be expressed in language form can be expressed by means of the common verbal language. However, as mentioned previously, the common language forms do not lend themselves for computational usage. Hence, translation into more succinct number language becomes necessary. This can be illustrated by the following problem which was presented about 1500 A.D.

"Out of a heap of pure lotus flowers, a third part, a fifth and a sixth were offered respectively to the Gods Siva, Vishnu, and then Sun; a quarter of the original heap presented to Bhavani. The remaining six lotuses were given to the venerable preceptor. Tell quickly the whole number of lotus flowers."[4]

Translating this problem into special number language terms is made as follows: first we select a pronumeral, that is, n, to represent the "whole number of lotus flowers." Then we proceed to construct number symbols depicting the common language number ideas.

to Siva   to Vishnu   to Sun   to Bhavani   to Preceptor   in all

$$\frac{1n}{3} \quad + \quad \frac{1n}{5} \quad + \quad \frac{1n}{6} \quad + \quad \frac{1n}{4} \quad + \quad 6 \quad = \quad n$$

The development of language media that aptly expresses its subject-matter is an important aspect of every phase of human concern. Since the subject-matter of mathematics as contacted in the elementary and secondary schools has been well thought out and conventionally established, the process of communicating it to the pupils is basically a language function. While each learner must conceive his own ideas, he can be greatly facilitated in that process by understandingly following maps provided by those who have already traversed that route. Competence with language can expedite and enrich experience.

[4] Charles T. Salkind, *The Contest Problem Book*, published by Random House and Yale University for the Monograph Project of the School Mathematics Study Group. Quotation from preface by L. Bers and J. H. Hlavaty. New York: 1960, p. 1.

ILLUSTRATIVE LESSON

The following lesson illustrates the ideas presented in this chapter.

Lesson
NUMERICAL ORTHOGRAPHY

The teacher and children had discussed ideas of number language. They had talked about how easy it is to spell the number names when they used numerals compared with writing the number names in common language. The following are some of the spellings that they had compared:

COMMON LANGUAGE	NUMERAL LANGUAGE
eleven	11
forty-five and twenty-seven hundredths	45.27
eight million, nine hundred forty-five thousand, nine hundred seventy-six, and nine hundred ninety-nine thousandths	8,945,976.999

The following are statements that indicate the thinking of the children:

Sally: Man surely made spelling easy when he made the numerals. Why didn't he make it as easy to spell words?

Bill: Almost anyone can spell the names of numerals.

Keith: I always get mixed up when I spell *forty* and *ninety*. I can't see why we don't use the word *four* in *forty*. We use *nine* in *ninety*.

Number sentences are easy to read.

Kim: My daddy has been in Germany and Denmark and other countries, and he told me that sometimes a 7 is made like this in those countries [showed a 7̄] . . . . It looked funny to me, but Daddy thinks that the extra line is a good idea. You aren't as likely to get a 7 mixed with a 1. Sometimes people write a 7 so that it looks like a 1 or a 1 so that it looks like a 7. I think my daddy is right.

Jack: But, all of the other numerals are like ours (meaning in Germany and Denmark). I think that's great! I could go to France and could read the numerals they write. Miss North, do all of the countries of the world agree on how to spell the numerals?

Miss North: It is likely true that you could read the numerals that are written in most of the countries of the world — certainly in the countries of Europe. There may be places, however, where the numerals are written in different ways. This question was pursued at a later date, and the common language and numeral language of various countries were discussed.

Jack: There aren't too many things that people of the world agree upon. We talked about how most people of the world use the calendar we use, and the decimal number system, and harbor markings, and . . . I think that if all people would say the names of the numerals as well as spell them the same, it would be a terrific idea.

It is shaped like . . .

Jill: It would be even more terrific if we all spoke the same language and wrote words the same way.

Miss North: Numerals are not the only things that are easy to spell. There are many symbols that make it easy to communicate in mathematics. Let's make a list of some of the symbols that you have used. [The symbols were discussed, and Miss North had two of the children make a chart for the classroom. (See Table 6.2.)]

TABLE 6.2

COMMON LANGUAGE	MATHEMATICAL LANGUAGE
Add	$+$
Subtract	$-$
Multiply	$\times$ or $\cdot$
Divide	$\overline{)\quad}$, $-$, $\div$, $\underline{)\quad}$, $:$, $/$
Equal to	$=$
Less than	$<$
Greater than	$>$
Not equal to	$\neq$
Not less than	$\not<$
Not greater than	$\not>$
Less than or equal to	$\leq$
Greater than or equal to	$\geq$
Not less than or equal to	$\not\leq$
Not greater than or equal to	$\not\geq$

Miss North: Can you think of anything about the numerals or these symbols that make them difficult to write? If you were going to start all over again and create the spelling for the numerals, what changes would you make?

Keith: I'd change the 2 because it is too hard to write when you are in a hurry.

Kim: I used to make my 3s like capital ε. I'd make a numeral that is easier to spell for three.

Jerry: I think that 6s and 9s are confusing when you are just beginning to read and write. It is hard to remember which direction to make the loops and which numeral has a loop at the top and which has it at the bottom.

Henry: I think that the sign for addition and for multiplication is too much alike. Sometimes my sign for multiplication looks like an addition sign.

Jill: But the dot for multiplication is even more confusing. It is harder to see, and you have to be very careful or it will look like a decimal point.

Further discussion ensued concerning the topic of the spelling of the symbols shown in Table 6.2. Later other charts were made for special symbols for sets, geometry, and so forth.

Discussion Questions

1.   Compare the simplicity of using the decimal alphabet of 10 digits with using our common language alphabet of 26 letters. Develop and illustrate specific points.

2.   What is meant by the term "numerical orthography?" Is it properly included within the language arts?

3.   Which of the digits of the decimal system are among the ones easiest to write and to spell? Which ones may be difficult for children who are beginning to read and to write? Tell why.

4.   The people who created the numerical orthography of decimal notation did a better job than was done with the common language. Discuss and illustrate this idea.

5.   Discuss the orthography of the symbols that you think show the greatest genius on the part of their inventors.

6.   Since people have not agreed upon a common verbal language, how do you account for the general use of a single, common number language?

7.   New symbols come into being to fit new ideas. Name and discuss one of the symbols, and evaluate it in terms of facile communication.

8.   Develop some ideas for a lesson that you may plan to teach to children concerning the orthography of a specific unit such as decimal fractions, sets, geometry, and so on.

Suggested Readings

Banks, J. Houston, *Elements of Mathematics*. Boston, Mass.: Allyn and Bacon, Inc., 1956, Chap. 1.

Bergamini, David, and the Editors of *Life, Mathematics*. New York: Time Incorporated, 1963.

Brune, Irvin H., "Language in Mathematics," *The Learning of Mathematics in Theory and Practice*, National Council of Teachers of Mathematics, Twenty-first Yearbook. Washington, D.C.: The Council, 1953, pp. 156–191.

Dantzig, Tobias, *Number: The Language of Science*. New York: The Macmillan Company, 1930.

Fouch, Robert S., and Eugene D. Nichols, "Language and Symbolism in Mathematics," *The Growth of Mathematical Ideas, Grades K–12*, National Council of Teachers of Mathematics, Twenty-fourth Yearbook. Washington, D.C.: The Council, 1959, pp. 327–369.

Glennon, Vincent J., "... and now synthesis: A theoretical model for mathematics education," *The Arithmetic Teacher*, vol. 12 (February 1965), pp. 134–141.

Gundlach, Bernard H., *The Laidlaw Glossary of Arithmetical-Mathematical Terms*. River Forest, Ill.: Laidlaw Brothers, Inc., 1961.

Hickerson, J. Allen, "Similarities between Teaching Language and Arithmetic," *The Arithmetic Teacher*, vol. 6 (November 1959), pp. 241–244.

Johnson, Harry C., "The Effect of Instruction in Mathematical Vocabulary upon Problem Solving in Arithmetic," *Journal of Educational Research,* vol. 38 (October 1944), pp. 97–110.

Schaaf, William L., "Mathematics As a Cultural Heritage," *The Arithmetic Teacher,* vol. 8 (January 1961), pp. 5–9.

Spencer, Peter L., and David H. Russell, "Reading in Arithmetic," National Council of Teachers of Mathematics, Twenty-fifth Yearbook. Washington, D.C.: The Council, 1960, pp. 202–223.

Young, W. E., "The Language Aspects of Arithmetic," *School Science and Mathematics,* vol. 57 (March 1957), p. 172.

7

Concepts Underlying Computation:
Decimal Integers

7.1 COUNTING: the ONE FUNDAMENTAL OPERATION

The basic number scale was developed as a device for measuring "how many." Hence, there is only one fundamental operation — counting — that is associated with its use. The statement that there are "four fundamental operations with computation" is questionable and misleading. Actually, computation consists in determining the number-value that correctly represents the result of an operation with two quantitative amounts. This is accomplished by a process of *directional counting*. The nature of the relationship determines the direction of the counting operation.

Addition is the operation from which the scale was devised. Addition consists in measuring on the counting number scale to determine the equivalent of the combined values of two or more designated amounts. This is accomplished by beginning on the number scale at the value represented by referent term (the augend)[1] and counting along the scale the number of units expressed by the other terms (addends). The sum or total is the number on the scale that expresses their combined values.

A number line may be used as a scale for computation. An arbitrary beginning point on a line may be selected and labeled 0. Another point

---

[1] The group to which the addition is made is an *augend*. There is an advantage in using the term *augend* as it identifies the referent or group to be operated upon. Sometimes it is important that one know the original or referent group with which the operation started. Conventionally, however, the augend and addends are all termed addends.

may be selected and labeled 1. Using the unit of length between point 0 and point 1, consecutive points may be marked off. Numerals may be used to label the points so that there is a one-to-one correspondence between the designated points and the set of numerals.

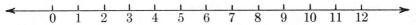

Addition and subtraction may be visualized by counting on a number line. The following table illustrates the example $3 + 2 = 5$. To add $3 + 2$, we first count to 3 on the number line and then count 2 more.

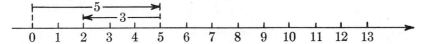

$5 - 3 = 2$. One group of 3 is counted out from a group of 5, leaving a remainder of 2.

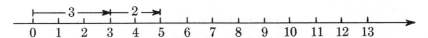

Multiplication and division may be illustrated as in Figs. 7.1 and 7.2.

Fig. 7.1   Fig. 7.2

Multiplication is merely a more facile way of performing the repeated addition when the respective groupings to be combined contain the same number of elements. Hence, multiplication is a special case of addition. Actually, this is implied by the term itself: the prefix, *multi*, means *many;* the root term, *plica*, means *fold*. Together they imply that a designated amount is to be considered many times as an addend.

The labels for the terms of a multiplication situation refer to the addend: the *multiplicand* refers to the number value that is to be added, and the *multiplier* indicates how many times the addend is to be used, or "folded." The multiplicand and the multiplier are called the *factors*. the result of the process is termed the *product*.

Addition

$$\left.\begin{array}{c} 2 \\ 2 \\ 2 \end{array}\right\} \text{ addends}$$

$$\overline{6} \text{ sum}$$

$$2 + 2 + 2 = 6$$

Two and two and two are six

Multiplication

2 multiplicand (addend)
3 multiplier (specifies
   number of times the
   addend is used)
—————————————————
6 product   (also a sum)

$$3 \times 2 = 6\,[2]$$

Three twos are six

Subtraction

Subtraction is the inverse of the addition process. Subtraction determines an amount equal to the difference between two quantities rather than that which is equal to their combined amounts. The function of the subtraction process is implied by its name. *Traction*, the root term, refers to *pulling*. *Sub*, the prefix, means *down* or under. Hence, subtraction labels a process of "pulling away" or of "drawing out." The grouping from which the drawing out is done is called the *minuend*, meaning that which is to be diminished. The amount that is to be drawn out is called the *subtrahend*, that which is taken away. The result of the operation is called the *remainder* or difference.

Sometimes a situation normally handled by subtraction is more expeditiously solved by adding to the subtrahend an amount that makes a sum which is equal to the minuend. The amount that is added represents the measure of the difference. This is a procedure commonly used in making change when a cash purchase is made. The clerk uses the

[2] The multiplier is usually written to the left of the multiplication sign when the equation is written in horizontal form. There is lack of consistency in interpreting expressions of multiplication. If the expression 3×2 is read "three times two," there is likely to be confusion as to which term is used as the multiplicand, that is, the addend. We propose that for the sake of clarity, the expression be read "three twos" and that all multiplication expressions be similarly expressed — at least, in the early stages of work with them. The statement "three twos" clearly indicates that 2 is the addend and that it is used 3 times.

purchase price as an augend (first addend) and then counts by adding on to the augend convenient coin units until the amount offered in payment is equaled. The counted addends constitute the change to be handed to the purchaser.

Division

Division is a special case of subtraction. Just as multiplication is concerned with totaling the results of a repeated use of the same addend, division is concerned with determining how many times a given subtrahend can be withdrawn from a specified minuend. Hence, division reverses the process of multiplication, as stated in a common definition, "Division is a process for determining the value of one factor when the product and its other factor are known."

$$
\begin{array}{llll}
\text{(a)} & \text{(b)} & \text{(c)} & \text{(d)} \\
\quad 2 & \quad 2 & \quad 8 & 8 \div 2 = 4 \\
+\,2 & \times 4 & -\,2 \;\; ① \\
+\,2 & \overline{\;\;8\;\;} & \overline{\;\;6\;\;} \\
+\,2 & & -\,2 \;\; ② \\
\overline{\;\;8\;\;} & & \overline{\;\;4\;\;} \\
& & -\,2 \;\; ③ \\
& & \overline{\;\;2\;\;} \\
& & -\,2 \;\; ④ \\
& & \overline{\;\;0\;\;}
\end{array}
$$

The examples above illustrate the nature of the respective processes and their interrelationships. The addition example, (a), shows that the cumulative result of combining 4 addends of 2 is 8. The multiplication example, (b), states that finding more succinctly: a group of 4 twos produces a group of 8. The subtraction example, (c), reverses the arrangement shown in the addition situation by successively drawing out groups of 2 from an original group of 8. Four such groups are drawn out. The division example indicates that a group of 8 when divided into groups of 2 will produce 4 such groups.

Obviously, as the situations to be solved become more complex and particularly when the number ideas are expressed by more extended numerals, special algorisms (methods of procedure) will be needed. These are discussed in subsequent chapters.

7.2   BASIC CONCEPTS UNDERLYING the FUNDAMENTAL OPERATION

The interpretation of the relationships that underlie computation is essential for efficient work with numerical computation. Concepts underlying addition and multiplication will be developed in the first part of this section. The inverse operations — subtraction and division — will be considered in the second part.

ADDITION AND MULTIPLICATION: direction toward increase

1. Does the sum of two numbers depend upon the order in which they are added?

$$\begin{array}{r} 5 \\ +\ 7 \\ \hline 12 \end{array} \qquad \begin{array}{r} 7 \\ +\ 5 \\ \hline 12 \end{array}$$ Does $5 + 7 = 7 + 5$?

Generalization

The order in which two numbers are added does not affect their sum. This property is called the commutative property of addition. (See Chapter 5.)

2. Does the product of two factors depend upon the order in which they are multiplied?

$$\begin{array}{r} 6 \\ 6 \\ +\ 6 \\ \hline 18 \end{array} \qquad \begin{array}{r} 3 \\ 3 \\ 3 \\ 3 \\ 3 \\ +\ 3 \\ \hline 18 \end{array}$$

$$3 \times 6 = 6 \times 3$$

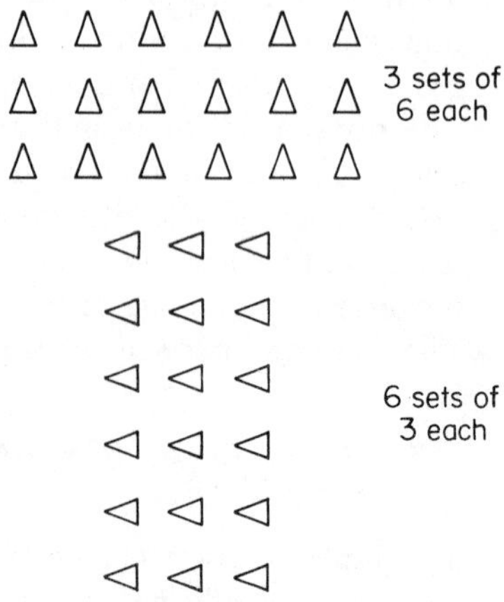

3 sets of 6 each

6 sets of 3 each

Fig. 7.3

The number of equal addends and the numerical value of the addends may be interchanged without altering the sum.

From Fig. 7.3 we see that:

3 sets of 6 each = 6 sets of 3 each

Generalization

The order in which two numbers are multiplied does not affect their product. This property is called the commutative property of multiplication.

3. How does the number of addends affect the value of the sum?

Addition

(a)	(b)	(c)	(d)
3	3	3	3
3	3	3	3
6	3	3	3
	3	3	3
	12	3	3
		3	3
		3	3
		3	3
		24	3
			3
			3
			3
			3
			3
			3
			48

Multiplication

(a)	(b)	(c)	(d)	(e)
3	3	3	3	3
× 1	× 2	× 4	× 8	× 16
3	6	12	24	48

Look at the set of examples above. Are your findings about in this order?

The multiplicand in each example is 3. The multipliers vary. The larger the multiplier, the larger the product when the multiplicand is constant.

The smaller the multiplier, the smaller the product when the multiplicand is constant.

Compare Example (b) with Example (a). The multiplicands are constant. The multiplier of Example (b) is two times as large in

Look at the set of examples above. Are your findings somewhat in this order?

The addend in every example is 3. The number of times 3 is used as an addend varies in each example.

The greater the number of addends, the greater the sum when the addend value is constant.

Compare Example (b) with Example (a): the addend value is constant. In Example (b), there are two times as many addends as in Example (a), and the sum is two times as large. And so forth . . .

Generalization

If the number value of the addends is constant, the sum is directly proportional to the number of addends.

number value as that of Example (a), and the product of Example (b) is two times that of Example (a).

Compare Example (a) with Example (c). And so forth . . .

Generalization

If the multiplicand is constant, the product is directly proportional to the multiplier.

4. How does the numerical value of the addends affect the value of the sum?

		Addition					*Multiplication*		
(a)	(b)	(c)	(d)	(e)	(a)	(b)	(c)	(d)	(e)
1	2	4	8	16	1	2	4	8	16
1	2	4	8	16	$\times 2$	$\times 2$	$\times 2$	$\times 2$	$\times 2$
2	4	8	16	32	2	4	8	16	32

In the set of examples above, the number of addends per example is constant. Each example has two addends.

Compare Example (a) with Example (b). The addend value of (a) is two times as small as that of (b), and the sum of (a) is two times as small as that of (b).

Compare Example (c) with Example (a). And so forth . . .

Generalization

If the number of addends is constant, the sum is directly proportional to the number value of the addends.

In the above set of examples, the multipliers are constant, but the multiplicands are variable.

Compare Example (a) with Example (b). The multiplicand of (a) is two times as small as that of (b), and the product of (a) is two times as small as that of (b). The multipliers are the same in number value.

Compare Example (d) with Example (a). And so forth . . .

Generalization

If the multiplier is constant, the product is directly proportional to the multiplicand.

Generalization Combining Points 1 and 2

The amount of a sum is determined by the number and the numerical value of the addends which produce it.

The value of a product is determined by the values of the multiplier and of the multiplicand.

5. In adding three or more addends, is the sum the same no matter how the addends are associated or paired?

Does $(5 + 3) + 4 = 5 + (3 + 4)$?
$$8 + 4 = 5 + 7$$
$$12 = 12$$

Generalization

When three or more numbers are added in a stated order, the sum is the same no matter how the numbers are paired. This property is called the associative property of addition.

6. In multiplying three or more factors, does the product depend upon the order in which the numbers are associated or paired?

Does $(4 \times 5) \times 3 = 4 \times (5 \times 3)$?
$$20 \times 3 = 4 \times 15$$
$$60 = 60$$

Generalization

When three or more factors are multiplied in a stated order, the product is the same no matter how the numbers are associated or paired.

7. Does one factor of a multiplication example distribute itself over the terms of the other factor?

$$2 \times 23$$

Does $2 \times (20 + 3) = (2 \times 20) + (2 \times 3)$?
$$2 \times 23 = 40 + 6$$
$$46 = 46$$

Generalization

Multiplication is distributive with respect to addition.

SUBTRACTION AND DIVISION: inverse direction from addition and multiplication

1. If the value of the minuend is constant, how does a change in the value of the subtrahend affect the number of times it can be subtracted from the minuend?

Subtraction

(a)	(b)	(c)	(d)
8	8	8	8
− 1	− 2	− 4	− 8
7	6	4	0
− 1	− 2	− 4	
6	4	0	
− 1	− 2		
5	2		
− 1	− 2		
4	0		
− 1			
3			
− 1			
2			
− 1			
1			
− 1			
0			

Division

(a)	(b)	(c)	(d)
8	4	2	1
1) 8	2) 8	4) 8	8) 8

The minuend value is constant in the examples above. Reading from left to right, as the subtrahend value *increases,* the number of times it can be taken away *decreases.* Conversely, reading from right to left, as the subtrahend value *decreases,* the number of times it can be taken away *increases.*

When the minuend is constant, the *smaller* the subtrahend value, the more times it can be subtracted. The *larger* the subtrahend value, the fewer the times it can be subtracted.

In the examples above, the dividends are constant. Reading from left to right, as the divisors *increase,* the quotients *decrease.* Moving from right to left, as the divisors *decrease,* the quotients *increase.* Compare Example (a) with Example (b). The dividends are the same. The divisor of Example (b) is two times as *large* in number value as that of Example (a). The quotient of Example (b) is two times as *small* as that of Example a. Compare Example (a) with Example (d). And so forth . . .

Generalization

If the minuend value is constant, the number of times the subtrahend can be withdrawn varies inversely with the numerical value of the subtrahend.

Generalization

When the dividend is constant, the value of the quotient varies inversely with the value of the divisor. The quotient decreases correspondingly with increases in the divisor. The quotient increases correspondingly with decreases in the divisor.

2. If the value of the subtrahend is constant, how does a change in the value of the minuend affect the value of the remainder?

Subtraction

(a)	(b)	(c)	(d)
6	12	24	48
6	− 6	− 6	− 6
	6	18	42
	− 6	− 6	− 6
		12	36
		− 6	− 6
		6	30
		− 6	− 6
			24
			− 6
			18
			− 6
			12
			− 6
			6
			− 6

Division

(a)	(b)	(c)	(d)
1	2	4	8
6) 6	6)1 2	6)2 4	6)4 8

In the examples above, the subtrahend values are constant.

Compare Example (c) with Example (a). The minuend of Example (c) is four times as large in number value as that of Example (a). The number of times the subtrahend can be withdrawn from the minuend in Example (c) is also four times that of Example (a).

The divisor is constant. Moving from left to right, as the dividends *increase*, the quotients *increase*. Moving from right to left, as the dividends *decrease*, the quotients *decrease*.

Compare Example (c) with Example (a). The divisors are the same. The dividend of Example (c) is four times as large in number value as that of Example (a), and the quotient of Example (c) is four times that of Example (a).

Compare Example (d) with Example (b). And so forth . . .

Compare Example (d) with Example (a). And so forth . . .

Generalization

When the subtrahend value is constant, the number of times it can be taken from the minuend is directly proportional to the size of the minuend.

Generalization

When the divisor is constant, the quotient is directly proportional to the value of the dividend.

3. If the number of subtractions is constant, how are the minuend and subtrahend related?

Subtraction

(a)	(b)	(c)	(d)
2	4	8	16
$-\,1$	$-\,2$	$-\,4$	$-\,8$
1	2	4	8
$-\,1$	$-\,2$	$-\,4$	$-\,8$

Division

(a)	(b)	(c)	(d)
$8\overline{)1\,6}\;2$	$4\overline{)8}\;2$	$2\overline{)4}\;2$	$1\overline{)2}\;2$

The number of subtractions in each example is constant. Each example shows two subtractions. Moving from left to right, the minuend value *increases* and the subtrahend value *increases*. Moving from right to left, the minuend value *decreases* and the subtrahend value *decreases*.

Compare Example (a) with Example (b). The number of subtractions for each example is the same. The minuend value of Example (a) is two times as small as that of Example (b), and the subtrahend value of Example (a) is two times as small as that of Example (b).

Compare Example (c) with Example (a). And so forth . . .

The quotients are constant. Moving from left to right, the divisors and dividends *decrease correspondingly*. Moving from right to left, the divisors *increase* correspondingly to the *increase* in the dividends.

Compare Example (a) with Example (b). The quotients are constant. The divisor of Example (a) is two times as large in number value as that of Example (b), and the dividend of Example (a) is two times that of Example (b).

Compare Example (c) with Example (a). And so forth . . .

Generalization

Generalization

When the number of subtractions is constant, the minuend value and the subtrahend value are directly related.

When the value of the quotient is constant, the divisor and dividend may vary in direct proportion.

4. Is subtraction an inverse direction of change compared with addition?

$$\overrightarrow{3 + 6} = 9$$
$$\overleftarrow{9 - 6} = 3$$

We add 6 to 3, and the sum is 9. We can "undo" the addition expressed above by subtracting the 6. We are then back where we started — at 3. The subtrahend and remainder are related as addends are related to the sum in addition.

7.3 IMPLICATIONS of ONE FUNDAMENTAL OPERATION

FAMILIES OF RELATED FACTS

When primary combinations for addition, subtraction, multiplication, and division are taught as separate facts, there are 390 facts: 100 primary combinations with addition, 100 with subtraction, 100 with multiplication, and 90 for division. (These will be developed later in this chapter.) When the 390 combinations are grouped into families of related facts, there are 100 families. An example of a related family of facts is:

$$8 + 8 = 16 \qquad 2 \times 8 = 16 \qquad \text{2s in } 16 = 8$$
$$16 - 8 = 8 \qquad 8 \times 2 = 16 \qquad \text{8s in } 16 = 2$$

Related facts developed as intradependent ideas facilitate the recall of facts and are a logical outgrowth of thinking from the earliest development with any one of the given facts. This does not imply that the words "multiplication," "times," "division," "divided into," and so forth, need be developed in the early stages of teaching primary combinations. However, the multiplication and division language patterns should emerge in their simplest forms during the early stages of teaching combinations. Expressions such as "2 eights" and "how many groups of 8 can be made from a group of 16?" illustrate this point. They symbolize the multiplication and division concepts much more clearly than many of the more frequently used terms such as "times," "multiplied by," and so on.

CONCEPTS THAT DETERMINE TECHNIQUES

There are concepts of the decimal system that determine the techniques to be applied with all numerical computation. Consider the following examples.

(1) Only terms within the same grouping category are added or subtracted. This is an important principle used throughout arithmetic computation and in algebra. Groups of ones are added to, or subtracted from, groups of ones; groups of tens are added to, or subtracted from, groups of tens, and so forth.

(2) The largest value that we write in any given position in a decimal numeral is 9. When the value is greater than 9 for any position, it is regrouped to higher terms. For example, 15 ones is regrouped as 1 group of 10 in the tens' position and a group of 5 ones in the ones' position.

(3) We group number values to fit our purposes. For example, the number value is the same if we have 9 grouped as 9 ones or as $4 + 5$, as $(3 + 3) + 3$, and so forth.

Twenty-six may be thought of as 2 groups of 10 each and 6 ones or as 1 group of 10 and 16 ones, or as a group of 26 ones.

Eleven cents may be thought of as 11 pennies, or as 1 dime and 1 penny, or as 2 nickels and 1 penny, or as 1 nickel and 6 pennies.

In $62 = 60 + 2$, we may group 62 as $50 + 12$ if we wish; $50 + 12$ names the same amount as $60 + 2$.

The way that a number value is grouped depends upon how we are going to use it.

7.4   ADDITION and SUBTRACTION

PRIMARY COMBINATIONS

The set digits that are used for a given number system determine the number of primary combinations that occur with that system. The 10 digits that are used for decimal notation determine the 100 primary combinations for addition. If each of the 10 digits is used once as a first addend (or augend) combined with each of the 10 digits, the combinations may be indicated as in Fig. 7.4.

For each primary combination for addition, a subtraction combination may be paired with it. In subtraction, the remainder and the subtrahend are related as the addends are related in the paired example for

ADDITION

First Addend (augend)

+	0	1	2	3	4	5	6	7	8	9
0	0	1	2	3	4	5	6	7	8	9
1	1	2	3	4	5	6	7	8	9	10
2	2	3	4	5	6	7	8	9	10	11
3	3	4	5	6	7	8	9	10	11	12
4	4	5	6	7	8	9	10	11	12	13
5	5	6	7	8	9	10	11	12	13	14
6	6	7	8	9	10	11	12	13	14	15
7	7	8	9	10	11	12	13	14	15	16
8	8	9	10	11	12	13	14	15	16	17
9	9	10	11	12	13	14	15	16	17	18

Second Addend (left label, rows)

Fig. 7.4

addition. The sum and the minuend, respectively, represent the total quantitative number value. The addends are indicated in boldface.

$$2 + 4 = 6$$
$$6 - 4 = 2$$

The subtraction chart in Fig. 7.5 shows the 100 primary combinations for subtraction. The mastery of the primary combinations for addition

SUBTRACTION

Subtrahend
(corresponds to first addend)

	0	1	2	3	4	5	6	7	8	9
0	0	1	2	3	4	5	6	7	8	9
1	1	2	3	4	5	6	7	8	9	10
2	2	3	4	5	6	7	8	9	10	11
3	3	4	5	6	7	8	9	10	11	12
4	4	5	6	7	8	9	10	11	12	13
5	5	6	7	8	9	10	11	12	13	14
6	6	7	8	9	10	11	12	13	14	15
7	7	8	9	10	11	12	13	14	15	16
8	8	9	10	11	12	13	14	15	16	17
9	9	10	11	12	13	14	15	16	17	18

Remainder
(corresponds to second addend) (left label)

Minuend Enclosed (right label)

Fig. 7.5

and subtraction is facilitated through teaching them in related family groups. For example, $2 + 3 = 5$ and $3 + 2 = 5$ should be taught together (commutative property of addition). Relating $5 - 3 = 2$ and $5 - 2 = 3$ facilitates the recall and applicability of all four combinations for use for whichever direction of change is called for in any given problem.

In the initial stages of learning primary combinations, counters and materials to facilitate "seeing" the combinations should be used. When the ideas are experienced concretely, recall of them is facilitated. Visual, tactile, aural, kinesthetic, and other types of stimuli operate in using counters and developing number stories through their use. Many teachers have noted that, when counters are used to teach families of related combinations, children achieve mastery of them with relatively little effort and in a short period of time. Children in kindergarten and grade one appear to "just know" the combinations when they are learned in an organized teaching situation in which counters and other materials are efficiently used.

CARRYING IN ADDITION AND REGROUPING IN SUBTRACTION

The word *carrying* in addition is an unfortunate term because it does not express well the idea of what is done. However, the word is established and it is likely to be used for many years. The basic idea is that of a subgrouping of number values: $7 + 7 = 14$ involves interpreting the idea of grouping 14 ones as 1 group of 10 and 4 ones. The inverse procedure for this is to subtract 7 from 14. We add 7 to find the sum, and then we subtract it to find the missing addend. By subtraction, we undo what we did in addition.

$$
\begin{array}{r}
26 \\
+\ 36 \\
\hline
12 \\
5 \\
\hline
62
\end{array}
\quad
\begin{array}{l}
\text{partial} \\
\text{sums}
\end{array}
$$

Only terms having the same positional value are added. In adding numbers of two or more digits, there is a column sum for each position. The sum of the ones' position is 12 which is grouped as 1 in the tens' place and 2 in the ones' place. The sum of the tens' value is 5 tens which is written in the tens' position. We can then combine the values of the partial sums. We have 6 in the tens' position and 2 in the ones' position or 62.

The extended form used above emphasizes the concepts of subgroupings by tens. The column sums are written in their respective places, and the sums are available for checking their accuracy. Many of the difficulties of carrying are reduced if not wholly eliminated.

The procedure has been found helpful by many groups of students. It can be dropped after the student has achieved facility with the addition process if that seems desirable. It is, however, a well-established procedure which has many advantages. We reverse what we did in addition when we regroup the minuend value for subtraction:

$$62 = 60 + 2$$
$$-\,36 = -(30 + 6)$$

In the units' position, we have $2 - 6$. The answer to this subtraction is not a member of the set of positive integers. Therefore, we need to regroup the minuend value. We can take 1 group of 10 from the group of 6 tens which leaves a group of 5 tens or 50. We can then regroup the 1 ten as 10 ones and add the 10 ones to the 2 ones of the units' position, making a group of 12 ones.

$$62 = 50 + 12$$
$$-\,36 = -(30 + 6)$$
$$\overline{20 + 6 = 26}$$

When the number combinations are directly visible as illustrated, they are in their "seen" form. However, the procedure is not desirable for extensive use, as it is time-consuming and awkward. The following example indicates the shortcut procedure that may be used.

$$\overset{5}{\cancel{6}}{}^{1}2$$
$$-\,3\ 6$$

Technically, this procedure is incorrect, since a two-digit value cannot be expressed in any single position.[3]

[3] The crutch illustrated above is used extensively. Actually, it violates the principle that 9 is the largest value that can be written in a single position within a numeral. However, as long as it appears to be helpful in visualizing the subtraction algorism, its use can be tolerated.

The procedure illustrated below avoids the violation by regrouping the value in a way that brings out the opposite direction of change in quantitative value as addition.

$$\text{check by addition}$$

6 2	12	3 6
−3 6	5	+2 6
2 6	~~6 2~~	1 2
	−3 6	5
	2 6	6 2

In adding, $36 + 26$, the partial sums are 12 and 50. Similarly, the regrouped minuend values are 50 and 12. Actually, since numbers and numerals are designed to help us in quantifying things, it is questionable if one should be pedantic about minor aspects of procedure.

As the learner achieves facility with subtraction, he may drop the step of showing the regrouped value. It is helpful, however, to return to the procedure for the introductory steps of regrouping for common and decimal fraction numbers, and denominate numbers.

Regrouping number values for subtraction involves potential sources of difficulty. The preceding type of example that was illustrated called for regrouping for the units' position only. It is an easy type of example. The two following examples are two of the types that produce high percents of error as determined in pupil responses to tests of subtraction.

Regrouping for the Units' Position Only

$$
\begin{array}{r}
2\ 0\ 0 \\
-\ 1\ 8\ 8 \\
\hline
\end{array}
$$

In this example, 200 may be grouped as 2 hundreds $+$ 0 tens $+$ 0 units or as 20 tens $+$ 0 units or as 200 ones. The most economical grouping for this type of example is to consider the 200 as 20 tens $+$ 0 units.

The steps of regrouping are: (1) Take 1 ten from the group of 20 tens which leaves 19 tens. (2) Regroup the 1 ten to 10 ones. (3) Add the

$$
\begin{array}{r}
{\scriptstyle 1\ \ 9} \\
2\ \cancel{0}\ {}^{1}0 \\
-\ 1\ 8\ 8 \\
\hline
1\ 2
\end{array}
$$

ten ones to the 0 ones making 10 ones. The regrouped value is 1 hundred, 9 tens, 10 ones. Then subtract as follows:

units' position: $10 - 8 = 2$

tens' position: $9 - 8 = 1$

hundreds' position: $1 - 1 = 0$ (not recorded)

Analyses of pupil response to test items of the type of the example above reveal high percents of error. The errors persist at grade levels where regrouping for subtraction supposedly has been mastered. The procedure illustrated above simplifies the regrouping and makes the type of example a relatively easy one.

Regrouping for the Units' and the Tens' Positions

$$
\begin{array}{r}
3\ 1\ 5 \\
-\ 2\ 8\ 8 \\
\hline
\end{array}
$$

Examples of this type need special consideration. They are potentially difficult from the standpoint that regrouping is needed for both the units' and the tens' position. Also, there is an "unseen" zero in the tens'

position of the minuend. The steps of regrouping may be developed as
follows:

$$\begin{array}{r} \overset{0}{3} \ \cancel{1} \ ^{1}5 \\ - \ 2 \ 8 \ 8 \end{array}$$

Regroup for the units' position: (1) Take 1 ten from the 1 ten (tens'
position) leaving 0 tens. (2) Regroup the 1 ten to 10 ones. (3) Add the
10 ones to the 5 ones making 15 ones for the units' position.

$$\begin{array}{r} \overset{2}{\cancel{3}} \ \overset{10}{\cancel{1}} \ ^{1}5 \\ - \ 2 \ 8 \ 8 \\ \hline 2 \ 7 \end{array}$$

Regroup for the tens' position: (1) Take 1 hundred from 3 hundreds
leaving 2 hundreds. (2) Regroup the 1 hundred to 10 tens. (3) Add the
10 tens to the 0 tens making 10 tens in the tens' position. The regrouped
value of the minuend is 2 hundreds, 10 tens, 15 ones. We then subtract:

units' position: $\qquad 15 - 8 = 7$

tens' position: $\qquad 10 - 8 = 2$

hundreds' position: $\qquad 2 - 2 = 0 \quad$ (not recorded)

7.5 MULTIPLICATION and DIVISION

PRIMARY COMBINATIONS

The primary combinations for multiplication can be charted in a way
similar to that which was done for addition (see Fig. 7.6). Each of the ten

MULTIPLICATION

Factor I (multiplicand)

×	0	1	2	3	4	5	6	7	8	9
0	0	0	0	0	0	0	0	0	0	0
1	0	1	2	3	4	5	6	7	8	9
2	0	2	4	6	8	10	12	14	16	18
3	0	3	6	9	12	15	18	21	24	27
4	0	4	8	12	16	20	24	28	32	36
5	0	5	10	15	20	25	30	35	40	45
6	0	6	12	18	24	30	36	42	48	54
7	0	7	14	21	28	35	42	49	56	63
8	0	8	16	24	32	40	48	54	64	72
9	0	9	18	27	36	45	54	63	72	81

Factor II (multiplier)

Fig. 7.6

digits of the decimal system may be used as a factor to multiply with each single digit as a second factor.

With the exception of using zero as a divisor, each combination for multiplication may be paired with a combination for division. Zero is not used as a divisor, since it is a meaningless situation to ask the question: "How many sets containing *not any* elements can be made from a group containing *some* elements?"

DIVISION

Divisor
(corresponds to Factor I – multiplicand)

		1	2	3	4	5	6	7	8	9
	0	0	0	0	0	0	0	0	0	0
	1	1	2	3	4	5	6	7	8	9
	2	2	4	6	8	10	12	14	16	18
Quotient	3	3	6	9	12	15	18	21	24	27
(corresponds to	4	4	8	12	16	20	24	28	32	36
Factor II –	5	5	10	15	20	25	30	35	40	45
multiplier)	6	6	12	18	24	30	36	42	48	54
	7	7	14	21	28	35	42	49	56	63
	8	8	16	24	32	40	48	54	64	72
	9	9	18	27	36	45	54	63	72	81

Fig. 7.7

Division is the inverse operation of multiplication. The divisor and quotient are related to division as the factors are related to multiplication (Fig. 7.7).

MULTIPLICATION

Types of Settings

The ideas of multiplication are experienced in many types of settings, such as the following:

1. Multiplication is a special case of addition. (See p. 130.) This is likely to be the learner's initial experiencing of multiplication. For example, four children were given two cookies each. How many cookies were they given? The idea of $(2 + 2) + (2 + 2)$ may be verbalized as 4 twos from the earliest experiencing of the problem situation.

2. Multiplication as interpreting the sets within an array may be an early experience with multiplication. Sets may be noted in the array of 12 rectangles.

The array may be considered as:

4 sets (each row as a set) of 3 each (3 + 3 + 3 + 3)

or

3 sets (each column as a set) of 4 each (4 + 4 + 4)

The product is the same whether the sets within the array are considered as 4 sets of 3 each or as 3 sets of 4 each. We may generalize that if a stands for the rows and b stands for the columns, the product will be $a \times b$.

3. Later, in the reading and making of graphs, the child will interpret multiplication in examples such as the one shown in Fig. 7.8.

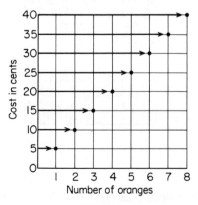

Fig. 7.8

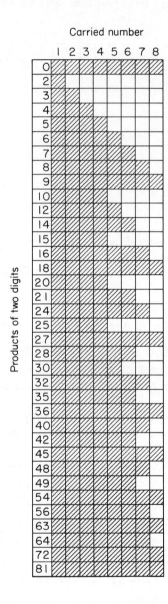

Fig. 7.9 The addition facts that can occur as carry facts with multiplication.

MULTIPLICATION—TECHNIQUES FOR COMPUTATION

Many of the techniques developed for addition are applicable with multiplication. One of the potential sources of difficulty in multiplication is that of regrouping in situations in which the right-hand digit of the product of two facts is recorded and the remaining value is kept in mind to be added to the product of the next multiplication fact.

$$\begin{array}{r} 69 \\ \times\,9 \\ \hline 621 \end{array}$$

In the example, the addition fact, $54 + 8$, is involved. $9 \times 9 = 81$. Write 1 in the units' position and carry 8 to tens' position. $9 \times 6 = 54$ tens. 54 tens $+$ 8 tens $=$ 62 tens.

There are 219 of these addition carry facts. There are 37 different products from the multiplication tables. The only product with which a carry fact cannot occur is 1. ($1 \times 1 = 1$, and no carry is possible.) The 36 other products, together with the numbers that can be carried to each of these products, constitute the 219 addition facts.

Studies reveal that the carry facts account for many errors that pupils make with multiplication examples and that an over-proportionate amount of pupil time is spent in performing the additions. A study by Jenkins reports that approximately 68 percent of the time consumed in multiplying examples that involve carrying is spent in making the required additions.[4]

Figure 7.9 shows the 36 different products and the carried numbers that are possible for each product.[5] This figure should be read as follows: (1) The column to the left contains a listing of the 36 products of two primary factors to which a carry may be made. (2) The row at the top lists the 8 possible carry values. (3) The bar to the right of each of the products indicates each of the carry values which may occur with that product. There are 219 addition facts depicted by the table.

For example, the product 81 is produced by the factors 9×9. The following situations will produce a carry step to that product:

$$\begin{array}{cccccccc} 92 & 93 & 94 & 95 & 96 & 97 & 98 & 99 \\ \times\,9 & \times\,9 & \times\,9 & \times\,9 & \times\,9 & \times\,9 & \times\,9 & \times\,9 \end{array}$$

[4] Marjorie Mahaffey Jenkins, *An Analytical Investigation of the Multiplication Process with Integers.* Unpublished Masters Thesis, Claremont College, Claremont, Calif., 1935, 339 pp.

[5] Melba Koonter, and Peter L. Spencer, "An Analytical Study of Certain Aspects of the Multiplication Process," *California Journal of Elementary Education,* vol. 1 (May 1933), pp. 168–176.

Likewise, the product 24 may be produced by the single digit factors — 4×6, 6×4, 8×3, 3×8. Since 8 is the largest primary factor of 24, it is used as the multiplier because the larger the multiplier, the larger the potential carry. To the product 24, the following situations for adding a carry may occur:

$$
\begin{array}{cccccc}
32 & 34 & 35 & 37 & 38 & 39 \\
\times 8 & \times 8 & \times 8 & \times 8 & \times 8 & \times 8
\end{array}
$$

Possibly there is no way to avoid this procedure when the multipliers contain two or more digits. However, at the initial stages of teaching multiplication examples, when the multiplier is a single digit and the multiplicand contains two or more digits, the extended form of working that was illustrated for addition has merit for multiplication. While the primary combinations are being taught, the extended form offers the opportunity to use the combinations in a variety of settings and at the same time to strengthen ideas of positional value. The carry facts are isolated and made visible. The following example illustrates the extended form. It is a procedure that clearly shows the operation of the distributive property of multiplication over addition.

$$4 \times 659 \text{ is } 4(600 + 50 + 9) = 4(600) + 4(50) + 4(9).$$

This same idea is illustrated with the extended form below.

				Add
6 5 9	6 0 0	5 0	9	6 5 9
=	+	+		6 5 9
× 4	× 4	× 4	× 4	6 5 9
3 6	2 4 0 0	2 0 0	3 6	6 5 9
2 0	partial			3 6
2 4	products			2 0
2 6 3 6				2 4
				2 6 3 6

The product of the units' value is 36 units, which is recorded as 3 in the tens' position and 6 in the units' position. The product of the tens' value is 20 tens which is recorded as 2 in the hundreds' position and not any in the tens' place. The product of the hundreds' position is 24 hundreds which is expressed as 2 in the thousands' position and 4 in the hundreds' position. Adding the values of the partial products, we have 2 in the thousands' position, 6 in the hundreds' position, 3 in the tens' position, and 6 in the units' position, or 2636. This procedure more clearly illustrates the operation of the distributive property than does the technique of carrying that is commonly used.

DIVISION OF DECIMAL INTEGERS

Division is related to subtraction in the same manner that multiplication is related to addition. Division is the process for determining the amount of one factor when the amounts of the product (dividend) and the other factor (divisor) are known. For example, $7 \times 6 = 42$ and $6 \times 7 = 42$. Then $42 \div 6 = 7$ and $42 \div 7 = 6$.

Division is a complicated process because it involves each of the other procedures — multiplication, addition, and subtraction, and it also includes principles and techniques that are peculiar to division alone.

$$\begin{array}{r} 9 \\ 54)\overline{5\ 1\ 4} \\ 4\ 8\ 6 \\ \hline 2\ 8 \end{array}$$

As may be noted in the example, skills of addition, multiplication, and subtraction are involved. Multiplication that occurs within division involves the use of the 100 primary combinations for multiplication and the 219 carry facts that are used in multiplication. All 100 primary combinations with subtraction may occur, and the types of regrouping for examples such as $514 - 486$ are a potential source of difficulty. In the example given, regrouping is required for both the units' and the tens' positions, and in regrouping, there is an unseen zero in the tens' position. (514 is regrouped to $400 + 10$ tens $+ 14$.)

In addition to the skills needed for the addition, subtraction, and multiplication that occur within division, there are division facts, principles, and techniques that are needed for division alone. As indicated in Fig. 7.7, there are 90 primary combinations for division. There are also 324 division facts that correspond to the primary combinations, but these divisions have remainders. For example, $4)\overline{12}$ and $4)\overline{16}$ are even division facts, but in between them are the following uneven facts: $4)\overline{13}$, $4)\overline{14}$, and $4)\overline{15}$. The set of whole numbers is not closed with respect to division as may be noted through the uneven division facts. For example, the quotient for $3)\overline{14}$ is 4 and 2 remainder. That quotient is not an element of the set of whole numbers. Mastery of the uneven and of the even division facts is important for achievement of facile computation in division.

Estimation of the quotient figure, correct placement of the digits in the quotient, bringing down the proper digit to continue division if more than a one-digit quotient is involved, and so forth, are all techniques that are specifically part of the division procedure.

The techniques for division reverse those used in addition, subtraction, and multiplication. In addition, multiplication, and subtraction the conventional procedure for working is from a right to a left direction. The operation of division is performed from left to right.

There are many techniques for making division easier. Five procedures to answer the problem, "How many subgroups of 57 each are there in a group of 456?" are presented below.

Procedure One—Seried Subtraction

```
    456
  −  57   ①
    ───
    399
  −  57   ②
    ───
    342
  −  57   ③
    ───
    285
  −  57   ④
    ───
    228
  −  57   ⑤
    ───
    171
  −  57   ⑥
    ───
    114
  −  57   ⑦
    ───
     57
  −  57   ⑧
    ───
      0
```

Subtract or draw out the subgrouping until the group of 456 is reduced to a value less than 57. Then count the number of times 57 has been subtracted. There are 8 subgroups of 57 in 456.

Procedure Two—"Guesstimation"

The idea is to start by taking as many of the divisor values from the dividend value as one selects to take. The partial quotient figures may be written to the right of the example and then summed to find the final quotient figure.

```
          8
      ─────
  57) 456
      114 │ 2 × 57
      ───
      342
      228 │ 4 × 57
      ───
      114
      114 │ 2 × 57
      ─────
          8 × 57
```

How many groups of 57 each can be made from a group of 456? *Answer:* 8 groups of 57 each and no remainder.

The procedure of "guesstimation" should grow out of the seried subtraction procedure above. As the learner develops his ability to estimate the quotient figure, he will need fewer and fewer steps in the "guesstimation."

Procedure Three—Initial Digit Method of Quotient Estimation

$$\begin{array}{r} 9 \\ 57\overline{)456} \\ 513 \end{array}$$

$$\begin{array}{r} 8 \\ 57\overline{)\,456} \\ 456 \end{array}$$

Fives in 45 are 9. Use 9 as a trial quotient. $9 \times 57 = 513$; $513 > 456$. Hence, 9 is too large for the quotient. *Decrease* the trial quotient to 8. $8 \times 57 = 456$.

Procedure Four—Increase by One Method for Quotient Estimation

$$\begin{array}{r} 7 \\ 57\overline{)456} \\ 399 \\ 57 \end{array}$$

$$\begin{array}{r} 8 \\ 57\overline{)\,456} \\ 456 \end{array}$$

Since the units' digit is large, it will tend to produce a large carry when the divisor is multiplied by the trial quotient. Hence, increase the trial divisor (5) by one. That will decrease the estimated quotient and also thereby decrease the size of the carry. Sixes in 45 are 7. Use 7 as a trial quotient. Then $7 \times 57 = 399$; $456 - 399 = 57$. The remainder is as large as the divisor, so we *increase* the trial quotient figure to 8. This increase-by-one procedure is frequently suggested for use when the divisor has a large value in its units' position. It does produce a higher percentage of correct estimates for divisors of that type than are produced by the initial digit procedure with such divisors. However, as the values in the units' place decrease, the accuracy of the increase-by-one procedure decreases and that of the initial digit procedure increases. Since the increase-by-one procedure is applicable for only a few divisors, and since it produces incorrect estimates even within that limited usage, one may reasonably question the advisability of teaching it to students. However, that does not mean that pupils should not be stimulated to derive it by themselves.

Procedure Five—Mental Long Division

With this procedure as with the two preceding ones, we need to find a multiple of the divisor that does not exceed the dividend and which when subtracted from the dividend does not leave a remainder that is equal to, or greater than, the divisor.

The procedure is basically a method of dividing separately by each digit of the divisor. Using a two-digit divisor, one divides first by the tens' digit and then by the ones' digit.

When we multiply, there is likely to be a "carry" to add to the product of the next multiplication. When we reverse the process by dividing, there must be a remainder that is as great as the carry.

$$\overset{9}{57)\,\overline{456}}$$

$$\overset{8}{57)\,\overline{456}}$$

One thinks fives in 45 equal 9. There is no remainder. But 9×7 produces a carry, so 9 is too large try $8 - 8 \times 5 = 40$. Subtract 40 from 45 which leaves 5. The 5 is combined with the value of the next position to make 56. There are 8 sevens in 56, so 8 is the correct quotient.

Comparing the verbal description of this process with its representation illustrates nicely the economy of numerical computation. The steps of this procedure are carried out for the most part without recording them. The number facts are known. All that is needed is a clear idea of the aspects of the procedure and meticulous accuracy in carrying them out. Errors with this process are less likely to be made than with the other processes described, and the multiplication and subtraction difficulties are greatly decreased.

ILLUSTRATIVE LESSONS

The following illustrative lessons and lesson plans are presented in this chapter:

Lesson 1. Baking cookies
Lesson 2. Multiplier-multiplicand-product relationships
Lesson 3. Introduction of written work with addition examples in which carrying is involved
Lesson 4. Division as a special case of subtraction
Lesson 5. Divisor-dividend-quotient relationships

In Lesson 1, the kindergarten group of children sensed a mathematical relationship that is very pertinent for interpretation of certain types of division situations and for understanding of an inverse type of change in quantitative amount. Let the cooky batter stand for the dividend, and the size of the cooky cutter for the divisor of a division example. The number of cookies can represent the quotient.

$$\text{size of cooky cutter}\,)\,\overline{\text{amount of cooky batter}}^{\text{number of cookies}}$$

If the amount of batter (dividend) is constant, the size of the cutter (divisor) and the number of cookies (quotient) are inversely related. This relationship of an inverse change was sensed and interpreted in several ways by the group of kindergarten children. It is this type of relationship that many learners fail to sense when it is placed in the computational setting of division of decimal and common fraction numbers. The relationship is equally simple in its setting of numerical computation if the ideas underlying the computation are understood.

The other lessons in this chapter follow the development of the concepts as presented in the first part of the chapter.

Lesson 1
ACTIVITY — BAKING COOKIES[6]
Kindergarten level

Kent: Be sure to get the right-size cooky cutter to get the most cookies.
Phyllis: Roll the dough thin, and you'll get more, too.
Sandra: If they're too thick, they won't get done in time.
[Later, with another group of kindergarten cooks (same kindergarten class) cutting their cookies. Their batter seemed to them to be too thin.]
Joe: It's too wet. The cutters won't work. How are we going to make cookies?
Teacher: Well, we could use a teaspoon and make drop cookies.
Marilee: They'll be awfully thick. Better make the oven awfully hot.

Generalizations:

(1) The amount of cooky batter being constant, the size of the cookies (cooky cutter used) determines the number of cookies. That is, the larger the cutter, the fewer the cookies; and the smaller the cutter, the greater the number of cookies.

[6] Read Schuster, "The Formation of Certain Arithmetic Concepts in the Pre-Primary Child," an unpublished study.

(2) The amount of cooky batter and the size of the cookies being constant, the thinner the batter, the more cookies that can be made; and the thicker the batter, the fewer cookies that can be made.

(3) The oven temperature being constant, the thicker the cookies, the longer the time to bake them; and the thinner the cookies, the shorter the time to bake them.

Lesson 2
MULTIPLIER-MULTIPLICAND-PRODUCT RELATIONSHIPS
Grade Three Class

Purpose of lesson: To lead the children to discover, to generalize, and to state in their own words the following relationships: (a) If the multiplicand is constant, the multiplier and product are in direct proportion. (b) If the multiplier is constant, the multiplicand and product are in direct proportion. (c) Factors and product are directly proportional.

Background of children: The children had developed simple work with multiplication using two-digit multiplicands and one-digit multipliers and had evolved the multiplier-multiplicand-product relationship in its addition setting.

Materials used: The teacher had made the charts that are described in this lesson.

Lesson Procedure

[The teacher had the following chart on the board where the children could see it easily.]

(a)	(b)	(c)	(d)	(e)
5	5	5	5	5
$\times\ 1$	$\times\ 2$	$\times\ 4$	$\times\ 8$	$\times\ 1\ 6$
5	1 0	2 0	4 0	8 0

Marilyn: That's all multiplication.

Kenneth: Yes, that is easy. We've had harder work than that. That's too easy.

Teacher: It is easy multiplication, but I'll make a problem about the examples so you will need to do very good thinking to have a good answer. Study the set of examples and see how many things you can discover about them. I'll give you about a minute to think and to be ready with your discoveries.

[*Note:* The time allowed for organization of thinking challenged the children to go beyond initial awareness of the concept and to refine their ideas and their statements.]

Marilyn: The numerals at the top are the same — all 5's.

Janice: The numerals at the top are the multiplicands, Marilyn. The multiplicands are alike and the answers increase as you go from left to right. The multipliers increase, too.

Ronnie: As you go from right to left, the opposite is true. The multipliers and answers decrease.

Judy: The multipliers get twice as large. [Example (a) through Example (e)]

Tom: So do the products — 5, 10, 20, 40, 80.

Jim: That's like the addition examples we had. The more addends, the bigger the sum. We added all twos.

Teacher: Who can compare Example (b) with Example (a) and state *all* of the things that are true?

Beth: Examples (a) and (b) are alike at the top — multiplicands are alike. Example (b) has a multiplier that is twice as big as (a)'s, and (b)'s product is twice as big as (a)'s.

Teacher: Very good thinking, Beth. You told about the multiplicands, the multipliers, and the product. This is even more difficult. Who can compare Example (a) with Example (d)? Start with Example (a).

James: The multiplicands are alike. The multiplier of Example (a) is smaller than (d)'s and the product is smaller.

Susan: You didn't tell how much smaller. The multiplier of Example (a) is 1 and the other multiplier is 8. The multiplier of Example (a) is 8 times as small as (d)'s. The same is true with its product.

[Other comparisons were made, and the children were asked to tell what was true about the set of examples by making a general statement.]

Ronnie: When the multiplicands are alike, the bigger the multiplier, the bigger the product.

Mary: And the smaller the answer, the smaller the multiplier.

Sandra: If the multiplier is 8 times as large, the product is 8 times as large.

Teacher: If we reverse the multipliers and multiplicands, let's see what is true.

[The children had generalized that the multiplier and the multiplicand can be interchanged, and the product remains constant. Four fives equal five fours, and so forth. The teacher then placed the following chart on the board.]

(a)	(b)	(c)	(d)	(e)
1	2	4	8	1 6
× 5	× 5	× 5	× 5	× 5
5	1 0	2 0	4 0	8 0

Mary: That is just the same. You've just turned the top and middle around.

Kenneth: You changed the multiplicands and multipliers. The answers are the same.

Dennis: Now the multipliers are the same, and the multiplicands change.

Teacher: This is a much harder question. Think before you give an answer. Who can tell what is true about the set of examples? Don't just compare two or three examples, but tell what is true about all of them.

Marilyn: I think I can. The multipliers are alike. As the multiplicands get larger, so do the products. As the multiplicands get smaller, so do the products.

Sandra: Yes. When the products get larger, the multiplicands get larger, too.

Teacher: You boys and girls do very good thinking in mathematics. Here is a small piece of paper for you to write some examples of your own. Listen carefully and see if you can do this. Write two examples in which the multiplicands are alike and the multipliers are different. Be able to compare your two examples and show how what we have talked about this morning is true.

The period ended with the children's writing their own examples. After the teacher had checked the children's examples, the children wrote them on the chalkboard and explained their work. Making their own examples challenged them to write examples that would be simple to compare and to sense and state the concept more clearly. The children didn't develop the language expression of direct proportion, but their concept of the relationship was at a high level of refinement.

Lesson 3
INTRODUCTION OF WRITTEN WORK WITH ADDITION EXAMPLES IN WHICH CARRYING OCCURS
Grade Two Class

Purpose of lesson: To have the child refine his concepts of number relationships and to introduce written work with addition examples in which carrying occurs.

Background of children: The children had learned many number combinations through grouping of objects such as tiles, blocks, and beads and through experiences with things within their environment. The children's concepts concerning the constant and positional value of numbers were at a fine degree of refinement for that given grade level and for the given group of children.

Materials used: Tiles, blocks, and chalkboard.

Lesson Procedure

[The children had developed the story of how shepherds, in days long ago, kept an account of how many sheep they had through the use of pebbles as counters. The children had used pebbles and acted out the story. In their activity, they had discovered many basic ideas that underlie the decimal system of notation.]

Kenneth: That was fun when we gathered pebbles and told number stories.

Keith: The way we count is a lot easier. I can count to 1000, and I don't need pebbles to count with.

Teacher: What are some of the things that you discovered when you used pebbles to tell about how many sheep a shepherd had?

Marilyn: I made a line of pebbles. Then I took 10 pebbles out and used one (of the 10 pebbles) in a place at this side [pointed to left] to say ten. Then I took 10 out again and used one (of the 10 pebbles) to say ten. You can keep doing that as long as you still have 10 pebbles in a line.

John: I used an eraser to hold the place in a line when there weren't any pebbles in a line.

Sue: And I used a pencil.

Mary: And I used a long line. I marked it with a stick.

[Others told ways that they used. Discussion also ensued concerning how the tens' position can be regrouped to hundreds, and so on.]

Teacher: When you write 35, what does the 3 stand for?

Jimmie: It stands for 3 tens. If you had a long line of 35 pebbles, you could take 30 out and put 3 in a line to this side. I'll show you. [Jimmie went to the board and showed his grouping like this.]

```
        *    *
        *    *
        *    *
             *
             *
```

The 3 pebbles in this position (tens' position) stand for 30 in this position (units' position).

Teacher: When we write this example, what things do we do that are similar to what we did with pebbles?

[Teacher wrote the following problem on the board.]

$$
\begin{array}{r}
9 \\
+\ 9 \\
\hline
1\ 8
\end{array}
$$

Sonja: If you had 18 pebbles in a long line, you could take 10 out of the long line and put 1 to the left side of the 8 pebbles. The 1 stands for 10.

Bill: That is just like when we write 18. The 1 stands for 1 ten.

Paul: Yes. And you should write the 1 where it belongs. It belongs over to the left side. If you wrote it in the wrong place, it wouldn't say 1 ten.

Bill: If you wrote the 1 to the right of the 8, you would have 81.

Teacher: You boys and girls do very good thinking. You are very careful where you place your numerals, and you make very few errors. You haven't had examples like the one I'm writing on the board, but I think you will know how to work it.

[Teacher wrote the following on the board.]

$$
\begin{array}{r}
2\ 9 \\
+\ 3\ 9
\end{array}
$$

Teacher: Will the answer to the example be as large as 100?

Judy: No, 50 and 50 equal 100, and 29 and 39 are smaller than 50 and 50.

Sally: But the answer will be larger than 50. 25 and 25 are 50.

Teacher: Let us add the digits in the units' position just as we did in the example of 9 + 9. Where should we write the 18?

Paul: The 1 should be written under the 2 and the 3. It means 1 ten. I'll write it.

[Paul went to the board and wrote the 18 as shown here:]

$$
\begin{array}{r}
2\ 9 \\
+\ 3\ 9 \\
\hline
1\ 8
\end{array}
$$

Teacher: How many tens do we have here? [Teacher pointed to 2 + 3.]

Peter: Five tens. I know where to write it. The 5 should go under the 1 ten. I'll write it.

[Peter wrote the 5 tens under the 1 ten.]

$$
\begin{array}{r}
2\ 9 \\
+\ 3\ 9 \\
\hline
1\ 8 \\
5 \\
\hline
\end{array}
$$

Teacher: What do you think we need to do now?

Sally: Wouldn't we bring down the 8 units and then add the 1 ten and 5 tens? May I write it? [Sally recorded the sum, 6 8.]

Sue: That is just the way we did it when we used pebbles. That's easy. I want to do one (example).

Teacher: Sue, you may go to the board and write this example and try to work it. 3 5 + 3 5. The rest of the class may help Sue if she needs help.

[Sue did not need help. She did the written work with addition as readily as she had done the regrouping of pebbles.]

Kenneth: That's too easy. Why don't you give us a harder problem?

Teacher: All right. This example is harder. Look at it and think before you suggest how to do it.

[Teacher wrote the following example on the board.]

```
   1 8 6
+  1 8 6
```

Michael: Let me do the first part: 6 + 6 equals 12. You would write the 1 in the tens' place under the 8 and 8.

[Michael wrote the 1 2 in its correct column position.]

Teacher: What do you notice about the next part of the example? 8 + 8 equals 16, but what is true about the position of the digits?

Michael: The 8 and 8 stands for 80 and 80 (8 tens and 8 tens). The 16 stands for 160; 80 and 80 equals 160. You have to write the 1 in the hundreds' place. The 6 goes with the tens. And 1 and 1 stands for 100 and 100 (1 hundred and 1 hundred). You write the 2 in the hundreds' place.

[Michael went to the board and placed the 16 and the 2 in the proper position.]

```
   1 8 6
+  1 8 6
     1 2
   1 6
   2
─────────
```

Teacher: Now all that we have to do is to add the units together, then the tens, and then the hundreds. Would you like to do it, John? [John combined terms and the answer 3 7 2 was shown.]

Sonja: That is harder. I'm not sure I can do that.

Teacher: That is true, Sonja. We will do easier ones first and will save the harder ones until later. How many of you are very sure that you could do this example? [Teacher wrote 4 8 + 3 6 on the board.]

Some of you may go to the board and work it if you are very sure you know how to do it.

The teacher selected a group of those who were very sure that they knew how to do the example and had them work the example on the chalkboard. The children were asked to wait until they really understood a new step before they tried to perform the written computation. This was a general procedure that produced good self-analysis and excellent results. Most of the children were able to analyze their readiness to do written work and were confident when they expressed their readiness. Such analysis reduced percents of computational error and decreased the amount of repetitive material needed for mastery.

Lesson 4
DIVISION IS A SPECIAL CASE OF SUBTRACTION
Grade Three Class

Purpose of lesson: To help the children formulate and refine concepts of division, and to help the teacher sense the level of readiness of his group of learners.

Background of children: The children had used the language of multiplication such as 3 fours, 5 threes, and so forth, but multiplication and division forms as such had not been introduced. As can be determined through the responses of the children, they had a high level of readiness for division. Many simple division facts were given with facility.

Materials used: One counter with a string of 10 beads, and one counter with a string of 20 beads. Egg cartons.

Lesson Procedure

Teacher: [Held up the counter with 10 yellow beads.] How many beads do you think there are on this wire?

Jane: Ten.

Teacher: How do you know?

Jane: It just looks like (as if) there are 10.

Joyce: I'll count them.

[Joyce took the counter, counted by twos, and confirmed Jane's statement.]

Teacher: Can you divide these 10 beads into 2 groups that would have the same number of beads in each group?

Joe: Yes. There would be 5 beads in each group because 5 and 5 is ten.

Teacher: Can you divide the 10 beads into 3 groups that would have the same number of beads in each group?

Tom: It wouldn't work. Since 3 and 3 and 3 are 9, 1 bead would be left over.

Joyce: There is 1 extra when you count by threes.

[Teacher held up counter that had 20 beads. The frames of the 2 holders were the same length.]

Teacher: Would you say that these 2 holders are about the same length?

Class: Yes.

Teacher: What do you notice about the 2 counters?

Richard: There are more red beads than yellow beads.

Susan: The red beads are smaller and stick out farther in the holder. [The children counted the 20 red beads in groups of 2s as the teacher pointed to the beads.]

Teacher: If we divide the 20 beads into 2 groups that have an equal number of beads in each group, how many beads would be in each group?

Judith: Ten. Ten and ten equals twenty.

Teacher: Can you divide the 20 beads into 4 groups that have the same number of beads in each group?

Marjorie: [After a few seconds of deliberation] There would be five and five and five and five.

James: Yes. Five and five is ten. Ten and ten is twenty. Four fives.

Teacher: Can you divide the 20 beads into 3 groups that are equal in number?

James: No. It wouldn't work with 10 so it won't work with 20.

Judith: [After short period of deliberation] There would be 6 and 6 and 6. There would be 2 beads left over. [Judith took the counter and showed her grouping.]

Teacher: That is fine, Judith. Let us see if you can do as well in dividing with our next problem. [Teacher held up an egg carton with the box divided as in the figure.]

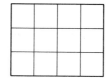

Let us pretend that this carton is full of eggs. If you took 2 eggs at a time out of this carton, how many times would you need to take out eggs to empty the carton?

Jane: That's easy. Six. Six and six equals twelve.

Teacher: Can you figure different ways to empty the egg carton? Take out the same number of eggs each time. Here are 12 tiles that you can use to represent eggs. Use the tiles to check your answer.

Class: [The following combinations were given:]

3	taken out at a time	4	times
4	taken out at a time	3	times
6	taken out at a time	2	times
1	taken out at a time	12	times
2	taken out at a time	6	times

Billy: The more eggs you take out at a time, the fewer the times you have to take them out.

Richard: The fewer eggs you take out at a time, the more times you have to take them out. If I had to fill many egg boxes, I'd put in 6 eggs at a time. I'd take 3 eggs in each hand. That would be less work than fooling around and putting in only a few at a time.

Teacher: Let us show our problems on the board. Judith, how many eggs did you take out at a time?

Judith: Three. I had 12 eggs. I took out 3, and 3 again, and 3 again, and 3 again.

Teacher: Does this tell how you did it?

[Teacher wrote on blackboard:]

$$
\begin{array}{r}
1\ 2 \\
-\ \ 3 \\ \hline
9 \\
-\ \ 3 \\ \hline
6 \\
-\ \ 3 \\ \hline
3 \\
-\ \ 3 \\ \hline
0
\end{array}
$$

① Took 3 out one time

② Took 3 out a second time

③ Took 3 out a third time

④ Took 3 out a fourth time

This lesson continued with showing the subtraction procedure illustrated above. The problems that the children had developed were worked, and then several examples with uneven division facts were worked. $14 - 3, - 3, - 3, - 3$, and 2 remainder, and several other examples were evolved to develop the concept of uneven division facts. A brief time after this lesson the division signs, $\overline{)}$ and $\div$, and the division form were developed with the class.

Lesson 5
DIVISOR-DIVIDEND-QUOTIENT RELATIONSHIPS
Grade Five Class

Purpose of lesson: To lead the pupils to discover and identify the inverse relationship between the numerical size of the divisor and the numerical size of the quotient in a division situation.

Lesson Procedure

The procedure is that of "sciencing" with numbers. A secondary purpose of the activity was to bring out and to apply scientific methodology in the pursuit of new ideas and new procedures.

The class session opened with an informal discussion of scientists and what scientists do. This led to the formulation of a working definition of a scientist: "A scientist is one who sees more and sees better than do people who are not scientists." At that point a test was proposed to determine who among the pupils might have this ability to "see more and to see better." Attention was brought to a high pitch, and then the following activity took place:

Teacher: Let's see who of us may be scientists. Follow closely what I do. [Teacher drew a square approximately a foot wide on the chalkboard.] What is the name of the figure I drew?

Class: A square.

Teacher: How many squares did I make?

Class: One.

Teacher: That is right! Everyone can see that! Now watch carefully, here comes the test to find out who can see more and see better than the others. [Teacher drew lines cutting the square into 9 equal segments. When the lines were drawn he asked:] What did I do?

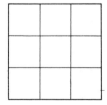

Pupil: You divided it into a lot of little squares.

Teacher: Good! At least, that is what I tried to do. Now here is our test! How many squares are pictured by this figure?

Class: Nine!

Teacher: Yes. There are 9 squares, but is that all there are?

Pupil: No. I see 10 squares! The first square is still there. You just drew lines in it.

Teacher: Good for you! You saw more and saw better than those who saw only 9 squares. But are 10 squares all there are?

Pupil: Hey! I see 14 squares there!

Teacher: Are you sure? We must be careful not to mislead others if we are to be scientists.

Pupil: Sure, there are 14. Look! I'll show you.

[Pupil went to the board and pointed out the 9 squares and the tenth square that had been mentioned. Then he showed that the 4 little squares in each corner of the large square make another square. That made 14 in all. After they had been pointed out, everyone was able to see them, but the 14 squares had not been seen at first.]

Teacher: That's fine! That's what it takes to be a scientist. One must observe carefully, and try to see things in different ways to find whether that helps him to "see more." Now you know that it is possible to see more and to see better if we really try.

Scientists sometimes perform experiments to help them to see more and see better. In those experiments they may do something several times, keeping some parts unchanged and making changes in the other parts. That way they may be able to tell better how the parts work together. Let's do an experiment with numbers to see what we can find out. Now all of you scientists watch carefully! Let's see who can see more and see better this time!

[The teacher wrote the figure 16 on the chalkboard 5 times in a row, placing the numerals about a foot apart in the series.

16   16   16   16   16

Teacher: Does what I have done so far represent constancy or does it represent change, variability?

Class: It is the same. All the numerals are alike. They are all 16.

Teacher: Now watch carefully. I am going to write sentences on the board. They will tell you to do something. A sentence must have a verb. So, I shall now write the verbs in the sentences. [The teacher made division signs to include each of the numerals.]

$\overline{)16}$ $\overline{)16}$ $\overline{)16}$ $\overline{)16}$ $\overline{)16}$

Teacher: What does the verb in the statements tell us to do?

Class: It tells us to divide. That is the sign for division.

Teacher: Is the verb the same in all? Is it constant or does it change, that is, vary?

Pupil: It doesn't change. It is constant.

Teacher: That's right! Now, I'll finish my sentences. They will tell you what you are to do.

[Teacher wrote divisors for each example as shown below:]

$$1)\overline{16} \quad 2)\overline{16} \quad 4)\overline{16} \quad 8)\overline{16} \quad 16)\overline{16}$$

Teacher: What did I write this time?

Pupil: You wrote the divisors. They are not alike.

Teacher: That is good seeing! What other way might you have said that the divisors are not alike?

Pupil: They are not the same. They differ. They *vary.*

Teacher: Yes. Vary is a good word for scientists. If we are to be scientists, we must learn to use the language of science. The sentences tell you to do something. What do they tell you to do?

Pupil: They say to divide 16 by the numbers shown.

Teacher: That is correct. There are five examples for us to solve. So we have a science experiment. In the examples, the dividends are constant and the divisors vary in size. If we solve the examples and watch carefully as we do so, we may see something interesting. As scientists we must try to see more and to see better. Let's solve them. I'll write a letter above each example. That will help us in comparing the examples.

[With the help of the pupils, answers were obtained for each of the examples.]

(a)	(b)	(c)	(d)	(e)
16	8	4	2	1
$1)\overline{16}$	$2)\overline{16}$	$4)\overline{16}$	$8)\overline{16}$	$16)\overline{16}$

[A brief pause followed to permit study of the statements.]

Teacher: Do you see something of interest?

Pupil: Yes, the answers are not the same.

Pupil: Yes. As the divisors get larger, the answers get smaller.

Teacher: Do you all agree?

[General assent was shown.]

Teacher: Harry made a good observation according to the way he saw the examples. He must have been reading from left to right the way we read from books. Can we read the examples another way?

Pupil: Sure you can! Reading from right to left they show that as the divisors get smaller the quotients get larger. That says the same thing that Harry said, but in a different way.

Teacher: That's fine! These statements tell us more than the statement "the answers are not alike." It often helps to say things in different ways. Sometimes one way of saying an idea gives more meaning to it than does another way. I'd say that we have gotten our experiment with numbers about to the place we were with the squares when we discovered that there were 10 squares instead of only 9 which everyone saw so easily. Can anyone think of a way to make the experiment more meaningful? We have seen that as the divisors get larger the quotients get smaller, and as the divisors get smaller the quotients get larger. How much smaller? How much larger? Is there an exact relationship?

Pupil: Oh! I see something. [Pupil went to board and pointed as he spoke.] As this divisor [pointed to Examples (a) and (b)] becomes 2 times as large, the quotient becomes half as large. Then as this divisor [Example (c)] is made 2 times as large, the quotient again becomes $\frac{1}{2}$ as large. That happens clear through the examples as you go from (a) to (e).

Teacher: Now, that's something that we can use! So long as we said only that the quotients became larger or smaller and didn't indicate how much larger or how much smaller, we didn't tell the relationship of the change.

We have found that as the divisor is made 2 times as large, the quotient becomes $\frac{1}{2}$ as large! I wonder if someone can think of a better way to say that. We want to indicate opposite directions for the change, but we refer only to one direction in the statement.

Pupil: Wouldn't it be better to say when the divisor is made 2 times as large, the quotient becomes 2 times as small, and when the divisor is made 2 times as small, the quotient becomes 2 times as large? I think that tells the direction better.

Teacher: What do the rest of you think about it? Do you agree that this way of stating the relationship is clearer?

[There was general agreement.]

Teacher: What other comparisons can you make?

Pupil: The divisor of Example (c) is 4 times as large as the divisor of Example (a). The quotient is 4 times as small for Example (c) as for Example (a).

Pupil: The divisor of Example (a) is 8 times as small as the divisor of Example (d). Example (a)'s quotient is 8 times as large as Example (d)'s.

Pupil: The divisor of Example (e) is 16 times as large as (a)'s divisor, and its quotient is 16 times as small.

Constant: distance
Variable: speed
Variable: time

The *faster* the comet travels, the *less* time it takes to go around
the sun.

Teacher: Can you bring our experiment to the 14-square level by
stating what is true about the whole set of examples? Can you state
the discovery about division examples in which the dividend is constant and the divisor is variable?

Pupil: I think I can. I'll try. We discovered that as the divisor gets
larger, the quotient gets smaller if the dividend stays the same. And,
if the divisor gets smaller, the quotient gets larger.

Teacher: Can you state those two ideas in one sentence? That is
a harder problem.

Pupil: You could say that as the divisor changes, the quotient
changes in the opposite direction from the divisor when the dividend
is constant.

Teacher: What you have said is true, but how does it change?

Pupil: The divisor and quotient change in opposite directions by
the same amount. If one gets 3 times as large, the other one gets 3 times
as small.

Teacher: That is not an easy idea to express in words, but you can
use the idea in your work with division. Can anyone think of an experience he has had that shows this idea without using numbers?

Pupil: In playing games, the more games we win, the fewer the other
side wins.

Pupil: The more time we waste getting ready for recess, the less time we have for play.

Pupil: If you take popcorn from a bag, the more you take out each time, the fewer the times you can take it. The less you take out each time, the more times you can take it.

At another time, the children were led to write out their examples in problem form and to set the problem up as a divisor-dividend-quotient relationship.

Discussion Questions

1. Show the regrouped value and state the steps of regrouping for the following subtraction examples:

$$
\begin{array}{r}
5\ 0\ 0 \\
-3\ 7\ 5 \\
\hline
\end{array}
\qquad
\begin{array}{r}
4\ 1\ 6 \\
-3\ 8\ 8 \\
\hline
\end{array}
\qquad
\begin{array}{r}
8\ 5\ 8 \\
-6\ 8\ 5 \\
\hline
\end{array}
$$

2. Write three word problems that illustrate each of the following ideas of multiplication: (a) multiplication as a special case of addition; (b) multiplication as sets of an array; (c) reading graphs to interpret multiplication.

3. Use the example, 9×748, and illustrate the distributive principle of multiplication.

4. Use the example in Question 3 to illustrate the extended form for multiplication. List the products and the carry facts that are involved.

5. List the uneven division facts that can occur: (a) between $9)\overline{45}$ and $9)\overline{54}$; (b) between $7)\overline{35}$ and $7)\overline{42}$.

6. How many uneven division facts can occur with 9 as a divisor and with a one-digit quotient? List them.

7. Use the "guesstimation" procedure for division and show the steps you would use to solve the example: $23)\overline{142}$.

8. Use Fig. 7.9, which shows the addition facts that can occur as carry facts with multiplication. Do you see that for the products 0 through 9, the sum of the product and the carried number will be 17 or less. These are among the primary combinations that were described on p. 141. Using the figure, determine how many of the facts are higher decade facts (sums greater than 18).

9. In Lesson 2 of Chapter 4, the children invented a base five numeral system. The symbols that they used were as follows:

COMMON LANGUAGE	NUMERAL
zero	0
one	1
two	∩
three	△
four	☐
onefi	1 0

Using 10 digits, there are 100 primary combinations that are possible for addition and 100 for multiplication. Use the base five numeration system invented by the children and chart the primary combinations that are possible for addition and for multiplication.

10. Write the primary combinations for addition, multiplication, and division that belong in the family group of $18 - 9$.

11. How does the identification of addition, subtraction, multiplication, and division as ways of counting show relationships among them? What does it suggest regarding instruction and the learning of those procedures?

12. In addition, there is always a directional grouping; that is, one set or group is "brought to" the other. The term "augend" is sometimes used to identify the term *to* which addition is made. What advantage or disadvantage do you think using the term would have?

13. In column addition, people sometimes "skip around" and add numbers out of order. What properties of addition are they applying?

14. What advantages or disadvantages do you see in bringing out the root meanings of terms such as *multiplicand* and *minuend?*

15. Some persons point out that division is a procedure for answering the following different questions: (a) "How many sets of a certain size can be made from the dividend set?" (measurement concept of division). (b) If the dividend set is broken up in a specified number of equal groups, how many would be in each group? (partition concept of division). In what way does the division procedure vary as applied to each of these different questions?

16. In checking the accuracy of their subtraction, people sometimes add the remainder to the subtrahend and compare the sum with the minuend. What idea of subtraction are they applying?

17. How many primary addition combinations would there be in a number system using an alphabet of 20 digits?

18. Since 9 is the largest number value that can be expressed in any position within a decimal numeral, how do you justify the algorism which uses a regrouped value greater than 9 in any decimal position?

$$\begin{array}{r} \overset{8}{9}{}^{1}2 \\ -4\ 8 \\ \hline \end{array}$$

Suggested Readings

Banks, J. Houston, *Learning and Teaching Arithmetic*, 2d ed. Boston, Mass.: Allyn and Bacon, Inc., 1964, Chaps. 5, 6, and 7.

Beatty, Leslie S., Janet S. Briggs, Edwena B. Moore, and Richard W. Oliver, *Mental Arithmetic in Subtraction and Division*. San Diego: Department of Education, San Diego County, San Diego, Calif., 1961. This is one of a series of Independent Learning Booklets which were part of an experimental program in San Diego County. Booklets of the series are *Probability and Statistics, We Travel with Money, Understanding the Slide Rule, We Learn to Measure,* and *We Measure to Learn.*

Brumfiel, Charles F., Robert E. Eicholz, and Merrill E. Shanks, *Fundamental Concepts of Elementary Mathematics*. Reading, Mass.: Addison-Wesley Publishing Company, Inc., 1962, Chap. 6.

Capps, Lelon R., "Division of Fractions," *The Arithmetic Teacher*, vol. 9 (January 1962), pp. 10–16.

Clark, J. R., "The Use of Crutches in Teaching Arithmetic," *The Arithmetic Teacher*, vol. 1 (October 1954), pp. 6–10.

Dutton, Wilbur H., and L. J. Adams, *Arithmetic for Teachers*. Englewood Cliffs, N. J.: Prentice-Hall, Inc., 1961, Chaps. 2,3,4, and 5.

Flournoy, Frances, "Controversy Regarding the Teaching of Higher-Decade Addition," *The Arithmetic Teacher*, vol. 3 (October 1956), pp. 170–173.

Gibney, Thomas, "Uses and Abuses of the Number Line," *The Arithmetic Teacher*, vol. 11 (November 1964), pp. 478–482.

Grossnickle, Foster E., "Discovering the Multiplication Facts," *The Arithmetic Teacher*, vol. 6 (October 1959), pp. 195–198.

Gunderson, Agnes G., "Thought-Patterns of Young Children in Learning Multiplication and Division," *Elementary School Journal*, vol. 55 (April 1955), pp. 453–461.

Hannon, Herbert, "A New Look at the Basic Principles of Multiplication with Whole Numbers," *The Arithmetic Teacher*, vol. 7 (November 1960), pp. 357–361.

Hartung, M. L., "Estimating the Quotient in Division," *The Arithmetic Teacher*, vol. 4 (April 1957), pp. 100–111.

Lay, L. Clark, *Arithmetic: An Introduction to Mathematics*. New York: The Macmillan Company, 1960, Chaps. 1,2, and 3.

Mueller, Francis J., *Arithmetic, Its Structure and Concepts*, 2d ed. Englewood Cliffs, N.J.: Prentice-Hall, Inc., 1964, Unit 6.

Osburn, W. J., "Levels of Difficulty in Long Division," *Elementary School Journal*, vol. 46 (April 1946), pp. 441–447.

Reckzeh, John, "Addition and Subtraction Situations," *The Arithmetic Teacher*, vol. 3 (April 1956), pp. 94–97.

Ruddell, Arden K., "Levels of Difficulty in Division," *The Arithmetic Teacher*, vol. 6 (March 1959), pp. 97–99.

Sauble, I., "Development of Ability to Estimate and to Compute Mentally," *The Arithmetic Teacher*, vol. 2 (April 1955), pp. 33–39.

Smith, Rolland, "Meaningful Division," *The Mathematics Teacher*, vol. 43 (January 1950), pp. 12–18.

Spitzer, Herbert F., *The Teaching of Arithmetic*, 3d ed. Boston: Houghton Mifflin Company, 1961, Chaps. 3–6.

Spross, Patricia, "Enrichment for Understanding," *The Arithmetic Teacher*, vol. 7 (December 1960), pp. 404–408.

Stern, Catherine, "The Natural Way to Numbers," *The Journal of Education*, vol. 132 (December 1949), pp. 248–250.

Weaver, J. Fred, "A Bibliography of Selected Summaries and Critical Discussions of Research on Elementary School Mathematics," *The Arithmetic Teacher*, vol. 7 (November 1960), pp. 364–366.

Williams, Catherine M., "The Function of Charts in the Arithmetic Program," *The Arithmetic Teacher*, vol. 2 (October 1955), pp. 72–76.

Zweng, Marilyn, "Division Problems and the Concept of Rate," *The Arithmetic Teacher*, vol. 11 (December 1964), pp. 547–556.

8

Concepts Underlying Computation: Decimal Fractions

Little and mighty —
A locative dot —
Powerful to use
In the right spot.

Pay proper respect,
But be in command.
A Lamp of Aladdin
You hold in your hand.

8.1 THE POINT of DECIMAL NUMERALS

The decimal point is one of the smallest of mathematical symbols. However, size is not a good index of its importance. By means of that simple dot, properly placed, the pattern for spelling the decimal whole number symbols is made applicable for use with a comparable set of fraction number values.

As stated previously, one whole thing is the basic referent for scaling "how many." All whole numbers refer to respective groupings of ones; therefore, they are not directly applicable for expressing values less than one. However, human concern often includes such amounts, so that a way of symbolizing such ideas is needed. This presents a problem: must a new type of symbol be devised or can an adaptation of established type be made?

In Chapter 7, the pattern for constructing decimal numerals was discussed. That pattern has a characteristic directional property: the ones' position is the referent position. All other positional values are determined by relation to the ones' position. Reading from right to left, positional values *increased*. Hence, by reading from left to right, positional values correspondingly *decrease*. This suggests that by continued extension of the pattern toward the right, values *less than one* may be symbolized. All that is needed in order to make such an extension of the orthographic pattern feasible is in some way clearly to identify which of the positions within the symbol refers to ones only, that is, the basic referent position.

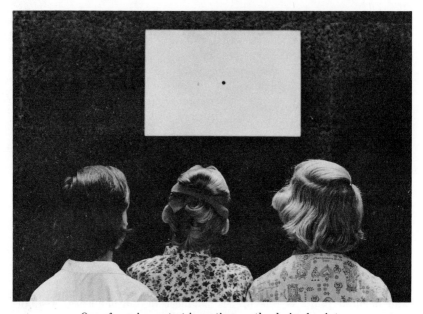

One of man's greatest inventions — the decimal point.

A dot is a simple convenient device for symbolizing location. It is commonly used to indicate position on maps and other points of reference. Its use in numerical orthography is consistent with its other usages. Hence, a dot is used to point out the location of the ones' position in a numeral. This is the basis of its verbal name, *decimal point.*

Since the decimal point is as important for depicting the number value of a numeral as is any of the digits of the numeral, it should be made visibly legible. Failure to give it prominence comparable to that given to other symbols has been a common source of difficulty. There is need to "see the point" both visually and intellectually speaking.

The distinguishing dot is placed immediately to the right of the ones' position since the positions toward the right of that referent express values less than the value of one. Throughout the pattern, however, each position is ten times as great in value as the position immediately to the right, and contrariwise, each position is ten times as small as the position next to the left.

8.2   BASIC CONCEPTS of DECIMAL FRACTIONS

LOCATING THE ONES' POSITION

The decimal point serves a locative function in decimal orthography. By convention it is placed immediately to the right of the basic referent position (ones' place) in the symbol.

SCALING DECIMAL FRACTIONS

Decimal fraction values are scaled in the same manner as are decimal whole number values. They differ, however, in their number reference values as shown by the following diagram.

Positions on this side indicate the digit value *multiplied* by 10 or a power of 10.	Positions on this side indicate the digit value *divided* by 10 or a power of 10.

Because of their orthographic pattern, decimal fraction numerals express clearly quantitative values based on division. The cue to the

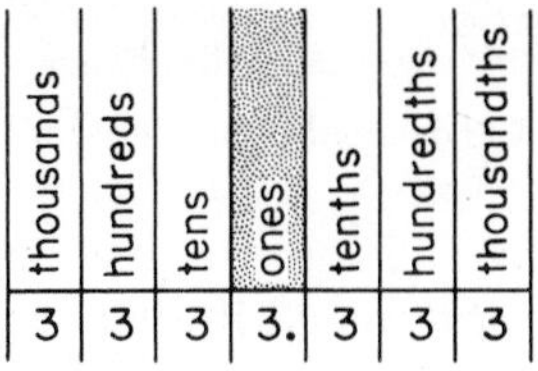

Fig. 8.1   Values in relation to ones' position.

value is the diminutive suffix, *ths*. The first position to the *left* of the ones' in the integer system is called tens; the comparable position to the *right* of the ones' position is called *tenths*. The position two places to the *left* of the ones' position is called hundreds; the comparable position to the *right* of the ones' position is called *hundredths*. The system continues with thousands and thousand*ths*, ten thousands and ten thousand*ths*, and so on. Fig. 8.1 illustrates the relationship between the names of the positions on the left and on the right of the ones' position.

RELOCATING THE DECIMAL POINT

Since the purpose of the decimal point is to "point out" the ones' position, it follows that relocating it within the numeral pattern automatically changes the ones' position and creates a different numeral. Obviously, the decimal orthographic pattern is maintained. Throughout the pattern, the directional characteristic is constant. Reading from right to left, the positional values *multiply* by 10. Reading from left to right, the positional values *divide* by 10.

By shifting the ones' position toward the right in a numeral, the value expressed is *multiplied* by 10 (made 10 times as large) for each position

"I shall place the decimal point here for our problem."

of the shift. Likewise, by shifting the ones' position toward the left, the value expressed is *divided* (made 10 times as small) for each position of the shift. Writing the decimal point within the numeral is an integral part of the correct spelling of the number symbol. Its position is determined by the idea that is being expressed. It should not be determined merely by rules.

3   .3

The 3 at the left is in the ones' position. The decimal point is understood to be to the right of the 3. When the decimal point is placed to the left of the 3, the expression is .3 (three tenths). The ones' position is to the left of the 3 in that case. The expression .3 is 10 times as small in number value as 3. Similarly, in these expressions, relocating the decimal point establishes a new ones' position and creates an expression with a different value.

345   34.5   3.45

In 345 the decimal point is not used because the ones' place is understood to be the position at the far right. The expression 345 is made 10 times as small in number value by placing the decimal point between the

the 4 and the 5. The ones' position is then to the left of the 5 which makes the 5 refer to five tenths. Conversely, 3.45 is made 100 times as large in number value by removing the decimal point from the symbol.

COMPARING NUMBER VALUES

Comparisons of numerical value operate with decimal fractions in the same way that they operate with decimal integers.

(a)	(b)	(c)	(d)
5	5	5	5

Example (a) 5 is 10 times as large in number value as (b) 5; 100 times as large in number value as (c) 5; and 1000 times as large in number value as (d) 5. Example (d) 5 is 10 times as small in number value as (c) 5; 100 times as small in number value as (b) 5; and 1000 times as small in number value as (a) 5.

INTERPRETING ZERO

Zero, when used in decimal numeral orthography, has the meaning "not any." In whatever position it occurs, it signifies "not any in this position."

Suffixing a zero to a decimal integer forms a symbol that is 10 times as large in number value, for example, 3 compared with 30. Each zero so attached similarly represents the value made 10 times as large, as in the following examples:

3
30 — 10 times as large as 3
300 — 10 times as large as 30 and 100 as large as 3

Contrariwise, deleting a terminal zero from a decimal integer forms a symbol that is 10 times as small in number value, that is, that number divided by 10.

The situation with regard for zero when used in a decimal fraction expression is somewhat different. Recall that in the decimal fraction, the referent positional base is to the left. Therefore, shifting to the right decreases positional values. Hence, a zero suffixed to a decimal fraction does not alter the fraction's value. It merely changes its name, for example, 0.2 = 0.20 (two tenths is equivalent to twenty hundredths). However, the suffixing of zero may be appropriate when measurement has been made to that degree of refinement.

Prefixing a zero to a decimal fraction divides the value of the fraction by ten, because it places the expression one space farther to the right from the positional referent (the units' place), for example, 0.2 > 0.02

(two tenths is greater in value than is two hundredths). Contrariwise, prefixing a zero to a decimal whole number does not change its number value.

The opposite nature of this function of zero when applied to decimal whole number symbols compared with decimal fraction number symbols complies with the principles of the orthographic pattern. However, special attention needs to be given to developing an understanding of these ideas and to their use in writing and reading decimal number symbols.

GROUPING LIKE TERMS

With decimal fractions as with decimal integers, only terms representing the same positional values are added or subtracted, that is, units are added to or subtracted from units, tens with tens, tenths with tenths, and so forth. Of course, all the values of the several positions are added to determine its number reference.

8.3   READING and WRITING DECIMAL FRACTION and MIXED DECIMAL EXPRESSIONS

Decimal fractions symbols are read first as though they were decimal whole number symbols; then their positional reference is given; for instance, .425 is read as "four hundred twenty-five," then the diminutive reference "thousandths" is given.

When mixed decimal numerals are read, the position symbolizing the whole number is read first; then a cue term *and* is given followed by the reading of the decimal fraction expression: 124.5 is read "one hundred twenty-four and five tenths." Since *and* is needed to indicate the shift from whole numbers to fraction designation, it should be reserved for that purpose. Careless usage produces poor mathematical communication. Three hundred and twenty-five thousandths means 300.025. It does not mean .325.

8.4   CONCEPTS and COMPUTATIONAL PROCEDURES: addition and multiplication

As pointed out previously, addition is the primary use of number, and multiplication is initially experienced as a special case of addition. Hence it is logical to begin the discussion of computation with those procedures. Since decimal fraction expressions conform to the orthographic pattern used with decimal integers, they may be treated in the same manner as decimal integers. The only new element involved is the fact that the units' position may no longer be assumed to be at the far right in the numeral pattern. The units' position is now identified by a decimal point, but it still retains its property as the basal referent position which determines the value of each of the other positions within the numeral. Sensing and interpreting the functions of the decimal numeral pattern is essential for utilizing decimal expressions meaningfully.

ADDITION

The procedures for addition of decimal fractions or for mixed decimal expression are substantially those used with decimal integers. Since only terms having the same positional values are added, it is essential that the decimal points be carefully observed and each digit in the numeral be interpreted in reference to the units' position so identified. When this is done, every concept and operation that pertains to decimal whole numbers has equal relevance to decimal fractions or mixed decimal expressions.

The main concepts that underlie the addition of decimal fractions are:

1. Concepts of function (dependence). As determined with decimal integers, the numerical value of the sum is directly determined by the numerical value of the addends and by the number of them.

2. Concepts of operation. The order of combining the values of any two addends does not affect the sum (commutative property of addition). Addition is a binary operation. When more than two addends are added in a stated order, the sum is the same no matter how the numbers are associated (associative property of addition). As is true for decimal integers, the sum of zero and any decimal fraction is that decimal fraction (identity for addition), and when decimal fractions are added, the sum will produce another grouping of that scaled value (closure property of addition). Only terms having the same positional value are added.

The similarity of addition of decimal integers and of decimal fractions may be noted in the following examples:

Add 62 and 34

$$
\begin{array}{r}
6\ 2 \\
+\ 3\ 4 \\
\hline
9\ 6
\end{array}
$$

Only terms alike in positional value are added: 2 ones + 4 ones = 6 ones; 6 tens + 3 tens = 9 tens.

Add 6.2 and 3.4

$$
\begin{array}{r}
6.2 \\
+\ 3.4 \\
\hline
9.6
\end{array}
$$

Only like terms are added: 2 tenths + 4 tenths = 6 tenths; 6 ones +

3 ones = 9 ones. Similarly, we add hundredths to hundredths, thousandths to thousandths, and so on.

Add .25, .42, 1.06, and 2.61

```
    .2 5
    .4 2
   1.0 6
 + 2.6 1
   ─────
     1 4
   1 2
   3
   ─────
   4.3 4
```

The sum of the hundredths' position is 14 hundredths, which is regrouped as 1 tenth and 4 hundredths. The sum of the tenths' position is 12 tenths, which is regrouped as 1 unit and 2 tenths. The sum of the units' position is 3. The partial sums that are recorded are added to find the grand total, and the decimal point is placed directly to the right of the units' position. If vertical addition is used, the decimal points must be kept in vertical column arrangement.

MULTIPLICATION

Multiplication was identified in Chapter 7 as a special technique for use when an addend is used repeatedly, for .example, 4 threes is a more succinct way of expressing a grouping of $3 + 3 + 3 + 3$. When the multiplication procedure is used with decimal whole numbers, the product is *usually* greater in value than the factors which produce it.[1] However, when we deal with numerical values of less than one, such as decimal fraction values, that relationship is changed. The nature of that change can be readily inferred from the characteristics of the product-factor relationships previously discussed, but it needs to be carefully developed and a technique for expressing the changed value needs to be derived.

Concepts Underlying the Multiplication Operation

1. Concepts of function (dependency). The numerical value of a product is determined directly by the value of its factors. When the multiplier is constant, the value of the product is directly related to the value of the multiplicand, and when the multiplicand is constant, the value of the product is determined directly by the value of the multiplier. This is an extremely important relationship. It serves as the basis for the placement of the decimal point in the product.

---

[1] Any whole number multiplied by 1 is equal to that number, and any whole number multiplied by 0 equals zero.

2. Concepts of operation or procedure. Multiplication is a binary operation. The order of the factors may be interchanged without affecting the value of the product (commutative principle). Since the decimal fraction numeral pattern conforms with the pattern for decimal integers, all of the techniques used with decimal integers apply also for use with decimal fractions and with decimal mixed numbers.

Decimal points, as elements in the numerals of the factors, do not enter into or affect the computational procedures. However, *their function as indicators of the value expressed by the numeral must be recognized and properly expressed in the product*. This is the only new aspect of the multiplication process that is introduced by decimal fraction numbers. Its operation is illustrated and developed in the examples that follow.

Examples in Which There Is a Decimal Fraction Expression in the Multiplier Only

The following concept was developed with decimal integers in Chapter 7. When the multiplicand is constant, the value of the product depends directly upon the value of the multiplier. If the multiplier is made 10 times as small, 100 times as small, and so forth, the product is made correspondingly as small in value. For example:

(a)	(b)	(c)	(d)
3	3	3	3
× 1	× 10	× 100	× 1000
3	30	300	3000

The multiplicands are alike in the examples above. As the multipliers increase, the products increase; as the multipliers decrease, the products decrease. Example (a) may be compared with Example (b). The multiplicands are constant. The multiplier of (a) is 10 times as small in value as the multiplier of (b), and the product of (a) is 10 times as small in value as the product of (b). The other examples may be compared in a similar way.

Similarly in the following examples, the multiplicands of the two examples are alike. The multiplier of Example (b) is 10 times as small in number value as the multiplier of Example (a). Therefore, the product of Example (b) is 10 times as small as the product of Example (a). The placement of the decimal point between the 7 and the 5 in the product indicates 75 is divided by 10 or 75 made 10 times as small in value. $(75 \div 10 = 7.5)$

(a)	(b)
1 5	1 5
× 5	× .5
7 5	7.5

The following type of example may need specific interpretation.

$$
\begin{array}{cc}
\text{(a)} & \text{(b)} \\
1\ 6 & 1\ 6 \\
\times\quad 8 & \times\ .0\ 8 \\
\hline
1\ 2\ 8 & 1.2\ 8 \\
\end{array}
$$

The multiplicands of the two examples are alike. The multiplier of Example (b) is 100 times as small in number value as the multiplier of Example (a). Therefore, the product of Example (b) will be 100 times as small in number value as the product of Example (a). One hundred twenty-eight can be made 100 times as small by locating the decimal point two places to the left of the ones' position (128 ÷ 100 = 1.28).

Generalization: In multiplication with examples in which there is a decimal fraction in the multiplier but not in the multiplicand, the product will contain a decimal fraction having as many decimal fraction places as there are in the multiplier.

Examples in Which There Is a Decimal Fraction or Mixed Decimal Expression in the Multiplicand Only

The interpretation of the commutative property of multiplication should lead to the generalization that when one factor is constant, the product is directly proportional to the other factor. However, interpreting the idea that multiplication is a special case of addition is a simpler generalization that may logically precede the interpretation of examples such as the following ones, which have a decimal point in the multiplier only.

$$
\begin{array}{cc}
Add & Multiply \\
3 & \\
3 & \\
3 & 3 \\
+\ 3 & \times\ 4 \\
\hline
1\ 2 & 1\ 2 \\
\end{array}
$$

Four 3's may be expressed as $3 + 3 + 3 + 3$ or as 4×3. The sum or product is regrouped as 1 ten + 2 ones. The 1 ten is written in the tens' position and the 2 is written in the ones' position.

$$
\begin{array}{cc}
Add & Multiply \\
.3 & \\
.3 & \\
.3 & .3 \\
+\ .3 & \times\ 4 \\
\hline
1.2 & 1.2 \\
\end{array}
$$

.3 + .3 + .3 + .3 = 12 tenths. The 12 tenths is regrouped as 1 unit and 2 tenths. 4 × 3 = 12; 4 × .3 = 12 tenths = 1.2.

From simple examples like these, it is logical to infer that when the multiplier is constant, the value of the product depends directly upon the value of the multiplicand. This generalization was developed with whole numbers and is applicable for use with decimal fraction and decimal mixed numbers.

Generalization: In multiplication of decimal fraction examples in which there is a decimal fraction in the multiplicand but not in the multiplier, the product will contain a decimal fraction having as many decimal fraction places as are found in the multiplicand.

Multiplication Examples in Which There Is a Decimal Fraction or Mixed Decimal Expression in Both the Multiplicand and the Multiplier

```
  (a)          (b)
   2.6          2 .6
 ×  7         × .7
 ─────        ─────
 1 8.2        1.8 2
```

We may use Example (a) as the referent example and compare Example (b) with it. The multiplicands of the two examples are alike. The multiplier of Example (b) is 10 times as small in number value as the multiplier of Example (a). Therefore, the product for Example (b) should be 10 times as small as the product for Example (a). We can make 18.2 ten times as small by moving the decimal point one place to the left: (18.2 ÷ 10 = 1.82).

The preceding interpretation is simple to understand and is recommended for initial work with multiplication of decimal fractions. The following interpretation is also good, but it may be more difficult to develop in the early stages of learning.

```
  (a)          (b)
   2 6          2 .6
 ×  7         × .7
 ─────        ─────
 1 8 2        1.8 2
```

Example (a) may be used as the referent example and Example (b) compared with it. The multiplicand of Example (b) is 10 times as small in value as that of Example (a). The multiplier of Example (b) is 10 times as small in value as that of Example (a). It follows that the product for Example (b) will be 100 times as small as that of Example (a). (182 ÷ 100 = 1.82.)

Generalization: In multiplication examples in which there is a decimal fraction in both factors, the product will contain a decimal fraction having decimal fraction places equal to the sum of those found in both factors.

It is not intended that such generalizations be taught to the pupils. They should be conceived by the pupils themselves as they work with the computational situations. The examples presented by the instructor should be selected in such a manner that they clearly and repeatedly illustrate the idea which the pupils are to perceive. The examples are part of the materials for use in a laboratory for learning.

8.5 CONCEPTS and COMPUTATIONAL PROCEDURES: subtraction and division

Direction is an important mathematical concept. It is applied in many types of situations and in many ways. One common application is that of *directional counting*. Basically, addition is a process of finding the *sum* of two numbers. The inverse of that operation is one of finding the *difference* between two numbers. Subtraction as a process will undo what has been accomplished by addition, and vice versa. Hence, either operation may be used as a check of the accuracy of the other.

Since the decimal fraction numeral pattern conforms with the orthographic pattern for decimal integers, all of the ideas and procedures developed for computing with the numerals of whole numbers are applicable with decimal fractions or with mixed decimal expressions. The only new element introduced by decimal fractions is that of the placement of positional values to the right of the units' position. This entails the use of care in sensing and interpreting the decimal points in the numerals.

SUBTRACTION

The main concepts and techniques of procedure are:

1. Only terms having the same positional values are subtracted. This is a source of difficulty which, unless properly understood, produces some characteristic errors, as shown in the examples. The identification of the units' position and its use as a referent for the positional value of each digit expressed in the numeral is extremely important.

2. Subtraction may be performed by an additive procedure or by a subtractive procedure. One may withdraw the value of the subtrahend from that of the minuend to determine the difference of their respective values (subtraction). Or, one may add to the subtrahend a value such that the sum equals the value of the minuend. If the additive procedure

is used, the terms minuend and subtrahend are no longer appropriate. The following examples illustrate typical situations with subtraction.

Decimal Integers	*Decimal Fractions*
Subtract 245 from 368	Subtract 2.45 from 3.68

$$\begin{array}{r} 3\ 6\ 8 \\ -2\ 4\ 5 \\ \hline 1\ 2\ 3 \end{array} \qquad\qquad \begin{array}{r} 3.6\ 8 \\ -2.4\ 5 \\ \hline 1.2\ 3 \end{array}$$

Only terms of like positional value are subtracted.
8 ones − 5 ones = 3 ones
6 tens − 4 tens = 2 tens
3 hundreds − 2 hundreds = 1 hundred

Only terms of like positional value are subtracted.
8 hundredths − 5 hundredths = 3 hundredths
6 tenths − 4 tenths = 2 tenths
3 ones − 2 ones = 1

From 68.8 subtract 24.75:

$$\begin{array}{r} 6\ 8.8\ 0 \\ -2\ 4.7\ 5 \\ \hline 4\ 4.0\ 5 \end{array}$$

Only like terms are subtracted. The decimal point locates the ones' position. Terms must be arranged according to their positional value. Since 24.75 is refined to hundredths of a unit, 68.8 should be expressed as a mixed decimal to the hundredths' place, 68.80. Not any hundredths is less than 5 hundredths. We can regroup one of the tenths to 10 hundredths. The regrouped value of the minuend is 6 tens + 8 ones + 7 tenths + 10 hundredths.

$$\begin{array}{r} {\scriptstyle 7} \\ 6\ 8.\cancel{8}\ {}^{1}0 \\ -2\ 4.7\ 5 \\ \hline 4\ 4.0\ 5 \end{array}$$

10 hundredths − 5 hundredths = 5 hundredths
7 tenths − 7 tenths = 0 tenths
8 ones − 4 ones = 4 ones
6 tens − 2 tens = 4 tens

DIVISION

Division is the most complicated of the operational processes. As it is usually performed, it makes use of each of the other processes. The introduction of decimal fractions produces an additional element to its complexity.

Concepts Underlying the Division Operation

1. Concepts of function (dependence). The value of the quotient is directly related to the value of the dividend. The value of the quotient is inversely related to the value of the divisor.

2. Concepts of operation. Distinction is sometimes made between the operation that seeks to determine the size of a designated number of equal sets which can be made from a given grouping (measurement), and the operation that seeks to determine how many groups of a specified size may be made from a given grouping (partition). However, the same operational procedure is used for either situation. Whether one performs "partitive" division or "measurement" division is largely a matter of what the quotient is intended to represent.

Since the dependence relationships between the divisor and the quotient and between the dividend and the quotient are the inverse of each other, both the divisor and the dividend can be multiplied by the same amount without altering the value of the quotient. That observation provides a basis for a commonly used technique of multiplying both the divisor and the dividend by 10 or some power of 10 such that the decimal fraction is eliminated from the divisor. However, such a procedure is unnecessary and, when it is presented merely as a rule of computational procedure, it can interfere with true mathematical learning.

Division with decimal fractions can be performed just as division with whole numbers is performed. The adjustment needed to express properly the meaning of the fractions can be made in the quotient. That procedure is preferred because it utilizes the basic concepts of function and of numerical writing. It is less amenable to treatment by an arbitrary rule of procedure.

Rules of procedure by which computational operations are performed should be drawn up by the students as they work with examples. Rules so derived have an experiential meaningful basis: they help and do not interfere with mathematical behavior.

There are many sources of difficulty with the algorisms commonly employed with division. These need to be identified and to have their potency reduced by awareness and by clear understanding of their nature. The examples that follow illustrate specifically some of the important division concepts and how they may be applied in operational procedure.

Division Examples in Which There Is a Decimal Fraction or a Mixed Decimal Expression in the Divisor but Not in the Dividend, and the Quotient Is a Decimal Integer

$$.4)\overline{16}\qquad .012)\overline{24}$$

Examples of the type shown above produce high percents of error as indicated on tests of pupil response. However, the examples are among the most simple to interpret. The key concepts that underlie their interpretation are: (1) interpretation of decimal fraction expressions, and (2) interpretation of the quotient and divisor relationship.

The quotient and divisor relationship was developed in Chapter 7, and it may be noted here by comparing the following examples:

$$\begin{array}{cccc} 1 & 10 & 100 & 1000 \\ 1000)\,\overline{1000} & 100)\,\overline{1000} & 10)\,\overline{1000} & 1)\,\overline{1000} \end{array}$$

The dividends are constant. As the divisors decrease, there is a corresponding increase in the quotients and, as the divisors increase, there is a corresponding decrease in the quotients. This idea of inverse proportion may be applied in this way:

(a)   (b)

$$\begin{array}{cc} 6 & 60 \\ 4)\,\overline{24} & .4)\,\overline{24} \end{array}$$

The dividends of the two examples are the same. What is true about the divisor of Example (b) compared with Example (a)? What should be true about the quotient of Example (b) compared with that of Example (a)? How can you make 6 ten times as large in number value?

$$\begin{array}{cc} 2 & 2000 \\ 12)\,\overline{24} & .012)\,\overline{24} \end{array}$$

The dividends of the two examples are alike. The divisor, .012, is 1000 times as small in value as 12. Therefore, what should be true about the quotient for $.012)\,\overline{24}$?

Division Examples in Which There Is a Decimal Fraction or a Mixed Decimal Expression in the Dividend but Not in the Divisor

$$\begin{array}{cc} 3)\,\overline{6\ 3} & 3)\,\overline{6.3} \end{array}$$

Examples of the type shown above are simple to interpret. The key ideas that underlie their interpretation are: (1) interpretation of decimal fraction expressions, and (2) interpretation of the dividend and quotient relationships.

The quotient and dividend relationship was developed in Chapter 7. As may be noted in the set of examples below, when the divisor is constant, there is a directly proportional relationship between dividend and quotient.

$$\begin{array}{cccc} 5 & 50 & 500 & 5,000 \\ 2)\,\overline{10} & 2)\,\overline{100} & 2)\,\overline{1000} & 2)\,\overline{10,000} \end{array}$$

This idea may be utilized as the basis for interpretation of examples such as the following:

$$\begin{array}{ccc} & 2\ 1 & 2.1 \\ \text{(a)} & 3)\,\overline{6\ 3} & \text{(b)}\quad 3)\,\overline{6.3} \end{array}$$

The divisors of the two examples are alike. The dividend of Example (b) is 10 times as small in value as the dividend of Example (a). Therefore, the quotient of Example (b) is 10 times as small in value as the quotient of (a). Similarly, the dividend for $5\overline{)\,.25}$ is 100 times as small in value as the dividend for $5\overline{)\,25}$. Therefore, its quotient must be 100 times as small.

$$5\overline{)\,.25}^{\,.05}$$

Division Example in Which There Is a Decimal Fraction or a Mixed Decimal Expression in Both the Dividend and the Divisor

After the two preceding generalizations have been formulated, an example such as $.5\overline{)\,25.5}$ should be readily interpreted.

$$\text{(a)}\quad 5\overline{)\,25.5}^{\,5.1} \qquad \text{(b)}\quad .5\overline{)\,25.5}^{\,5\,1} \qquad \text{(c)}\quad .05\overline{)\,25.5}^{\,5\,1\,0}$$

Example (a) may serve as a referent example. The dividends of Examples (b) and (a) are alike in number value, but the divisor of (b) is 10 times as small as that of the referent example. Therefore, its quotient must be 10 times as large: $(5.1 \times 10 = 51)$. Similarly, the dividends of Example (c) and Example (a) are alike, but the divisor of Example (c) is 100 times as small. Therefore, its quotient must be 100 times as large: $(5.1 \times 100 = 510)$.

The preceding development was designed to lead the reader to consider the concepts underlying computation. Many illustrations of the ideas, such as examples from common usages and use of the number line should be utilized. For example, $.1\overline{)\,2}$ may be visualized on the number line. There are 20 of the tenth segments in 2 units.

```
0                               1
├─┬─┬─┬─┬─┬─┬─┬─┬─┬──┬──┬──┬──┬──┬──┬──┬──┬──
0  .1 .2 .3 .4 .5 .6 .7 .8 .9 1.0 1.1 1.2 1.3 1.4 1.5 1.6 1.7 1.8
```

8.6   EXAMPLES of PUPIL INTERPRETATION of DIVISION of DECIMAL

To determine the learner's interpretation of the ideas underlying the division and multiplication of decimal fractions and common fractions, a test was devised in which the pupil was asked questions concerning the nature of his answers.[2] Eight simple questions were designed for grade six level. In these questions the student was asked to state his ideas. No specific numerical computation was to be done.

[2] Marguerite Brydegaard, "The Insatiable Quest: Mathematicking," *The Arithmetic Teacher*, vol. 7 (January 1960), p. 11.

The exercise was given to 243 college students, 167 pupils in grades seven and eight, 220 pupils in grade six, and one class of 27 children in a combined grade four-five class. The classes of children in grades six, seven, and eight were groups that were considered average or above average. Some of the college students had taken courses in college mathematics, but none of them had completed a course in methods for teaching mathematics in the elementary school.

The tests were given in several states of our 50 United States. The findings were reported as general findings. However, no state stood out as a bright and shining star as compared with another state. In other words, the findings of one state were typical of those of another.

The written directions for the test were: "Do Not Work These Examples. You will be asked simple questions concerning the answers. For each question, underline the answer that you think is true." The oral directions for the test included development of the idea that only *positive* number values were to be considered.

Some of the test questions and tables showing the percentages of incorrect response are given in the following pages.[3]

Question 1

Susan said, "The answer to 4348 divided by .25 will be larger than 4348." What Susan said is

(a) true. (b) false. (c) partly true. (d) partly false.

Question 7 was paired with Question 1.

Question 7

Betty said, "The answer to any number except zero divided by .85 will be larger than that number." What Betty said is

(a) always true. (b) sometimes true. (c) sometimes false. (d) always false.

The percentages of *incorrect* response were as follows:

Group	Question 1	Question 7
Combined population of college classes	65	63
Combined population of grades seven and eight	83	71
Combined population of grade six classes	84	75
Grade four-five combination class	78	63

Questions 4 and 8 were paired to check interpretation of division of common fractions.

[3] Op. cit., pp. 10–12.

Question 4

The answer to 7735 divided by $\frac{9}{10}$ will be
(a) larger than 7735. (b) smaller than 7735. (c) equal to 7735.

Question 8

Martha said, "The answer to any number except zero divided by $\frac{15}{16}$ will be smaller than that number." What Martha said is
(a) always true. (b) sometimes true. (c) sometimes false. (d) always false.

The percentages of *incorrect* response were as follows:

Group	Question 4	Question 8
Combined population of college classes	64	67
Combined population of grades seven and eight	78	78
Combined population of grade six classes	72	80
Grade four-five combination class	78	78

Questions 2 and 6 were paired to determine pupil interpretation of multiplication of common fractions. Questions 3 and 5 were paired for a similar treatment of multiplication of decimal fractions. Although the percentages of error were lower for multiplication than for division, only Questions 2 and 3 produced less than 50 percent error for any of the groups tested in the study.

USING A NEWER APPROACH

Are the concepts extremely difficult to comprehend? Are they teachable to young children? In order to delve into these problems, two classes in which the multiplication and division of common and decimal fractions had not been taught were used as experimental groups. In one class, a grade six group of 38 children, there had been an introduction to multiplication of common fractions, but the introduction as indicated by results on the pretest, did not interfere with the study. The other group was a mixed class of 27 children in grades four and five. The group was above average. Each was pretested, and teaching the concepts of division and multiplication of fractions was outlined. Emphasis was placed on building the concepts, and the work was carried on as a brief additional unit during the period allotted for mathematics. The regular work of the class continued since the classes were in a public school in which the program was set up in a definite way. The specific concepts were identified, and the teaching was designed to challenge the learner to sense, discover, and interpret the relationships that underlie the areas of multiplication and division of common and decimal fractions. Emphasis was placed upon making the relationships meaningful through selection of illustrations that were significant in the experiencing of the children.

The concepts grew out of simple, elemental ideas that children used and could interpret, and the generalizations evolved with power behind them.

In the experimental study, the concepts underlying division of decimal and of common fractions were taught as a single unit. In this report, the experiment with grade six will be described as considerable data concerning the study is available.

The teachers were led to identify the basic concepts that underlie the areas of division and multiplication of common and decimal fraction numbers. For example, the main concepts that underlie division of decimal fraction examples of the type used in Questions 1 and 7 were identified as

1. the interpretation of decimal integer and decimal fraction expressions
2. interpretation of the divisor-dividend-quotient relationship that functions when the dividend is constant and the divisor is variable

First, the teacher challenged the children to sharpen their understanding of decimal integer and decimal fraction expressions. An open-end abacus was used to refine concepts such as the constant and positional value of digits in a numerical expression, meanings of zero, and principles of grouping and regrouping, and so forth. The extension of the system of decimal integers led to developing the locative function of the decimal point and to interpretation of decimal fraction expressions such as .5, .25, and .09. Comparisons were made of the numerical value of decimal integer and decimal fraction expressions such as 25 and .25, and 9 and .09.

Secondly, ideas of divisor-dividend-quotient relationships were developed. The concept of the relationship that exists when the dividend is constant and the divisor and quotient are variable was isolated and developed. Illustrations without the use of specific number preceded development of examples with specific number. For example, if the dividend shows the distance traveled, the divisor may indicate the speed of travel and the quotient the time it takes for travel.

$$\text{speed}) \overline{\text{distance}}^{\text{time}}$$

If the distance traveled is constant (dividend), as we *increase* the speed of travel, we *decrease* the time for travel, and as we *decrease* speed, we *increase* time. The teacher challenged the children to interpret the divisor-dividend-quotient relationship as it occurred in settings familiar to them. The children illustrated their ideas on large sheets of paper, and the concept of the relationship became very meaningful. Refinement of the ideas through using specific numbers followed, and when examples such as 35 divided by .5, 6 divided by $\frac{1}{4}$, etc., were discussed, the children *just knew* the answers. Below are a few statements made by the children that indicate the nature of their thinking:

"Our answers come out larger instead of smaller when we divide by a fraction" (larger than the dividend).

"It is interesting to see that dividing can make answers larger than the dividend and that multiplication makes answers smaller than the multiplicand."

"When using a fraction as a divisor, division seems to be multiplication and multiplying by a fraction seems to make multiplication be division."

"Why don't we just change the names of processes around and call them what we are really doing . . . Well, I guess that wouldn't be too good because . . . "

The children were retested two weeks after the pretest. The change in percentages of incorrect response are indicative of the teachability of the concepts. In the grade six class, the chart below shows the gains on the retest compared with the pretest.

As was stated earlier, the experiment was an additional unit and no written computation pertaining to the unit was given to the classes during the experimental period. However, after the children had a vacation period of one week, they were tested on ten simple examples involving computation to test their generalizations. The test revealed mastery with computation that was similar to the mastery of concepts. For example, 72 divided by .12 and 20 divided by $\frac{1}{4}$ each produced only 8 percent error. One of the most interesting findings of the study was this evidence regarding a basic principle for practice exercise or drill. *Practice exercises should provide opportunity to practice correct response.* The experimental study demonstrated that, when sharpness of concept precedes practice, the principle operates in a positive way. In many classrooms, practice provides opportunity for pupils to practice their errors. Here lies one of the enemies of achievement of mathematical competency.

TABLE 8.1   GRADE 6
Percentages of Incorrect Response on Pretest and Retest
and Percentages of Gain

	% INCORRECT RESPONSE		
Question	*Pretest*	*Posttest*	*% Difference*
1	91.2	5.9	85.3
2	47.1	8.8	38.3
3	67.6	17.6	50.0
4	76.5	2.9	73.6
5	82.3	29.4	52.9
6	73.2	17.6	55.6
7	82.3	8.8	73.5
8	76.5	14.7	61.8

Source: The Arithmetic Teacher, vol. 7 (January 1960), p. 12.

ILLUSTRATIVE LESSONS

The following lessons are presented in this chapter:

Lesson 1. Concepts concerning decimal notation — a background lesson leading to the introduction of decimal fraction notation

Lesson 2. Introduction of decimal fraction notation

Lesson 3. Multiplication of decimal fractions — introductory lesson for evolving computational procedures

Lesson 4. Multiplication of decimal fractions — similar to preceding lesson, except that examples with decimal point in the multiplier only were used, and generalizations involved use of algebraic symbols

Lesson 5. Division of decimal fractions

Lesson 6. Percent — initial lesson introducing computational procedures

With each group of learners, the teacher needs to determine their developmental level and move ahead as far as seems desirable for that group. In the lessons presented in this chapter, one can readily sense that the learner had the background of concepts and skills prerequisite for making logical generalizations.

Lesson 1
CONCEPTS CONCERNING DECIMAL NOTATION — A BACKGROUND LESSON LEADING TO THE INTRODUCTION OF DECIMAL FRACTION NOTATION
Grade Three Class

Purpose of lesson: To challenge the children to refine their concepts concerning the decimal system and to develop specific background concepts for the introduction of decimal fraction notation.

Background of children: The children had evolved these concepts: (a) There are 10 primary digits in the decimal system of notation. (b) Each digit has a positional value. In the expression "33," they were aware that the 3 at the left has a value of 30 or 3 tens, and that the 3 at the right represents a value of 3 units. (c) A given digit in the tens' position has a value 10 times as large as if that digit were in the units' position. (d) A given digit in the units' position has a value 10 times as small as if that digit were in the tens' position.

Lesson Procedure

Teacher: You have discovered many things about the number system that we use. Can you name some of the things that you have discovered?

Edith: We can write very large numerals. We can keep writing figures and never come to an end.

Jim: We use only 10 different digits to write all numerals. The 10 digits are 0, 1, 2, 3, 4, 5, 6, 7, 8, and 9.

Marian: We can write large numbers by putting the 10 different digits in different positions.

Teacher: Let us see how well you can use the ideas that you have been discussing. I am going to write a digit on the blackboard.

[Teacher wrote a 4 on the blackboard. He placed his initial, B, above it.]

Teacher: This is your problem. Listen carefully! Can you write a digit that expresses a value 10 times as large as the value of my numeral? You are to write only 1 digit.

Mary: I think I can do it. I'd put a zero with your 4. That would make it 40. [Mary wrote the 0 where she intended it to be, and put an M above it to show that it was her 0.]

> B   M
> 4   0

Teacher: The value is 10 times what *I wrote*, Mary, but the value you expressed is only 0. The problem was for *you* to write the digit that is 10 times as large in value as my numeral.

Jerry: May I use your numeral?

Teacher: Surely, you may use it if you don't change its value by doing so.

Jerry: Oh! In that case, I think that I can write a value 10 times as large (in number value) as your 4. I'll try.

[Jerry went to the blackboard and wrote a 4 at the left of the teacher's 4.]

> J   B
> 4   4

Jerry: Your 4 still says 4. I haven't changed it. My 4 stands for 40. And, it takes 10 fours to make 40. My 4 is 10 times as large (in number value) as your 4.

Teacher: Do you agree with Jerry?

Meredith: Yes, it looks all right to me, but it seems as if it is too easy. Let's see if it works with another number.

Teacher: What number would you like to have us try, Meredith?

Meredith: Let me write a numeral on the blackboard.

[Meredith wrote a 5 on the blackboard.]

Teacher: Who can write a digit that stands for a value 10 times as large as the value of Meredith's 5, and not change the value of her 5? You may use only 1 digit.

Tommy: That's easy. May I do it?

[Tommy wrote a 5 at the left of Meredith's 5.]

Tommy: My 5 says 50, and Meredith's 5 says only 5. It takes 10 fives to make 50. My 5 is worth 10 times as much as Meredith's 5. That is too easy. Let's see if it works with 9.

Teacher: All right, but you may get stuck! Tommy, you may write your 9 on the blackboard.

[Tommy wrote his 9 on the blackboard, and put a T above it to indicate that it was his 9.]

Teacher: Can anyone write a digit that is 10 times as large in value as Tommy's 9?

Dick: I'm not sure, but I think I'm right.

[Dick wrote a 9 at the left of Tommy's 9.]

Dick: I don't know how many 9's it takes to make 90, but I think that it takes 10. Is that right, Teacher?

Teacher: How could we find out how many 9s it will take to make 90?

Richard: We could add 9s until we had 90.

Teacher: I'll write 9s on the blackboard as you add.

Class: 9, 18, . . . What is 18 and 9?

Richard: 27. Then 27 + 9 is . . .

Teacher: Shall I help you?

[Teacher helped children count by 9's as he wrote down each 9 until they came to 90. The Class counted how many 9's it took to make 90.]

Dick: I was right. It does take 10 nines to make 90. Boy, that was a hard one!

Jim: I think that I have discovered something. I think that we could take any digit, and it would work.

Mary: What do you mean by that, Jim?

Jim: I'll show you.

[Jim went to the board and wrote 22 and explained that the 2 at the left stood for 20 and that it represented a value 10 times that of 2 units. He continued with 33 and 11.]

Laura: It works with 99. We tried that.

Denny: And with 44 and 55. You're right, Jim.

Bill: Let's see if it works with 66 and 77.

Teacher: Each of you try it with 66 and with 77 and be ready to show the class about it tomorrow.

In subsequent lessons, the children were led to extend the idea to the hundreds' and thousands' positions. The concept was further developed through their handling of meters — water meters, light meters, and odometers (instruments to measure mileage). Through using an old odometer that they could manipulate and through observing odometers while riding in cars, they developed their understanding of the operation of positional value assigned to digits within a numeral. They became aware of measuring miles and realized that an odometer measures distances smaller than one mile. They formulated an idea of tenths of a mile.

Lesson 2
INTRODUCTION OF DECIMAL FRACTION NOTATION
Grade Three Class (not the class reported in previous lesson)

Purpose of lesson: To challenge the children to interpret decimal fraction expressions through extending the decimal system of notation.

Background of children: The children had a fine background of concepts concerning the decimal system of notation. They had observed odometers (instruments to measure mileage) and had formulated the concept that it takes 10 of the digits at the extreme right of an odometer to make 1 mile.

Lesson Procedure

Teacher: You have discovered many things about numbers and numerals. However, today you will need to be good thinkers to solve one problem that we shall discuss. This is the problem. I shall write a digit on the blackboard. [Teacher wrote a 2 on the blackboard.] My digit is 2. In this problem, you are not to change the value of my 2. I'll write my initial above my 2 so that we'll know it is my 2. Can you, using only one digit, write a digit that expresses a value that is ten times as small as my 2?

Janet: That is easy. I'll do it.
[Janet wrote a 2 at the right of the teacher's 2, and thus changed the the number value of the teacher's 2 to 20.]

Janet: My 2 is 10 times as small as your 2.

Stephen: But, Janet, look what you did! You made the teacher's 2 into 20. The teacher said to start with that you should not change her 2.

Teacher: What do you need?

Fred: Something to stop your 2. [Pause . . .] Can we make up something of our own to stop your 2?

Teacher: That would be a good idea, wouldn't it?

Fred: May I try how I would do it? [Fred went to the blackboard and wrote the following:]

$$\text{B} \parallel \text{F}$$
$$2 \parallel 2$$

I drew lines between your 2 and my 2. The lines are to stop your 2. My 2 is 10 times as small in value as your 2.

Janet: I have a way now.

[Teacher wrote a number of her B-over-2 symbols on the blackboard so that the children might show the different ways they had discovered to solve the problem of locating the units' position. [Janet went to the blackboard and wrote the following:]

```
B    J
2 x   2
```

Janet: My 2 stands for a number that is 10 times as small in value as your 2.

[Sharon, Carol, Harry, and others went to the blackboard and showed how they would divide the teacher's 2 from their 2. These were among the examples given.]

```
B   C    B   H    B   S    B   A    B   E
2 , 2    2   2    2   2    2 / 2    2  [2]

B   C    B   R    B   M    B   L    B ⌇ D
2  ②     2 x 2    2 . 2    2   2    2 ⌇ 2
                            =

B   J    B   P
2.. 2    2  :2
```

Fred: Isn't one of the ways that we have on the blackboard the way that is agreed upon in the United States?

The children had already discovered that all of the people of the world do not agree concerning how to measure. Hence, Fred's question was a natural one, but it brought the lesson to the given point faster than had been planned.]

Teacher: Yes, Fred, you are right. However, some of the ways that we have on the blackboard are ways that are used in other countries, and sometimes we use more than one way. Which of the ways that we've written on the blackboard do you think would be good ways and which ones would not be good ways?

Fred: The comma would not be good. We use it to separate groups of digits when we write large values.

Sharon: The way Fred used a line looks like a good way to me.

Teacher: We use the line — often a red line — for many things. We use it in the record that we keep to show how many days you were present at school and how many days you were absent. I'll show you the record book some day.

Carol: I think that the way that I used is a good way.

Harry: I think that my way was a good one.

[And others!]

Teacher: You have discovered many ways that are very good. When we write sentences, what do we use to stop one sentence and begin a new sentence?

Fred: We use a period. A period would be a good thing to use to stop your 2 and to begin a new 2. Is that what we use?

Teacher: Yes, that is what we use in our country. However, we do not call it a period. We use a special name — *decimal point.* The purpose of the decimal point is to show where the units' position is. As you write digits to the right of the decimal point, you express values smaller than one, and you call those values decimal fractions.

June: A decimal point is a good name for the way we separate your 2 from our 2.

Teacher: Mary, how many of your 2's would it take to make my 2?

Mary: It would take 10 because it would work the same way as with whole numbers.

Teacher: It would take 10 of your 2s to make 2 units. Do you know what we call your 2?

[Various suggestions were given, and the teacher developed the word "tenths." A summary of the discoveries ended this lesson.]

Further development of the concept of decimal and decimal fraction notation was developed through the use of meters. The children manipulated light meters, water meters, and odometers. By handling and observing odometers, the concept of tenths of a mile was made meaningful.

Lesson 3
MULTIPLICATION OF DECIMAL FRACTIONS
Grade Six Class

Purpose of lesson: To introduce computational procedures with multiplication of decimal fractions.

Background of children: The children had developed the basic multiplier-multiplicand-product relationships that are prerequisite for the lesson. They had also developed a refinement of vocabulary that kept pace with their ideas. The first part of the lesson was a refinement of previous work. Addition and subtraction of decimal fractions had been taught previously, and the children had a good background of understanding concerning the decimal system.

Lesson Procedure

[The teacher had the following set of examples on the chalkboard:]

(a)	(b)	(c)	(d)	(e)
1 0	1 0	1 0	1 0	1 0
$\times$ 1	$\times$ 2	$\times$ 4	$\times$ 8	$\times$ 1 6
1 0	2 0	4 0	8 0	1 6 0

Teacher: This morning we shall apply the multiplier-multiplicand-product relationship that is illustrated on the chalkboard. Can you state the ideas that are represented in the examples?

Dicky: When the multiplicand stays the same, if the multiplier changes, the product changes in the same way.

Jim: The multiplier and the product change in direct proportion — either way — increase and decrease. The multiplicands are constant.

Teacher: Look at the set of examples. Who can state the entire relationship that is true as you move from Example (a) through Example (e)?

Ricky: The multiplier is two times as large in each example as you move to the right. The same is true of the product. The multiplicands are constant.

Sara: And moving from right to left, the opposite is true. The multipliers become two times as small in each example as you move to the left, and the same for the products.

Gene: If the multiplicands are kept constant, the multiplier and the product will be in direct proportion.

Teacher: There are many other things that we have discovered about multiplication. Do you remember when we went to the *Journal* building to see a newspaper being printed? Billy's brother was in the station-wagon in which a number of us rode. Billy's brother is five years old. Do you recall how he counted the wheels on a truck that was in front of us as we rode along?

Ken: He counted the wheels in pairs. He counted by twos.

Teacher: Do you think that young children do multiplication?

Marguerite: They do multiplication, but they call it adding.

Teacher: Are all addition examples like multiplication? What about an example like this: 4 + 2 + 7? What must be true for the example to be multiplication?

Billy: The addends must be the same.

[Teacher demonstrated the idea by writing the following on the blackboard:]

```
    1 4      1 4
    1 4    × 4
    1 4    ─────
  + 1 4
```

Teacher: What is the sum?

Class: 5 6.

Teacher: If we place a decimal point between the 1 and the 4 in each addend [Teacher did so], what is the sum?

Laura: The sum is five and six tenths (5.6).

Teacher: Why?

Laura: Because the values were made 10 times as small.

Teacher: What does the decimal point do in the sum?

Margaret: It comes straight down. The decimal point makes the sum 10 times as small in number value. [Referred to 1.4 + 1.4 + 1.4 + 1.4 compared with 14 + 14 + 14 + 14.]

[Teacher changed 4 × 1 4 to 4 × 1.4.]

Teacher: What happens when we put a decimal point between the 1 and the 4 in the multiplicand?

Robert: The multiplicand is made 10 times as small (in number value). So the product will have to be 10 times as small. The product is five and six tenths (5.6).

Sara: The decimal point comes right down as it did in adding.

[Teacher erased decimal points so that the original examples were on the chalkboard.]

Teacher: What is true in this example? [Teacher placed decimal point so that the examples read .14 + .14 + .14 + .14 and 4 × .14. The children developed the ideas as they did in the other examples, except that the changes in the sum and in the product involved making the answers one hundred times as small in number value. Then Teacher wrote 7 × 2.1 on the blackboard.]

Teacher: What is the product of 7 × 2.1?

Joan: 14.7.

Teacher: How can you judge that 14.7 is the correct answer?

Margaret: By dividing the product by 7 to see if it gives you the multiplicand.

Teacher: True! I was thinking of another way.

Richard: Two times 7 would be 14.

Teacher: How would you know that 147 wasn't correct?

Ken: You know that 7 × 2 can't be near 147.

[Development of 7 × .21 followed.]

Teacher: If the decimal point is in the multiplicand only, what is true concerning the decimal point in the product?

Richard: It will go right down from the multiplicand.

Joyce: It will have the same positional value.

Tommy: What if the decimal point is in the multiplier?

Teacher: Let us work that out with this example. What is the product of 4 × 22?

Class: 88.

[Teacher placed a decimal point to the left of the 4 in the multiplier.]

Teacher: What did I do to the multiplier?

Susan: You made it 10 times as small in value.

Dicky: Then the product should be made 10 times as small in value. You can make it 10 times as small by placing a decimal point between the 8s. The product is 8.8.

[Teacher wrote .04 × 22 on the blackboard.]

Teacher: What will be true about the product in this example?

Joyce: It will be 100 times as small in value as if the multiplier were 4. The answer is .88.

[Teacher wrote the following example on the chalkboard. The class and the teacher together found the product.]

```
  2 8 8
× 1 2
  5 7 6
2 8 8
3 4 5 6
```

Teacher: Let us change the multiplier to one and two tenths (1.2).

Class: That makes the multiplier 10 times as small in value. The product will have to be made 10 times as small in value.

Billy: The answer is three hundred and forty-five and six tenths.

Margaret: Omit one "and," Bill. You should have said, "three hundred forty-five *and* six tenths."

Teacher: Yes. It is better to use "and" only at the decimal point.

[The multiplier was changed to .12 and .012 and the products discussed.]

Tommy: Can you keep adding zeros in the multiplier?

Teacher: Yes, but shall I suffix them or shall I prefix them?

Ricky: Prefix them.

[Teacher then made multiplier .0012.]

Tommy: You made the multiplier ten thousand times as small in value.

Joyce: The product will be three thousand four hundred fifty-six ten-thousandths.

Robert: What if you prefix more zeros now?

[Robert was referring to the fact that all figures in the product were now to the right of the decimal point.]

Jack: I know what happens if you prefix another zero in the multiplier. You prefix one in the product, too.

Teacher: What about the decimal point?

Jack: Prefix that, too. You can just keep on doing it.

Teacher: That is right. I don't know that you could keep on naming the values represented, though — could you?

Tommy: No, but you could make up names to suit yourself!

[Tommy and Jack got into a discussion about certain methods of writing large checks. The teacher stopped them with the remark that probably those present would never be faced with the need for a number that large on their checks. Jack said in termination of the discussion, "No, but we can dream!"]

Jack: What if there is a decimal point in the multiplier and in the multiplicand?

Teacher: Let us work that out. What is the product of 16 × 3?

[Teacher wrote the example on the board and placed the decimal point as the children discussed its position.]

Class: 48.

Teacher: What is the product of 1.6 × 3?

Class: 4.8.

Teacher: What is the product of 1.6 × .3?

Class: .48.

Marie: I don't get it.

Teacher: The product of 1.6 × 3 equals 4.8. Are you with us that far, Marie?

Marie: Yes, I understand that.

Teacher: With 1.6 × .3, what is true about the multiplier?

Marie: It is 10 times as small in value as if it were 16.

Teacher: Then what is true about the product?

Marie: It becomes 10 times as small in value. Yes, 10 times as small in value. So it would be .48.

Marguerite: Is that sometimes called "counting off"?

Teacher: Yes, it is. But, people who learn just a rule about how to "count off" usually have little understanding of what it means.

Aldon: Does it work the same if you have .3 × 1.6?

David: Yes it would — just as 3 × 6 equals 6 × 3.

Aldon: Are there ever two decimal points in the answer?

Teacher: What do you think, Aldon?

Aldon: It wouldn't make sense.

[Lesson continued with the children making up examples and stating procedures for the solution of them.]

Teacher: You boys and girls have done very well and have moved ahead very rapidly. We shall have more discussion before we have any written work. Do you think, however, that you understand the examples that we have been doing?

David: Yes, but if you stop to think, you would just about know where the point has to go in the product.

Lesson 4

MULTIPLICATION OF DECIMAL FRACTIONS
Grade Six Class

This lesson is similar to the preceding lesson except that examples with decimal point in the multiplier only were used, and generalizations involved the use of algebraic symbols.

Purpose of lesson: To introduce computational procedures with the multiplication of decimal fraction examples in which there is a decimal point in the multiplier only.

Background of children: The children had a good background of general concepts, and they thought logically and well in group discussion. The group had developed the following concepts previous to this lesson: (a) multiplier-multiplicand-product relationships with decimal integers; (b) concepts of decimal and decimal fraction notation including the interpretation that .5 is 10 times as small in number value as 5 units, that .005 is 1000 times as small in number value as 5 units, and so forth; and (c) concepts concerning the addition and subtraction of decimal fractions.

Lesson Procedure

Teacher: What have we done in arithmetic so far this semester that you have enjoyed most?

Terry: Decimal fractions.

Joan: Long division.

[Others listed things of special interest.]

Lorraine: Arithmetic is all fun when you really understand it. Most of our teachers help us understand our work before they hand us written papers to do.

Teacher: Today we are going to discuss something that we have not had before — multiplication of decimal fractions. Can you state some of the main ideas about multipliers, multiplicands, and products?

[The children stated the basic multiplier-multiplicand-product relationships and discussed their operation with things that they had observed.]

Teacher: What is the answer to this example?

[Teacher wrote this example on the board, and the children gave the answer.]

$$\begin{array}{r} 2\ 5 \\ \times\ 3 \\ \hline 7\ 5 \end{array}$$

[Teacher placed a decimal point in front of the 3.]

Teacher: Now what has happened to the multiplier?

Peggy: The product is 7.5.

Teacher: You are way ahead of me. What have I done to the multiplier?

Terry: You made it 10 times as small in number value, and the product must be 10 times as small in value, too.

Peggy: I didn't have to figure it the long way. I knew the answer. Will multiplication of decimal fractions be that easy?

Teacher: You will not have difficulty if you think about the meaning of the examples.

[Teacher changed the multiplier to .03, and then asked the children to state what was true about the example.]

Tim: The product will be 100 times as small in value as if the multiplier were 3. Place a decimal point in front of the 7. The product is seventy-five hundredths (.75).

[Teacher changed the multiplier to .003.]

Jim: The multiplier is now 1000 times as small as when it was 3. The product will be 1000 times as small. Put a 0 in front of the 7 and then the decimal point in front of the 0.

Teacher: What does the zero do?

Jim: It holds the position of the tenths. Otherwise, the answer would be **.75**.

Teacher: Excellent thinking, Jim.

[Teacher wrote the following example on the board:]

$$\begin{array}{r} 1\ 5 \\ \times\ R \\ \hline \end{array}$$

Teacher: Let R stand for any primary digit. What do you know about the product?

Jim: It could be anything from 15 to 9×15.

Denny: Not if R is equal to zero. Zero times any number would still be zero.

Teacher: Right, Denny. What should my question have been if we want Jim's statement to be true?

Denny: You should have said, "Let R be any primary digit except zero."

Teacher: What is the answer to the example if the value of R is 4?

Dick: 60.

[Teacher wrote a second example next to the one on the board so that these two examples were to be compared.]

$$\begin{array}{cc} (a) & (b) \\ 1\ 5 & 1\ 5 \\ \times\ R & \times\ .R \\ \hline \end{array}$$

Teacher: R stands for any primary digit excluding zero.

Terry: The product for Example (a) is 10 times as large (in number value) as the product for Example (b).

Paul: The multiplier and the product of Example (b) are 10 times as small (in number value) as Example (a)'s. The multiplicands are constant.

Teacher: What are the products if R equals 4?

Jack: 60 for Example (a).

Jim: For Example (b), the answer would be 6.

Teacher: What are the products if R equals 7?

Jim: 1 0 5.

Teacher: Wonderful, Jim. How did you know?

Jim: I figured it out. I thought you would ask 6, so when you asked 7, I just added 15.

June: Then the answer to Example (b) is 10.5. It is 10 times as small as the answer to (a), which is 105.

[Teacher wrote 5×20 and $.5 \times 20$ on the board and similar comparisons were made. The class continued with $.5 \times 25$, and $.5 \times 18$. These three examples were left on the board:]

$$
\begin{array}{ccc}
1\,8 & 2\,5 & 2\,0 \\
\underline{.5} & \underline{.5} & \underline{.5} \\
\end{array}
$$

Teacher: There is something interesting about these examples. What do you see that is true about them?

Mary: The products are 10 times as small as if you were multiplying by 5.

Teacher: That is true, but there is something else. What is the answer to $.5 \times 18$?

Mary: 9.

Teacher: To $.5 \times 25$? And to $.5 \times 20$?

[Class gave answers.]

Susan: The product goes into the multiplicand in each case. That's really interesting.

Joan: Two times the product equals the multiplicand. The multiplicand becomes 2 times as small. To multiply by .5 is the same as taking $\frac{1}{2}$ of the number.

Teacher: When you multiply by five tenths (.5), what is another way you could do the computation?

Denny: Take $\frac{1}{2}$ of the multiplicand. Divide the multiplicand by 2.

Teacher: Very good, Denny. What is the product of L multiplied by .5?

Denny: It would be L divided by 2. [He wrote $2\overline{)L}$ on the board.]

Joan: I have an example. [Joan went to the board and wrote her example.]

$$
\begin{array}{r}
4\,0 \\
\times\ .2 \\
\hline
\end{array}
$$

The answer would be 8.

The lesson continued with the children asking questions, presenting examples, and formulating generalizations concerning decimal integer expressions multiplied by decimal fraction expressions. The main generalizations that were evolved were the following:

(a) Any number multiplied by .5 is the same as that number divided by 2.

(b) Any number multiplied by .1 is the same as dividing that number by 10.

(c) Any number multiplied by .2 is that number divided by 5.

(d) Any number multiplied by a decimal fraction gives a product which is smaller in number value than the multiplicand.

Lesson 5
DIVISION OF DECIMAL FRACTIONS
Grade Five Class

This lesson on the division of decimal fractions was preceded by the development of (a) divisor-dividend-quotient relationships; and (b) concepts with regard for decimal fraction expressions.

Purpose of lesson: The development of concepts with regard for the division of decimal fractions.

Lesson Procedure

Teacher: Can you state what is true concerning division situations in which the dividend remains constant in value, and the divisor value is variable?

June: When the dividend is constant, if the divisor increases, the quotient decreases.

Sam: And, when the dividend is constant, if the divisor decreases, the quotient increases.

Richard: You could say both of those ideas in one sentence if you wanted to. You could say that if the dividend is constant, the quotient changes in the opposite way from the change in the divisor. [With this group of children, the language expression to state this relationship was developed soon after this lesson. The children's refinement of the concept was such that they were ready for comparable refinement of language to facilitate their expression of ideas. The words "inverse proportion" had significant meaning when they were developed.]

Teacher: If we keep the dividend constant and make the divisor 3 times as small in value, what would have to happen to the value of the quotient?

Class: The quotient would have to be made 3 times as large in value.

Teacher: Let us look at a few problems in which we use these numerals. [Teacher wrote on the blackboard:]

$$\frac{5}{3)\ 1\ 5}$$

Teacher: If we make the divisor 3 times as small in number value, what would the divisor be?

Class: 1.

[Teacher wrote on the blackboard:]

$$\frac{1\ 5}{1)\ 1\ 5}$$

Teacher: We have made the divisor 3 times as small in value, and the dividends of the two examples are the same. What is true about their quotients?

Gene: When you made the divisor 3 times as small in value, the quotient became 3 times as large in value: 15 is 3 times as large as 5.

Teacher: I am going to change the divisor of this problem:

$$3)\overline{1\ 5}^{\,5}$$

Watch while I change it.

[Teacher changed the divisor from 3 to .3.]

Nancy: You changed the divisor so that it is 10 times as small in value as when it was 3. I know what the quotient is. It would have to be 10 times as large in value. The quotient for 15 divided by 3 is 5. And, .3 (three tenths) is 10 times as small as small in value as 3. The quotient will have to be 10 times as large as 5.

Teacher: Class, is that correct?

Class: Yes.

Teacher: Very well, Nancy. What shall I do with the example to show that the quotient is made 10 times as large in value?

Nancy: Make the 5 into 5 0 by writing a 0 in the units' place.

Teacher: Let us try another example.

[Teacher wrote on the blackboard:]

$$4)\overline{3\ 2}^{\,8}$$

Teacher: I am going to change the divisor. Watch carefully, and be ready to tell what I have done.

[Teacher changed the divisor from 4 to .4.]

Evelyn: That is easy. The answer would be 80. You made the divisor 10 times as small in value, and the quotient will have to be 10 times as large in value. You didn't change the dividend.

Ray: Now write an example in which you make the divisor .04. I'll write it.

[Ray wrote .0 4)$\overline{2\ 4}$ on the blackboard.]

Ray: The answer is 600, isn't it? The answer would be 6 if the divisor were 4; .04 (four hundredths) is 100 times as small in value as 4. The quotient will have to be 100 times as large in value: 6 times 100 is 600.

Dorothy: The value of the quotient is larger than the value of the dividend. That looks strange! In division examples we've worked before, the quotient was always smaller in value than the dividend, wasn't it?

Robert: That isn't true, Dorothy. When one is the divisor, the value of the quotient is the same as the value of the dividend. Remember, any number divided by one is that number!

Nancy: We've divided by .3 (three tenths), .4 (four tenths), and .04 (four hundredths) today. With these divisors, the value of the quotient was larger than the value of the dividend.

Robert: Yes, but .3 (three tenths), .4 (four tenths), and .04 (four hundredths) are smaller in value than one unit. When your divisor is smaller than one, the quotient must always be larger than the dividend.

Nancy: Is that always true?

Teacher: Shall we see if Robert's idea works with some other examples?

The lesson continued with experimenting with the ideas concerning division of a decimal integer by a decimal fraction. The class formulated and stated the following generalizations concerning division:

(a) When the divisor value is smaller than one unit, the quotient value is larger than the dividend value.

(b) When a number is divided by five tenths, the quotient is twice the number value of the dividend.

(c) When a number is divided by one tenth, the quotient is 10 times as large in number value as the dividend.

Lesson 6
PERCENT — INITIAL LESSON INTRODUCING
COMPUTATIONAL PROCEDURES
Grade Six

Purpose of lesson: To lead the children to interpret the main relationships underlying computational procedures with percent.

Background of children: The children had a good background of concepts and skills concerning (a) multiplication and division of decimal fractions; (b) meaning of percent and interpretation of percents such as 50 percent, 25 percent, and 20 percent; and (c) divisor-dividend-quotient relationships.

Lesson Procedure

[Teacher had written on the blackboard:]

$$4 \times 8 = 32$$

Teacher: In this equation, if one part of the equation were unknown, how would you find the answer? Let us use a question mark to indicate the unknown part, and we can write the following problems:

(a) $4 \times 8 = ?$
(b) $? \times 8 = 32$
(c) $4 \times ? = 32$

In Example (a), what is known and how would you find the answer?

Jerry: The multiplicand and the multiplier are known, so I'd multiply $4 \times 8 = 32$.

George: In Example (b) the multiplier is unknown. You know the multiplicand and the product. To find the multiplier, I'd divide 8 into 32.

Teacher: Tell what your dividend and divisor correspond to in the multiplication example and show us on the blackboard.

George: The product becomes the dividend, and the multiplicand the divisor. [George wrote the following on the blackboard:]

$$\begin{array}{r} 8 \\ \times\, 4 \\ \hline 3\ 2 \end{array} \qquad 8)\overline{\begin{array}{c} 4 \\ 3\ 2 \end{array}}$$

The multiplier of the multiplication example would become the quotient in the division example.

Teacher: What can you tell about Example (c)?

Marian: The known parts are the multiplier and the product. The multiplicand is unknown. You find that (the multiplicand) by dividing the multiplier into the product. That is like George's example, except that the unknown is 8.

Teacher: You have expressed your ideas very well. Now let us work out these ideas we've developed by using this example. [Teacher wrote on the blackboard:]

$$40 \times \frac{1}{4} = 10$$

Teacher: In how many ways can you set up one unknown part? Let us have t stand for the unknown part.

[Three children were selected to go to the blackboard and write their equations. The following were written on the blackboard:]

Sue $\qquad 4\ 0 \times \dfrac{1}{4} = t$

Douglas $\quad 4\ 0 \times t = 1\ 0$

Doris $\qquad t \times \dfrac{1}{4} = 1\ 0$

Sue: In my example, you multiply $40 \times \frac{1}{4}$. The product is 10.

Douglas: In my example, you divide, but it surely looks funny to me to write it like this. [Douglas wrote on the blackboard $4\ 0)\overline{1\ 0}$.] The answer would have to be a decimal fraction.

Sue: Douglas, you could write it like this. This is the way we write the division example as a common fraction.

[Sue wrote on the blackboard $\frac{10}{40} = \frac{1}{4}$.]

Doris: In my example, the $\frac{1}{4}$ is the divisor and the dividend is 10. [Doris wrote the following on the blackboard:]

$$\frac{1}{4})\overline{\begin{array}{c} 1\ 0 \times 4 = 4\ 0 \\ 1\ 0 \end{array}}$$

Teacher: You have done very good thinking. Let us see how these ideas work when we express the common fraction, $\frac{1}{4}$, as a percent. One fourth is equal to what percent?

John: One fourth is the same as 25 hundredths or 25 percent.

Betty: Wouldn't that be just like the examples we've done except that we would use the percent sign and change the $\frac{1}{4}$ to 25 percent?

Teacher: That is correct. Can you write the equation on the blackboard?

George: That is easy.

[George wrote on the blackboard $40 \times 25\% = 10$. Then the children went to the blackboard and, using the letter t to indicate one unknown part of the equation, wrote the following equations:]

Marjorie $4\,0 \times 25\% = t$
Jack $t \times 25\% = 1\,0$
Bill $4\,0 \times\ t\ = 1\,0$

Marjorie: My example is very easy. I'll multiply $4\,0 \times .2\,5$.

[Marjorie showed the following multiplication on the blackboard:]

$$
\begin{array}{r}
4\ 0 \\
\times\ .2\ 5 \\
\hline
2\ 0\ 0 \\
8\ 0 \\
\hline
1\ 0.0\ 0
\end{array}
$$

Jack: I need to find the value of t. The multiplier is t, so I'll have to divide, but I'm not sure what to divide.

Teacher: Can you tell what your dividend has to be by thinking through what we have said about how the dividend corresponds to something in multiplication?

Jack: We found that the dividend of a division example corresponds to the product of a multiplication example. $1\,0$ would have to be the dividend, and the divisor would be 25 percent which is 25 hundredths. It would be like this. [Jack wrote on the blackboard:]

$$
.2\ 5\overline{)\ 1\ 0.0\ 0}\ ^{4\ 0}
$$

That's really easy. We've had examples like that in the division of decimal fractions.

Bill: My example is $4\,0 \times t = 1\,0$. To find the value of t, I'll divide. As in Jack's example, my dividend would be $1\,0$ because $1\,0$ is the product. [Bill wrote on the blackboard:]

$$
4\ 0\overline{)\ 1\ 0}
$$

The divisor is $4\,0$. The answer will be a decimal fraction. [Bill divided and came out with $.2\,5$.] Would you say the answer was $.2\,5$?

Mary: Wouldn't you have to change .2 5 to percent?

Teacher: What do you think? Would you need to unless the problem asked for the value of *t* to be expressed as a percent?

Doris: If you left the unknown as *t* and didn't say how *t* was to be said, you could say the value of *t* was .2 5 or $\frac{1}{4}$ or 25 percent.

Teacher: That is right. Would it be easier to use the common fraction to find the value of *t* in some examples?

Douglas: It would be easier in the example on the board because it is easier to divide 4 into 40 than it is to multiply 40 by .25. Sometimes it would be easier to multiply.

Sue: When would it be easier to multiply by .25? I can't think of any time.

George: How about 25 percent of 467?

Sue: It would be much easier to divide 467 by 4 than it would be to multiply 467 by .25.

George: I think I could multiply it as quickly as you can divide it. Let's both start at the same time and see.

[The teacher gave starting signal and George and Sue raced! The following examples were written on the blackboard:]

$$
\text{Sue} \quad 4\overline{)\,4\,6\,7\,} = 1\,1\,6\tfrac{3}{4} \qquad \text{George} \quad
\begin{array}{r}
4\;6\;7 \\
.2\;5 \\
\hline
2\;3\;3\;5 \\
9\;3\;4\; \\
\hline
1\;1\;6\,.7\;5
\end{array}
$$

Sue: I was through first.

George: I think that I can figure as fast as you can, Sue, but I had to do more writing.

Sue: That's what I said before — dividing is an easier way to work.

Teacher: As we do problems with percent, what are some things that you will have to watch?

Harold: What the problem asks you to find.

Paul: It's easy if you know what to multiply or what to divide, but you have to think about the problem to know that.

Teacher: Very true! You know the meaning of percent, and you know how to multiply and divide decimal fractions, so that the only thing that is new is deciding what the equation is and what part of it is unknown. That calls for good thinking.

Discussion Questions

1. In what sense does seeing the *"point"* in decimal numerals refer to more than the decimal point?

2. The decimal point serves a locative function in decimal orthography. What does the statement mean and what does it imply for instructional guidance?

3.   The place values in a decimal whole number toward the left of the units' position depict sets of ten or sets of "powers" of ten. Show that this principle holds true in the decimal fraction as well.

4.   The statement has been made that "the principal source of difficulty with decimal numerals is with the *decimal point.*" Do you agree with that observation? Why is placing a decimal point properly difficult to do?

5.   Construct a unit test consisting of at least four examples in division that require the use of zero in the quotient between the decimal point and the other digits in the quotient.

6.   Someone has stated that the invention of decimal notation contributed as much to the "industrial revolution" as did any of the inventions of machinery. How would you refute or support such a statement?

7.   Various ways are used to indicate the location of the units' position; $2\underline{50}$ is an example of one way. List five other examples and write a sentence telling about each of them.

8.   Illustrate the operation of the associative principle using decimal fraction expressions.

9.   Using decimal fractions or mixed decimal numerals, illustrate the principle that multiplication is distributive with respect to addition.

Suggested Readings

Banks, J. Houston, *Learning and Teaching Arithmetic*, 2d ed. Boston, Mass.: Allyn and Bacon, Inc., 1964, Chap. 11.

Brumfiel, Charles F., Robert E. Eicholz, and Merrill E. Shanks, *Fundamental Concepts of Elementary Mathematics*. Reading, Mass.: Addison-Wesley Publishing Company, Inc., 1962, Chap. 12.

Brydegaard, Marguerite, "The Insatiable Quest: Mathematicking," *The Arithmetic Teacher*, vol. 7 (January 1960), pp. 9–12.

Clark, John R., and Laura K. Eads, *Guiding Arithmetic Learning*. New York: Harcourt, Brace & World, Inc., 1954, Chap. 7.

Grossnickle, Foster E., "Kinds of Errors in Division of Decimals and Their Constancy," *Journal of Educational Research*, vol. 37 (October 1943), pp. 111–117.

Grossnickle, Foster E., "Types of Errors in Division of Decimals," *Elementary School Journal*, vol. 42 (November 1941), pp. 184–194.

Grossnickle, Foster E., and Leo J. Brueckner, *Discovering Meanings in Elementary School Mathematics*. New York: Holt, Rinehart and Winston, Inc., 1963, Chap. 12.

Guiler, Walter Scribner, "Difficulties in Decimals Encountered by Ninth-grade Pupils," *Elementary School Journal*, vol. 46 (March 1946), 384–393.

Guiler, Walter Scribner, "Difficulties Encountered by College Freshmen in Decimals," *Journal of Educational Research*, vol. 40 (September 1946), pp. 1–13.

Hauck, E., "Concrete Materials for Teaching Percentage," *The Arithmetic Teacher*, vol. 1 (December 1954), pp. 9–12.

Howard, Charles F., and Enoch Dumas, *Basic Procedures in Teaching Arithmetic*. Boston, Mass.: D. C. Heath and Company, 1963, Chap. 10.

Johnson, J. T., "The Case of Decimals versus Common Fractions," *The Mathematics Teacher*, vol. 39 (May 1946), pp. 221–224.

Kessler, Rolla V., "The Equation Method of Teaching Percentage," *The Arithmetic Teacher*, vol. 7 (February 1960), pp. 90–92.

Marks, John L., C. Richard Purdy, and Lucien B. Kinney, *Teaching Arithmetic for Understanding*. New York: McGraw-Hill Book Company, Inc., 1958, Chap. 9.

Mueller, Francis J., *Arithmetic: Its Structure and Concepts*. Englewood Cliffs, N.J.: Prentice-Hall, Inc., 1956, Chap. 5.

Potter, Mary A., "Corralling the Wandering Decimal Point," *The Mathematics Teacher*, vol. 40 (February 1947), pp. 51–57.

Spencer, Peter L., "Do They See the Point?" *The Arithmetic Teacher*, vol. 5 (November 1958), pp. 271–272.

Swain, Robert L., *Understanding Arithmetic*. New York: Holt, Rinehart and Winston, Inc., 1957, Chaps. 5 and 6.

Swenson, Esther J., *Teaching Arithmetic to Children*. New York: The Macmillan Company, 1964, Chap. 17.

9

Concepts Underlying Computation: Common Fractions

9.1 INTRODUCTION

"The simplest numbers are the positive whole numbers, 1, 2, 3, and so on, used for counting. These are called *natural numbers* and have been with us for so many millennia that the famous mathematician Kronecker reputedly said: 'God created the natural numbers; all the rest is the work of man.'

"The basic necessities of everyday life led to the introduction of common fractions like $\frac{1}{2}$, $\frac{2}{3}$, $\frac{5}{4}$, etc. Such numbers are called *rational numbers*, not because they are 'reasonable,' but because they are ratios of whole numbers."[1]

It is important that we recognize, as Niven has pointed out, "The basic necessities of everyday life led to the introduction of common fractions..." However, there is a definite lack of clarity in referring to them as "rational numbers." The term *rational* has a common connotation of *reasonable* which, when associated with the term number appears to imply that other numbers are lacking in reasonableness. In order to avoid this implication and to stress the basic nature of the fraction numbers, we have used the term *ratio number. Ratio* refers to "the quotient of one magnitude divided by another of the same kind."[2]

9.2 COMMON FRACTIONS PRODUCED by DIVIDING into EQUAL PARTS

In the process of quantitative scaling, we may use anything as a unit of measurement and group successive multiples of it on our number scale.

[1] Ivan Niven, *Numbers: Rational and Irrational.* New York: The L. W. Singer Company, 1961, p. 3.

[2] *Webster's New International Dictionary*, 3d ed.

If we choose a unit that is a *part of another whole*, however, there is an advantage in selecting a part such that some multiple of it will equal the whole of which the unit is a part. By so doing we establish a definite relationship between the whole-number scale and the fraction-number scale. Hence, we divide or "fracture" the whole into *equal parts* in order to produce ratio-numbers. The number of parts produced by the division does not matter as long as they are equal in amount. The parts are fractions of the whole.

The word *fraction* is commonly used to mean both *number* and *numeral*. The words "fractional number" and "fractional numeral" are also used. In this chapter, we have used the word "fraction" as it is commonly used unless there is need to emphasize the distinction between the number and its symbol.

9.3   COMMON FRACTION PATTERN

Since a common fraction is merely the ratio of two numbers, it seems evident that the scale of such numbers would conform with the scale of whole numbers that was discussed in previous chapters. Actually, all that is done in order to produce the fraction scales is to change the unit of measure that is being scaled.

For example, as discussed in the preceding chapter, with decimal fractions the unit of measurement is a "decimal part" of the whole or "identity unit" (one) which is basic to the whole-number scaling. Instead of referring to *one* dollar, we may refer to one tenth part of a dollar (one dime), or to one hundredth part of a dollar (one cent). However, should we so desire, we may change our basic reference and make either the dime or the penny the scaling unit. If the dime is chosen, the dollar is scaled as 10 dimes, and the penny is scaled as 1 of the 10 equal parts of a dime. Such scaling applies equally well with any unit we may care to use.

9.4   THE UNIT FRACTION: BASIC UNIT
in FRACTION SCALING

The unit fraction identifies the basic *ratio* that is being used. It has the same relationship to the fraction scaling as the unit (one) has to the whole-number scaling. The essential difference between the two measures is merely their comparative reference to size. Unit fractions can be grouped and treated just as unit wholes are treated.

When we use scaled measures, it is imperative that we designate clearly with which unit of measure we are concerned. In the common language, reference to fractions may be indicated by suffixing a diminutive syllable, *th*, to the customary number symbol. We note this idea in the words four*th*, six*th*, seven*th*, eigh*th*, and so forth. The halves, thirds, and fifths are exceptions to this practice.

In contrast to the common language, the number-language symbol for a unit fraction is more succinct and more uniformly used. It consists merely in depicting the *ratio* of 1 divided by the symbol that designates the number of equal parts into which the whole was divided. The symbol may be spelled in various ways:

$$\frac{1}{x}, \ x\overline{)\,1\,}, \ 1 \div x, \ 1/x, \ 1 : x, \ \ldots,$$

where x stands for any value that we wish to use. The choice of spelling for the symbol may be made for convenience in writing or for clarity in expressing a particular idea.

Every fraction is a ratio or an indicated division.

9.5   THE COUNTLESS NUMBER
of FRACTION-NUMBER SCALES

A whole may be divided into any number of equal parts, and one of the parts can be used as the basic unit for constructing a fraction-number scale. Each fraction-number scale makes feasible some measurement that it is not possible to measure by the whole-number scale. As greater precision in measurement is desired, smaller and smaller units of measure will be used. The very nature of scaling (matching groupings of units of measurement) determines that there will always be amounts so small that they cannot be measured by the unit being used. However, by choosing smaller and smaller units, the unmeasurable amounts will be reduced to practical insignificance. The field of micro-measurement is infinite, just as is the field of macro-measurement.

9.6   FRACTION-NUMBER SCALES SIMILAR
to WHOLE-NUMBER SCALE

Table 9.1 has been designed to illustrate the parallel nature as well as the comparative values depicted by different number scales. The scale at the top shows the first two spacings of the whole-number scale. For the sake of comparison, the numerals are presented in the form of fractions or ratios. This is not a violation of the whole-number value because they represent successive multiples of ones and, therefore, their value remains the same when it is divided by one. Each decimal whole number may be expressed as a rational (ratio) number. Scale number 2 shows the comparative measures when the unit of measurement shows division into *two equal parts* or *halves*, that is, divided by 2. Scale number 3 depicts comparable scalings for a division into *four equal parts* or *fourths*. Scale number 4 shows the measure divided into *eight equal parts* or *eighths*.

TABLE 9.1

Comparative Number Scales in Terms of Fraction Units

Scale 1	$\frac{0}{1}$				$\frac{1}{1}$				$\frac{2}{1}$ ...		
Scale 2	$\frac{0}{2}$		$\frac{1}{2}$		$\frac{2}{2}$		$\frac{3}{2}$		$\frac{4}{2}$ ...		
Scale 3	$\frac{0}{4}$	$\frac{1}{4}$	$\frac{2}{4}$	$\frac{3}{4}$	$\frac{4}{4}$	$\frac{5}{4}$	$\frac{6}{4}$	$\frac{7}{4}$	$\frac{8}{4}$ ...		

| *Scale 4* | $\frac{0}{8}$ | $\frac{1}{8}$ | $\frac{2}{8}$ | $\frac{3}{8}$ | $\frac{4}{8}$ | $\frac{5}{8}$ | $\frac{6}{8}$ | $\frac{7}{8}$ | $\frac{8}{8}$ | $\frac{9}{8}$ | $\frac{10}{8}$ | $\frac{11}{8}$ | $\frac{12}{8}$ | $\frac{13}{8}$ | $\frac{14}{8}$ | $\frac{15}{8}$ | $\frac{16}{8}$ ... |

In each scale, the unit 1 divided by the number of equal parts being scaled is the primary measure. Each of the other measures is made up of sets of those units, just as is done to establish the series of whole numbers. Obviously, the scalings may be continued indefinitely to include larger groupings of the unit of measure. They may also be paralleled by an infinite number of comparable scales based upon other units of measurement. Note that at some points all of the scales represent the same number value, for example, $\frac{1}{1}$, $\frac{2}{2}$, $\frac{4}{4}$, $\frac{8}{8}$, all symbolize the same value. This is determined by the fact that each scale is based upon equal divisions of the whole unit and, therefore, some multiple of each scale must equal the whole unit.

9.7   ORTHOGRAPHY of COMMON FRACTION (RATIO) NUMBERS

INDICATED DIVISION

Just as there is a pattern governing the spelling of decimal whole-number symbols, there is likewise a pattern for spelling the fraction-number symbols. Since the principal function served by the fraction numerals is that of scaling amounts produced by dividing wholes into equal parts, it is reasonable to use a symbol that expresses that idea. Hence, the common symbol for a fraction or ratio number is an *indicated division*. As mentioned above, a unit fraction is symbolized by the unit 1 divided by a symbol that tells what scale is being considered, for example, $\frac{1}{2}$, $\frac{1}{3}$, $\frac{1}{4}$, indicating respectively that the scale of halves, thirds, or fourths is being referred to. In this sense, the symbol is a succinct way of expressing a number sentence. For example, $\frac{1}{2}$ means 1 is divided by 2, or $2\overline{)\,1}$. The divisor in such a symbol identifies the particular scale to which the symbol refers. It is, therefore, commonly referred to as the *denominator* or *namer*. In this regard, it serves as a type of base (radix), indicating the particular number scale being used.

Since the unit fraction is the measure being scaled, it is evident that groupings of such measures will be considered. Hence, there is need for the numeral to indicate how many of such units are in the grouping being symbolized. This is accomplished by replacing the 1 in the unit fraction symbol by a number symbol that tells the number of such units. Since this element of the symbol tells the NUMBER of units, it is called the *numerator* or *"numberer."* It is also the *dividend* of the division that is expressed.

WAYS TO WRITE NUMERALS TO EXPRESS COMMON FRACTION NUMBERS

Fraction or ratio numerals may be expressed in different ways. The most common form, however, consists in naming the dividend, then indicating the division operation, and finally identifying the divisor. The symbol for division is usually a horizontal line or slanted line between the other terms of the symbol. It may, however, be a symbol like the colon used in punctuation. There are other variations, such as $\frac{2}{3}$, 2/3, $2 \div 3$, $2 : 3$, and $3\overline{)2}$, all symbols for the same fraction numeral. There is another form that is sometimes used to depict "ordered pairs" as a ratio idea, for example, (2,3), (4,6), and so forth.

CLASSIFICATION OF COMMON FRACTIONS

There are classifications of fractions. Since the primary purpose of the fraction unit is to provide for measurements of *parts* of wholes, such numerals would normally represent quantities less than one. Hence, fractions expressing values less than the value of the number 1 are called *proper fractions*. Set A shows examples of proper fractions.

$$A = \left\{ \frac{1}{9}, \ \frac{3}{4}, \ \frac{2}{3} \right\}$$

There is no reason why measurements on a fraction scale need to be limited. Since it is inevitable that values equal to, or in excess of, the whole number 1 will be experienced when using any fraction scale, such numerals are accepted. But, they are designated as *improper fractions*. See Set B.

$$B = \left\{ \frac{16}{4}, \ \frac{17}{9}, \ \frac{13}{5} \right\}$$

A combination of a whole number with a common fraction number produces a *mixed number*. Set C shows examples of mixed numerals.

$$C = \{1\tfrac{1}{2}, \quad 5\tfrac{2}{3}, \quad 19\tfrac{1}{4}\}$$

They are "mixed" because they combine two types of numerals that have different characteristics.

Only "proper fractions" are joined with whole numbers to form mixed numbers. Since the fraction value refers to "parts of one," it normally would be expressed within the ones' position in the numeral; for instance, $3\tfrac{1}{2}$ would be written

However, this would be a cumbersome symbol to write and it would be difficult to read. Hence the fraction is suffixed to the right of the whole-number symbol. Actually, this violates the pattern of decimal numeral orthography and it produces difficulty with reading the numeral because readers have been accustomed to interpret positional value with the numerals. A common error results from reading the fraction symbol as a placeholder, which *it is not*.

The term *similar fractions* is used to designate fractions that belong to the same fraction scale. Fractions belonging to different fraction scales, that is, having different divisors (denominators), are called *dissimilar fractions*. Set D shows examples of similar fractions; Set E illustrates dissimilar fractions.

$$D = \left\{\frac{1}{4}, \quad \frac{3}{4}, \quad \frac{2}{4}\right\}$$

$$E = \left\{\frac{1}{6}, \quad \frac{1}{8}, \quad \frac{1}{9}\right\}$$

THE DENOMINATOR (NAMER) IDENTIFIES
THE FRACTION-NUMBER SCALE

The idea that each *denomination* of fractions belongs to a particular number scale helps to suggest ways in which fraction numbers may be added or subtracted. For example, if one is counting apples, the unit of measure is *one apple*. Each grouping consists of a particular set of apples. Comparably, were we counting cows, each grouping would consist of cows. Should we wish to combine the groupings from these respective scales, the resulting grouping would be neither cows nor apples. However, the union of the two groupings can be made, but the set will need to have a name that is suitable for it. Perhaps *things* will serve, since apples are things and cows are things. Things, then, may be used as a common referent or *denominator*. We call such a referent a *common denominator*. It really identifies a scale upon which all of the measures of concern may be expressed.

9.8   ADDITION and SUBTRACTION of FRACTION NUMBERS

In Chapter 4, we discussed numbers having different subgrouping patterns (radices). While each of such numerals represents a number value, they cannot be combined without changing them to equivalent values upon the same number system. For example, one cannot combine Roman numerals with decimal numerals without changing them into numerals having a common pattern. Similarly, one cannot add or subtract fractions unless they are expressed in terms of the same fraction scale. Techniques for transforming fraction values into equivalent values on another fraction scale are an important part of the study of fractions. These techniques are derived from properties of the division operation.

9.9   COMMON FRACTION RELATIONSHIPS

Since fractions are indicated divisions, properties of the division operation apply to them. There are three such basic properties: (1) the value of the quotient is *directly* proportional to changes in the dividend, when the divisor is constant, (2) the value of the quotient is *inversely* proportional to changes in the divisor when the dividend is constant, and (3) *both* the divisor and the dividend may be *multiplied or divided* by the same number without changing the value of the quotient. This is the property that pertains particularly to transforming ratio values from one scale to another.

We may illustrate the properties of division as applied with fraction numbers as in the following numbered paragraphs.

1. The number value of a fraction is inversely proportional to changes in its divisor when the dividend is left unchanged.

$$\begin{array}{cccccc} \text{(a)} & \text{(b)} & \text{(c)} & \text{(d)} & \text{(e)} & \text{(f)} \\[4pt] \dfrac{1}{1} & \dfrac{1}{2} & \dfrac{1}{4} & \dfrac{1}{8} & \dfrac{1}{16} & \dfrac{1}{32} \end{array}$$

Using Example (a) as a referent, Example (b) has the same dividend, but its divisor is *two times as large* in value. Its ratio value is *2 times as small* as that of Example (a). It is evident that this is characteristic of each pair of examples as one reads from left to right.

By reversing the direction of our reading, we may use Example (f) as a referent and compare Example (e) with it. We see that Example (e) has a divisor that is *2 times as small* in value as the divisor in (f). However, the ratio value of (e) is *2 times as large* as that of (f). This relationship holds true for other comparisons in the right-to-left direction with the examples. Hence, we may generalize as follows: (1) one way to *divide* a common fraction value is to *increase* its divisor, and (2) one way to *multiply* the value of a common fraction is to *decrease* its divisor.

2. The number value of a fraction is directly proportional to changes in its dividend when the divisor is left unchanged. This should be evident because fractions having the same divisors are elements of the same fraction-number scale; hence, their positions within that scale are determined by their dividends:

(a)	(b)	(c)	(d)
$\dfrac{1}{9}$	$\dfrac{2}{9}$	$\dfrac{4}{9}$	$\dfrac{8}{9}$

These examples are all elements of the scale of ninths. Example (a) is the unit of measure for that scale. Each of the other examples is composed of a grouping of such units. Example (b) contains 2 times as many as does Example (a). Reading from left to right reveals that values increase directly in proportion to the increase in the dividends. By reversing the direction of the comparisons, we find that values decrease in direct proportion in the dividends. Hence, we may generalize as follows: (1) one way to divide the value of a common fraction is to divide its dividend, and (2) one way to multiply the value of a common fraction is to multiply its dividend.

3. Both the divisor and the dividend of a common fraction may be multiplied or divided by the same number without changing the value of the fraction. Consider the following examples:

(a)	(b)	(c)	(d)
$\dfrac{3}{1)\,3}$	$\dfrac{3}{2)}$	$\dfrac{3}{)\,12}$	$\dfrac{3}{8)}$

The quotients are constant. Use Example (a) as a referent. The divisor of Example (b) is 2 times as large in value. What must be true of its dividend as compared with that of (a)? Now compare Example (c) with Example (a). The quotients are the same. The dividend in Example (c) is 4 times as great in value as that of (a). Then what must be true of the divisor of (c) as compared with that of (a)? If one multiplies by 2 and then divides that product by 2, what will the answer be?

From the preceding discussion we may conclude the following: (1) to change a fraction to an equivalent value expressed in a higher denomination or number scale, *multiply both terms of the fraction* by a number that will make its divisor equal to the desired value, and (2) to change a fraction into an equivalent value expressed in a lower denomination or number scale, *divide both terms* by a number that will make its divisor equal to the desired value. The process of changing a fraction to an equivalent value having a smaller denominator is called expressing the value in simplest form.

9.10 COMPUTATIONAL TECHNIQUES
with COMMON FRACTION NUMBERS

The same principles govern operational work with fractions as govern such work with whole numbers. The only new aspect is that of interpreting the fraction expression. The interpretation which serves best is that *the numerical value of a fraction is the numerical value of its dividend* (*numerator*) MADE AS MANY TIMES AS SMALL *as is indicated by its divisor.* For example, as compared with 5 the value of the fraction $\frac{5}{6}$ is *6 times as small.* This is a difficult concept to visualize or to illustrate pictorially, but it is not particularly difficult to comprehend. By stressing the *ratio* concept, work with fractions can be greatly simplified. For example, in the specimens below, the value 12 is operated upon by different-sized divisors:

$$\text{(a)} \quad \text{(b)} \quad \text{(c)} \quad \text{(d)}$$
$$\frac{12}{1} \qquad \frac{12}{2} \qquad \frac{12}{3} \qquad \frac{12}{4}$$

$$\overset{12}{1) \overline{12}} \qquad \overset{6}{2) \overline{12}} \qquad \overset{4}{3) \overline{12}} \qquad \overset{3}{4) \overline{12}}$$

Stated as fractions these specimens express ratios as indicated divisions. By performing the indicated operations the values expressed by the ratios are 12, 6, 4, and 3, respectively.

However, it is not feasible to perform the divisions expressed by some fractions. We use them as "indicated divisions." This will become more easily accomplished as greater familiarity with the fraction symbol is achieved.

As was pointed out above, common-fraction values are changed to a common scale when we wish to add or subtract them. The process of converting fractions from one scale to another is in itself a potential source of difficulty for a beginner. Hence, it may be well to introduce computational work with fractions with the operation of multiplication. This may well be followed by the operation of division for reasons which will be evident when we discuss that operation.

MULTIPLICATION

The following concepts are important in the interpretation of multiplication of common fractions:

(1)   Common fractions are indicated divisions, or ratios.

(2)   The interpretation of divisor-dividend-quotient relationships underlies the use of fractions as factors in multiplication.

(3)   The concepts of multiplier-multiplicand-product relationships, (factor-product) are basic for the interpretation of the multiplication of common fractions.

(4)   A combination of the concepts mentioned above is the key to a rational understanding of the multiplication of common fractions.

Examples in Which One Factor Is a Decimal Integer and the Other Factor Is a Common Fraction

In Example (a), the multiplier is a decimal integer. In Examples (b) and (c), the multiplier is a common fraction.

(a)   (b)   (c)

$$5 \times \frac{2}{3} \qquad \frac{1}{2} \times 3 \qquad \frac{3}{5} \times 7$$

Consider Example (a). The problem is to determine how many thirds there would be in a set of five groupings of two thirds each. To make the value of a fraction 5 times as large, we multiply its dividend by 5; hence,

$$5 \times \frac{2}{3} \quad \text{will be} \quad \frac{5 \times 2}{3} \quad \text{or} \quad \frac{10}{3}$$

This can be illustrated by a number line as follows:

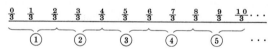

The symbol $\frac{10}{3}$ is an improper fraction. By performing the indicated division it can be changed into the mixed number, $3\frac{1}{3}$.

Consider Example (b) ($\frac{1}{2} \times 3$). The problem here is that of interpreting a fraction as a multiplier. We know that the size of the product is determined directly by the size of the multiplier when the multiplicand is constant.

(a) $8 \times 3 = 24$
(b) $4 \times 3 = 12$
(c) $2 \times 3 = 6$
(d) $1 \times 3 = 3$
(e) $\frac{1}{2} \times 3 =$

In the examples given, the multiplicands are constant. Reading from the top to the bottom, the multipliers decrease in a definite pattern. Each multiplier after the first is 2 times as small in value as the preceding multiplier. What is true about the products?

Compare Example (b) with Example (a). The multiplicands are the same. The multiplier of Example (b) is 2 times as small in number value as that of Example (a). What is true about the product for Example (b) as compared with that of Example (a)?

Compare Example (d) with Example (e). The multiplicands are constant. The multiplier of Example (e) is 2 times as small in number value as the multiplier of Example (d). What will be true about the product of Example (e) compared with that of Example (d)?

What is true concerning 3 multiplied by $\frac{1}{2}$?

From the initial development of multiplication of common fractions, the learner should become aware that multiplying a given expression by a proper fraction decreases the value of the given expression. Similarly, specific development of examples such as the ones below should produce generalizations of the following type:

(a) Any number multiplied by $\frac{1}{2}$ is that number divided by 2.

(b) Any number multiplied by $\frac{1}{5}$ is that number divided by 5.

(c) Any number multiplied by $\frac{1}{10}$ is that number divided by 10.

(d) Any number multiplied by $\frac{2}{3}$ is decreased in value because the number is multiplied by 2 and divided by 3.

(e) Any given number multiplied by a proper fraction produces a product that is smaller than that given number.

Similarly, in the example $\frac{3}{5} \times 7$ we need to interpret the idea that the size of the product is determined by the size of the multiplier when the multiplicand is constant. We may therefore compare a multiplier of 3 with a multiplier of $\frac{3}{5}$. The fraction value is 5 times as small as is that of the whole number. Hence the product that it produces will be 5 times as small as that produced by multiplying by 3. So we multiply by the 3 and divide that product by 5. Three fifths of 7 is

$$\frac{3 \times 7}{5} \quad \text{or} \quad \frac{21}{5}$$

This can be changed by performing the indicated division to the mixed number, $4\frac{1}{5}$.

Of course, we could have foreseen that Example (b) would be solved in the same manner as Example (a), because the commutative property of multiplication applies. In the multiplication of two factors, either factor may be used as the multiplier.

Examples in Which Both Factors Are Common Fractions

We still need to consider situations in which both factors are common fractions, such as $\frac{2}{3} \times \frac{4}{5}$. Here again we apply the principle that the size of the product is directly determined by the size of the multiplier, when the multiplicand is held constant. Hence, we use $2 \times \frac{4}{5}$ as a referent, that is,

$$\frac{2 \times 4}{5}$$

Now $\frac{2}{3}$ is 3 times as small in value as is 2. Consequently, the product should be made 3 times as small in value as the referent example, that is, divide it by 3. In order to make a fraction value 3 times as small, we make its denominator (divisor) 3 times as large, that is, multiply the denominator by 3. Hence

$$\frac{2}{3} \times \frac{4}{5} \quad \text{becomes} \quad \frac{2 \times 4}{3 \times 5} \quad \text{or} \quad \frac{8}{15}$$

By applying the properties of division and those of multiplication as shown in the preceding solutions we observe that, to multiply by a common fraction, we multiply the multiplicand by the numerator of the fraction and we divide that product by the denominator of the fraction.

Simplification (Cancellation)

"Cancellation" may be used to *simplify* multiplication with fractions. In the discussion above, we observed that dividing the dividend and divisor of a fraction by the same amount did not alter the value of the fraction. This is the principle that forms the basis for the procedure of cancellation (simplification). It consists in removing factors common to both terms of a fraction. It is essentially what is done when fractions are expressed in simplest form: $\frac{6}{8}$ may be expressed as

$$\frac{2 \times 3}{2 \times 4}$$

The factor 2 may be "canceled" since multiplying by 2 and then dividing by 2 does not change the value of the fraction.

Consider the application of this procedure in the following examples:

(a)   (b)   (c)

$$\frac{3}{8} \times 8 = \frac{3}{\cancel{8}} \times \overset{1}{\cancel{8}} \text{ or } 3 \qquad \frac{2}{5} \times 10 = \frac{2}{\cancel{5}} \times \overset{2}{\cancel{10}} \text{ or } 4 \qquad \frac{3}{4} \times \frac{2}{9} = \frac{\overset{1}{\cancel{3}}}{\underset{2}{\cancel{4}}} \times \frac{\overset{1}{\cancel{2}}}{\underset{3}{\cancel{9}}} \text{ or } \frac{1}{6}$$

In Example (a) the factor 8 is "canceled" from both the dividend and the divisor of the situation as expressed. In Example (b) a common factor 5 is similarly removed from both terms. Example (c) needs special attention. This type of example produces many errors because of failure to recognize that the common factor is used as a divisor and that it is not actually "canceled." For example, when 3 is divided by 3 the quotient is 1, and when 2 is divided by 2 the quotient is 1. Failure to recognize this fact sometimes leads to giving whole numbers for answers in situations like Example (c).

DIVISION

The development of understanding of the division procedures with common fractions has been neglected in the past. Understanding has too commonly been supplanted by *rules of procedure* that were often imposed and not meaningfully derived. Actually, they are easily explained by using the concepts of division that are made evident through working with whole numbers.

The main concepts underlying the division of common fractions are:

(1)   The concepts underlying division with decimal integers and decimal fractions also underlie division with common fractions.
  (a) The size of the quotient depends directly upon the size of the dividend, when the divisor is constant.
  (b) The size of the quotient changes in the opposite direction (in inverse proportion) from that of changes in the divisor when the dividend remains the same.
  (c) The size of the dividend and the divisor vary in direct proportion when the quotient remains the same.

(2)   The interpretation of common fraction expressions as indicated in division situations is fundamental to their use in division examples.

The process of inferential reasoning is helpful in deriving the procedures for division with common fractions. By using 1 as a divisor and then comparing other divisors with that referent, we derive the necessary steps. The following types of division situations need to be considered.

Examples in Which the Dividend Is a Decimal Integer and the Divisor Is a Unit Fraction: $6 \div \frac{1}{2}$.

It is suggested that the division form illustrated below may be helpful to use in the early stages of teaching the computational work with division of common fraction numbers. The placement of the quotient of the division example brings out the inverted form of the divisor. The multiplier is usually written to the left of the multiplication sign when the multiplication algorithm is expressed in horizontal form. The placement of the multiplier in the examples below is consistent with that practice.

The commutative property of multiplication leads us to generalize that interchanging the position of the factors does not change the value of the product. It is likely true that, after the introductory stages have been developed, the form used in the other pages of this chapter is desirable.

We may first consider this as our referent example. Any number divided by 1 is that number.

$$\frac{6}{1)\ 6}$$

When the divisor is 2 times as small and the dividend is the same,

$$\frac{}{\tfrac{1}{2})\ 6}$$

the quotient will be 2 times as large:

$$2 \times 6 = 12$$
$$\frac{}{\tfrac{1}{2})\qquad 6}$$

This can be illustrated on the number line as follows:

Scale of halves $\dfrac{0}{2}\ \dfrac{1}{2}\ \dfrac{2}{2}\ \dfrac{3}{2}\ \dfrac{4}{2}\ \dfrac{5}{2}\ \dfrac{6}{2}\ \dfrac{7}{2}\ \dfrac{8}{2}\ \dfrac{9}{2}\ \dfrac{10}{2}\ \dfrac{11}{2}\ \dfrac{12}{2}\cdots$

Scale of ones $\quad 0 \qquad 1 \qquad 2 \qquad 3 \qquad 4 \qquad 5 \qquad 6 \cdots$

Generalizations such as the following should be formulated in the early stages of interpreting examples of the type above:

(1) Any number divided by $\tfrac{1}{2}$ is equal to that number multiplied by 2, and (2) any number divided by $\tfrac{1}{5}$ is equal to that number multiplied by 5. Dividing by a unit fraction is achieved by inverting the fraction and then multiplying the dividend by the inverted fraction.

Examples in Which the Dividend Is a Decimal Integer and the Divisor Is a Common Fraction Larger Than a Unit Fraction: $6 \div \tfrac{2}{3}$

Following the same type of inferential reasoning as used with the unit fraction, we have the following referent example:

$$\frac{6}{1)\ 6}$$

When the divisor is 3 times as small and the dividend is constant,

$$\frac{}{\tfrac{1}{3})\ 6}$$

the quotient will be 3 times as large.

$$\frac{3 \times 6 = 18}{\tfrac{1}{3})\quad 6}$$

The divisor of this example is 2 times as large as $\tfrac{1}{3}$,

$$\tfrac{2}{3})\ \overline{6}$$

and the dividends of the two examples are the same. Therefore, the quotient will be 2 times as small as for $6 \div \tfrac{1}{3}$:

$$\frac{\frac{3 \times 6}{2} = \frac{18}{2} = 9}{\tfrac{2}{3})\quad 6}$$

We may note the generalization: *Dividing by a fraction is achieved by inverting the fraction and then multiplying the dividend by the inverted fraction.*

The inverted fraction is often called the *reciprocal* or the *multiplicative inverse.* Every whole number except 0 has a reciprocal, a value which when multiplied by that number produces 1. For example, the reciprocal of 6 is $\tfrac{1}{6}$. Similarly, the reciprocal of $\tfrac{2}{3}$ is $\tfrac{3}{2}$. We may generalize this idea by saying that, when a and b are whole numbers excluding 0,

$$\frac{a}{b} \times \frac{b}{a} = 1$$

ADDITION AND SUBTRACTION

The addition and subtraction operations with common fractions present somewhat different problems from those experienced with multiplication and division. Once again, however, the principal source of difficulty appears to be with language arts aspects, that is, with the fraction expression.

MAIN CONCEPTS UNDERLYING ADDITION AND SUBTRACTION WITH COMMON FRACTION NUMBERS

(1) The concepts basic to the addition and subtraction operations with whole numbers apply when adding or subtracting common fraction numbers.

(2) Only terms expressing values on the same number scale can be added or subtracted. Fraction number values from different fraction number scales must be transformed into values on the same scale.

(3) Recognizing that fraction numbers are "indicated divisions" is basic to deriving the technique for adding or subtracting them.

(4)   The process of regrouping fraction number values to whole number values or whole number values to fraction values is based upon the characteristics of fraction notation and not upon those of decimal whole-number notation.

Examples in Which Fractions to be Added or Subtracted Are Similar (Are Elements within the Same Fraction Scale)

Consider the following division situations: $2\overline{)4} + 2\overline{)6} = ?$ Since the size of the quotient depends directly upon the size of the dividend when the divisor is constant, we can combine these examples into a single division situation as follows: $2\overline{)4} + 2\overline{)6}$ is the same as $2\overline{)10}$ or 5. Hence,

$$\frac{4}{2} + \frac{6}{2} = \frac{10}{2} \text{ or } 5$$

In this example, we may note the *distributive property of division* with respect to addition. $10 \div 2$ may be interpreted as:

$$(4 + 6) \div 2 = (4 \div 2) + (6 \div 2)$$

Letting a, b, and c stand for whole numbers and c does not equal 0, we may say: $(a + b) \div c = (a \div c) + (b \div c)$. On the basis of this idea, we may conclude that *to add two or more similar fractions, we merely add their numerators and divide that sum by the common denominator*. However, if the sums are to be expressed in simplest form, there are five different types of such example situations:

Type 1   The sums are nonreducible.

$$\frac{1}{3} + \frac{1}{3} = \frac{2}{3}$$

Type 2   The sum is reducible to an integer.

$$\frac{1}{3} + \frac{2}{3} = \frac{3}{3} \text{ or } 1$$

Type 3   The sum is reducible to lower terms.

$$\frac{1}{4} + \frac{1}{4} = \frac{2}{4} = \frac{1}{2}$$

Type 4   The sum is reducible to a mixed number with a nonreducible fraction.

$$\frac{3}{5} + \frac{3}{5} = \frac{6}{5} = 1\frac{1}{5}$$

Type 5 The sum is reducible to a mixed number with a reducible fraction.

$$\frac{5}{6} + \frac{5}{6} = \frac{10}{6} = 1\frac{4}{6} = 1\frac{2}{3}$$

The fifth type of addition frequently produces a typical error which is really an error of expression, that is, the value that the student has in mind is incorrectly expressed:

$$\frac{10}{6} = 1\frac{4}{6} = \frac{2}{3}$$

Examples with subtraction of similar fractions present comparable types, except for instances where the subtrahend equals or exceeds the minuend. Consider the following examples:

Type 1 The difference is zero.

$$\frac{1}{3} - \frac{1}{3} = 0$$

The zero must be written if only fractions are involved, but it must *not* be written if these occur with mixed numbers. For example,

$$\frac{1}{3} - \frac{1}{3} = 0, \quad 4\frac{1}{3} - 2\frac{1}{3} = 2 \text{ and not } 20$$

Type 2 The remainder is nonreducible.

$$\frac{4}{7} - \frac{3}{7} = \frac{1}{7}$$

This may occur with mixed numbers requiring regrouping from the whole number to the fraction in the minuend:

$$13\frac{1}{5} - 3\frac{2}{5} = 9\frac{4}{5}$$

Type 3 The remainder is reducible to lower terms.

$$\frac{3}{4} - \frac{1}{4} = \frac{2}{4} = \frac{1}{2}$$

This may likewise occur with mixed numbers requiring regrouping in the minuend:

$$12\frac{3}{8} - 9\frac{5}{8} = 2\frac{6}{8} = 2\frac{3}{4}$$

Type 4 This situation occurs when a mixed number is subtracted from a whole number. Regrouping is required in the minuend:

$$16 - 6\frac{1}{4} = 9\frac{3}{4}$$

Comparable types of examples occur when we add or subtract dissimilar fractions. The first step is to transform the terms into elements on a common-fraction scale. There are three general types of these situations:

1. One of the divisors is a multiple of the other divisor, for example, $\frac{2}{3}$ and $\frac{1}{6}$ or $\frac{1}{4}$ and $\frac{3}{8}$, and so forth.

2. The divisors have a factor or factors other than 1 in common. Consider $\frac{1}{9}$ and $\frac{1}{6}$. One ninth factors into

$$\frac{1 \times 1}{3 \times 3}$$

and $\frac{1}{6}$ factors into

$$\frac{1 \times 1}{2 \times 3}$$

The factors are

$$(3 \times 3) \times 2$$

Hence, the least common denominator is 18, which is the product of the common factors.

3. The divisors have no common factor other than 1. Hence, the scale to which they must be transformed is identified by the product of the given divisors, for example, $\frac{1}{4}$ and $\frac{1}{3}$ or $\frac{2}{7}$ and $\frac{3}{8}$, and so forth.

Another procedure for finding the lowest common denominator is to locate the first point of intersection of the sets that are multiples of the denominators. For example, let Set A be the multiples of 8. Let Set B be the multiples of 6.

$$\begin{array}{ll} \dfrac{1}{8} & A = \{8, 16, 24, 32, 40,\ldots\} \\[2ex] +\dfrac{1}{6} & B = \{6, 12, 18, 24,\ldots\} \\[1ex] \hline \end{array}$$

$$A \cap B = \{24, 48, 72,\ldots\}$$

The first point of intersection of the multiples 8 and 6 is 24.

The major sources of difficulty with the addition or subtraction of dissimilar fractions are: (1) those of transforming the numbers to express equivalent values on a common scale, and (2) expressing answers in their simplest form. In subtraction situations when fractions are parts of mixed numbers, an additional difficulty is experienced when regrouping from the integer to the fraction is necessary. These aspects need careful attention.

Equality of Ratios

The equality of ratios is used as a powerful instrument in computing. It is sometimes referred to as "the rule of three." In an equation such as

$$\frac{2}{4} = \frac{n}{8} \quad \text{or} \quad 2 : 4 : : n : 8$$

if three of the number values are known, the fourth number value can be computed. This is accomplished by a procedure which amounts to multiplying a fraction by its reciprocal.

$$\frac{2 \times 8}{4 \times n}$$

A comparable technique is sometimes expressed as "the product of the means (inside terms) equals the product of the extremes (outside terms)."

$$2 : 4 : : n : 8$$

9.11   NONFRACTION EXPRESSIONS in FRACTION FORM

There are symbols having the appearance of fractions which are not intended to represent fraction ideas. For example, in the ocular profession, measures of visual acuity are presented as a comparison between a referent measure and the actual performance of the patient. The referent is commonly a standard target viewed at a distance of 20 feet. Targets calibrated for sight at nearer and farther distances are exposed in making the measure of the patient's acuity. If the measurement results in evidence of the ability to see at 20 feet what would normally be expected to be seen at 15 feet, the result is reported as 20/15. If, on the other hand, what is seen at 20 feet is what normally would be seen at 100 feet, the record is stated as 20/100. Such symbols are not intended to be "indicated divisions." They should not be transformed into percentage measures — they are designed for comparison purposes only.

Similarly, in music scripts a fraction-like symbol is used to indicate the composition of a measure. For example, symbolic expressions resembling fractions such as: $\frac{2}{4}$, $\frac{3}{4}$, $\frac{4}{4}$, $\frac{6}{8}$, and so forth, occur. They have a fraction reference in that the lower numeral (denominator) indicates the type of note that is used to establish the measure, and the upper numeral (numerator) indicates the number of such units that are found in the measure. This, however, ends the similarity with common-fraction numerals. The music symbol is not representative of a quotient value.

There are numerous other symbolic signs in the music language having fraction implications. An examination of them and of their service to that form of expression illustrates a convincing argument as to the need for fraction ideas in human behavior. (See Chap. 6.)

9.12   USE of PICTORIAL ILLUSTRATIONS

In the preceding discussion, pictorial illustrations have not been used. This was done deliberately in order to stress the process of inferential thinking. The idea of fractions as fragments resulting from fracturing is readily conceived by everyone. The process of refining such simple everyday experiencing into a powerful instrument for serving human needs is not so readily conceived. Its development is a matter of the "mathematics of algebra," in the sense of determining part-whole and whole-part relationships.

Postulating the equality of fragments in order to provide the unit fraction as a referent measure is an initial step in this development. Then, utilizing the unit fraction in the same manner that the unit whole is used to produce a graded scale of measurements provides us with innumerable number scales each capable of contributing something which the others cannot contribute.

Once the properties are made clear, it is possible to sense that there are properties of dependence that characterize the computational operations with any and all of these scales without resort to extraneous illustrations.

As with other aspects of mathematical development, the language forms and techniques needed for expressing and communicating ideas concerning fractions need careful consideration. Having an idea is one thing. Expressing it effectively in communication may be quite different.

There is no dearth of illustrative material for demonstrating the ideas of fractions or of fraction scaling. However, the so-called demonstrations must not be permitted to replace the creating of the ideas. The following illustrations taken from classroom discussions indicate that children are aware of fractions, and that they can express that awareness in many ways.

Understanding ideas and applying them go hand in hand. Ideas that are meaningful in mathematics may be applied to new settings and new meanings may be created. Similarly, ideas that are sensed and applied within the pattern of experiencing become powerful in behavior.

In teaching concepts, simple experiences should be selected that can be interpreted readily. Abstract situations should grow out of these simple meanings. For example, the following are types of situations that have been used by teachers to facilitate meanings of a whole number divided by a proper fraction. Miss Ross asked the children to write sentences using mathematical symbols as the ideas were developed:

"Here are 5 sheets of paper. To how many people can we give these if each person is given 1 sheet of paper?

$$\frac{5}{1)\,5}$$

"If we give each person ½ sheet of paper, to how many people can the paper be given? The paper was torn to represent halves, and the activity was demonstrated."

$$\frac{5 \times 2}{\frac{1}{2})\,5}$$

Miss Ross then continued: "If we give each person ¼ sheet of paper, to how many people could the paper be distributed?"

$$\frac{5 \times 4}{\frac{1}{4})\,5}$$

Mr. Stone challenged his children to develop examples that illustrate division of common fraction examples such as $\frac{1}{2})\,\overline{6}$ and $\frac{2}{3})\,\overline{8}$. The following are some of the illustrations presented by his class.

Sally said, "I have drawn a picture of a pie. You could never cut a pie so the pieces were exactly alike. However, they are enough alike that I can write my problem. I have shown the pie cut into 8 equal parts. If we served each person 1 of the 8 pieces, we could serve 8 persons. If we had 2 pies and cut each of them into eighths, we could serve 16 persons, and 3 pies would serve 24 persons."

$$\frac{1 \times 8 = 8}{\frac{1}{8})\,1} \qquad \frac{2 \times 8}{\frac{1}{8})\,2} \qquad \frac{3 \times 8}{\frac{1}{8})\,3}$$

Laura's illustration showed a rectangular dish filled with gelatin, and the contents were cut into 4 equal parts. She said, "My sentence is a picture. I have shown a pan of gelatin cut into 4 equal parts. Each

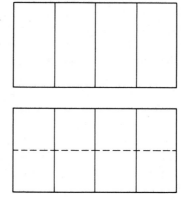

person was to have been given 1 piece. We could serve 4 persons. But, when we were ready to sit down to dinner, company came and suddenly we needed to serve 8 instead of 4. I cut each of the 4 pieces into halves, and there was dessert for all of us.

$$\frac{1}{4} \div 2 = \frac{1}{4} \times \frac{1}{2} = \frac{1}{8}$$

The teacher asked the children to think of other ways that Laura could have written her mathematical sentence. The following were suggested:

$$2)\overline{\tfrac{1}{4}} \text{ or } \tfrac{1}{8} \qquad \tfrac{1}{2} \times \tfrac{1}{4} = \tfrac{1}{8} \qquad 4)\overline{1} \div 2 = \tfrac{1}{8}$$

Denny offered this problem: If we had $10 to give away, we could give each person $1, and 10 people could be given the money.

$$\frac{10}{1)\ 10}$$

We could give each person 50 cents or half a dollar, and then twice as many people could share the fortune.

$$\frac{10 \times 2 = 20}{\tfrac{1}{2})\ 10}$$

If we gave each person one dime — $\frac{1}{10}$ of a dollar — then 100 people could be given the money.

$$\frac{10 \times 10 = 100}{\tfrac{1}{10})\ 10}$$

If we gave each person one penny — $\frac{1}{100}$ of a dollar — then 1000 people could be given the money.

$$\frac{10 \times 100 = 1000}{\tfrac{1}{100})\ 10}$$

Bill asked Denny, "If we gave each person a quarter, how many people would get money?"

Denny knew that Bill usually asked this type of question! He answered, "That depends, Bill. Do you mean a 'quarter of the money' or do you mean 'a quarter of a dollar?'"

A class was studying multiplication with fractions. They were illustrating the operation as follows:

$$\tfrac{3}{4} \times \tfrac{7}{8} = ?$$

A rectangle was drawn to represent the whole or referent. It was divided vertically into 8 equal sections, which were numbered as indicated. Since only 7 of the sections were included in the multiplicand, 1 of the 8 sections was crossed off.

Because they were concerned with a fourth part of the sections, they divided the referent horizontally into 4 equal sections as shown in the

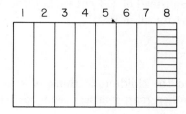

diagram. Since they were concerned with only three of those divisions, the one was crossed out. They noted that the rectangle had been divided into 32 equal parts and 21 of those parts were not marked out. Hence, their picture showed that

$$\frac{3}{4} \text{ of } \frac{7}{8} = \frac{21}{32}$$

Next they pictured a similar illustration of $\frac{2}{3}$ of $\frac{5}{8}$. By the time that was done, several pupils had observed that the answer appeared to

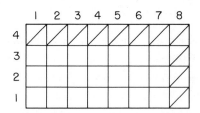

show that the product of the divisors gave the divisor of the answer and the product of the dividends gave the dividend of the answer. They pointed this out. Then the teacher asked them to demonstrate that their observation would hold true for other similar situations. This they did as follows:

$$1 \times \frac{7}{8} = \frac{7}{8}$$

$$\frac{1}{4} \times \frac{7}{8} =$$

must be 4 times as small because the multiplier is 4 times as small. Hence,

$$\frac{1}{4} \times \frac{7}{8} = \frac{7}{32}$$

$$\frac{3}{4} \times \frac{7}{8} =$$

must be 3 times as large because the multiplier is 3 times as large. There-fore,

$$\frac{3}{4} \times \frac{7}{8} = \frac{21}{32}$$

The class then tried to solve the following mathematical puzzles:

(1) There are 30 seconds in a half of a minute. How many thirty-seconds are there in a whole thing?

(2) The month of July has 31 days. Why then is the Fourth of July only one day?

(3) If each person is given a quarter, how many people can share $8?

ILLUSTRATIVE LESSONS

The following illustrative lessons are presented in this chapter:

Lesson 1. Concepts concerning common fraction expressions
Lesson 2. Concepts concerning common fraction expressions
Lesson 3. Multiplication of common fractions — introductory lesson
Lesson 4. Multiplication of common fractions — cancellation
Lesson 5. Division of common fractions — introductory lesson
Lesson 6. Division of common fractions

Lessons 1 and 2 indicate interest and readiness on the part of the learners. Young children like precision and accuracy. When the type of thinking demonstrated in these lessons is present in the child's experiencing, it facilitates sensing reasons for achieving accuracy with computation.

Lessons 3 and 4 indicate the type of generalizations that children formulate when they are challenged to interpret the concepts under-lying multiplication of common fractions. In terms of behavior, the concepts and interpretation of relationships are basically more important than computation. However, understanding of the relationships and skill in computation go hand in hand. Understanding facilitates achieve-ment of skill with computation.

Lessons 5 and 6 indicate the nature of thinking that children do when they have a fine background of the concepts and skills that are prereq-uisite for the instructional unit on division of common fractions.

Lesson 1
CONCEPTS CONCERNING COMMON FRACTION
EXPRESSIONS
Grade One Class

The children had been discussing measuring things, and one child mentioned that he divided a piece of toast into halves. The teacher asked what was meant by one-half.

Johnnie: One-half means half of something.

Marie: Like half an apple.

Others: And half the children in our room. And half an hour. And half a day.

Teacher: I have a piece of paper in my hand. What would one-half of the piece be?

Johnnie: Tear the paper in (into) two pieces.

[Teacher tore the paper into two pieces so that one piece was very small and the other very large.]

Johnnie: [Laughed disgustedly.] Not like that. You have to make the pieces alike. I'll show you. [He folded the paper into two pieces that were alike as far as he could see, tore them, and said . . .] See, this is what I mean.

Karen: But the pieces still aren't just alike. Look, the edges on this piece are different. It would be better if you cut the paper.

Ronnie: The pieces still wouldn't be *just alike*. The edges aren't the same.

Teacher: Do you think that Larry could divide a piece of toast so that the pieces were just alike?

Larry: No.

Karen: I don't think so, but I'll go home and try.

Others: I'll try, too.

[The following day, the lesson opened with many of the children in the group relating their experiences in trying to divide things equally.]

Johnnie: I tried to cut a piece of toast into two parts that were alike. It can't be done.

Ronnie: You could never make the two parts just alike. The crumbs aren't the same.

Larry: You can try and try, and it won't work.

Others: You just couldn't do it. It's impossible. It won't work no matter how many times you try. [And so on. . . .]

The lesson continued with a discussion of things that can come the nearest to dividing equally and things that would be most difficult to divide equally.

Lesson 2
CONCEPTS CONCERNING COMMON FRACTION EXPRESSIONS
Grade Two Class

Purpose of lesson: To lead the children to refine their concepts concerning common fraction expressions, and to introduce the written expression of unit fractions. Awareness of dividing things and concepts of one-half were not new to the group of children.

Materials used: Scissors and paper. However, in the following lessons, many types of materials were used.

Lesson Procedure

Teacher: You said that we couldn't divide our cake for our Halloween party so that each person would have exactly the same amount. You said that the teacher should cut the cake so that the servings were as equal as the teacher could cut them. What things do you think would be hard to divide into parts that are just alike?

Gail: Our cake!

Denny: It would be impossible for us to cut a pencil into two parts that were just alike.

Marian: We couldn't divide a book into two parts that were the same. One would have a front cover, and the other part would have a back cover.

Allen: We can't divide one of our tiles into two parts that are exactly the same. I don't think that anyone could divide one of our tiles so that the two pieces would be exactly alike.

John: My mother cuts a grapefruit into two parts for Daddy and me. She gives one piece to Daddy and one piece to me. Sometimes I get the bigger piece, and sometimes Daddy tries to trade his smaller piece for my bigger piece.

Peggy: My mother cuts the pieces so they are just alike.

John: I don't think your mother could do that, Peggy. You couldn't cut a grapefruit so that the two pieces would be exactly alike.

Gretchen: One piece is always a tiny bit different from the other piece.

Bonnie: I think that the teacher could cut that piece of paper she has on my desk so that she could have two pieces that are exactly alike.

Teacher: How do you think that I should make them just the same, Bonnie?

Bonnie: You should measure so that the two pieces will be alike.

Alexander: You could fold the paper right down the middle and then tear it very carefully so that the two pieces will be the same. [Teacher folded the paper as was suggested and tore the sheet into two parts that were as equal as she could make them with the given procedure. The children examined the parts. There was considerable debate concerning whether the two parts were "exactly alike."]

Sandra: The two pieces look alike, but see how the edges on this piece [pointed to one piece] are not just like the edges on this piece [pointed to the other piece]. You couldn't tear a piece of paper so the two pieces would be *exactly alike*. You could try and try, but the pieces wouldn't be *just the same*.

Arnold: They would be almost the same.

Roger: They would be more alike than if you tried to divide a piece of cake.

Gail: Or an apple.

Allen: Or a raisin.

Peggy: Or a piece of toast.

Teacher: [Took another sheet.] I'll fold this sheet and then cut down the middle of the fold so that the two pieces will be as equal as I can make them.

[Teacher did so.]

Marian: That is better. They are *almost* exactly alike.

Teacher: I should like to tell you what I have done by writing it on the blackboard. See if you can read the story that I write.

[Teacher wrote on the blackboard: "I had one piece of paper. I cut it into two parts. The parts were the same in size, so far as I could tell." The children, with the assistance of the teacher, read the statement.]

Teacher: We use many languages. One of the simplest languages that we use is number language. I am going to write what we did in number language. Do you think that you can read the story when I write it in number language?

[Teacher wrote $\frac{1}{2}$.]

Gretchen: Does that tell about what you wrote with all the words we read?

Teacher: Yes, it does, Gretchen. This line [she pointed to the division sign] says "divided into." See if you can read what I've written as I point to each part.

[Teacher pointed as the children read:]

Class: One divided into two equal parts. [The expression "equal parts" was facilitated by the teacher.]

Billy: That is surely a short way to tell about it.

Sandra: It surely saves a lot of paper.

Billy: You mean blackboard and writing.

Teacher: Would each of you like to try to divide a sheet of paper into two parts that are as much alike as you can make them?

The lesson ended with this activity. Later, concepts of one third, two thirds, one fourth, and so forth, were developed.

Lesson 3
MULTIPLICATION OF COMMON FRACTIONS —
INTRODUCTORY LESSON
Grade Six Class

Purpose of lesson: To challenge the child to discover, to refine, and to state some of the ideas that underlie the multiplication of common fractions.

Background of class: The group of children had a good background of concepts with regard for multiplier-multiplicand-product relationships and of interpreting the meaning of common fraction expressions.

Lesson Procedure

Teacher: Today, would you like to start a new topic in mathematics?

Class: Yes. [Various topics were suggested.] How about multiplication of common fractions?

John: We've been talking about common fractions, and you said that soon we could start multiplication of common fractions. I think I know how to multiply common fractions.

Teacher: Let us check your ideas about multiplication. [Teacher wrote on the board, and the children stated the products as she wrote them:]

(a)	(b)	(c)	(d)	(e)
8	8	8	8	8
× 1 6	× 8	× 4	× 2	× 1
1 2 8	6 4	3 2	1 6	8

Jim: The multiplicands are all alike, and the multipliers decrease as you go from Example (a) through Example (e).

Connie: As you move from (a) through (e) each multiplier grows 2 times as small and each product grows 2 times as small.

Jim: And moving from (e) through (a), the opposite is true. Each multiplier becomes 2 times as large, and each product becomes 2 times as large as the one next to it. The products vary in the same way as the multipliers.

Susie: I think the words *direct proportion* are better than saying *in the same way*. We learned the words when we were studying multiplication the other week.

Tommy: In the examples on the board, the multiplicands are constant. The multipliers vary and the products vary in direct proportion with the multipliers.

Teacher: You have expressed the idea very well. Now, let us review the meaning of common fraction expressions. What does $\frac{1}{3}$ mean to you, Donald?

Donald: One divided into 3 equal parts. One divided by 3 — just as the numbers and division sign say.

Teacher: What about the expression $\frac{5}{6}$?

Gail: Five divided into 6 equal parts. Five divided by 6.

Tommy: You make the five 6 times as small when you write the division sign and the 6.

Helen: In the fraction $\frac{5}{6}$, the 5 is the dividend and the 6 is the divisor.

Teacher: Let us look at these examples that I am writing on the board. [Teacher wrote these two examples:]

$$\begin{array}{cc} 8 & 8 \\ \times\ 1 & \times\ \dfrac{1}{2} \\ \hline 8 & \end{array}$$

Teacher: The multiplicands of these two examples are the same. The multiplier of the example at the right is how many times as small as that of the example at the left?

John: Twice as small. The product will be 4. The product has to be twice as small as 8 × 1.

Teacher: That is correct. What about these examples?

[Teacher added the following two examples so that these four examples appeared on the board:]

$$\begin{array}{cccc} 8 & 8 & 8 & 8 \\ \times\ 1 & \times\ \dfrac{1}{2} & \times\ \dfrac{1}{4} & \times\ \dfrac{1}{8} \\ \hline 8 & 4 & & \end{array}$$

Bert: In $\frac{1}{4} \times 8$, the multiplier is 4 times as small as in 1×8. The product would be 2.

Eddie: And in $\frac{1}{8} \times 8$, the multiplier is 8 times as small as in 1×8. The product would be 8 times as small as the product of 1×8. The product is 1.

Helen: I see something interesting. Look at our products. They are smaller than the multiplicand when we multiplied by $\frac{1}{2}$ and $\frac{1}{4}$ and $\frac{1}{8}$.

Bert: That sounds strange. Usually our answer was larger than the multiplicand. It has to be when you multiply by whole numbers.

Donald: That isn't true, Bert, when you multiply by 1. Any number times 1 is that number.

Bert: Of course, but I meant any number larger than 1. And what about 0? A number multiplied by 0 is 0.

Frances: Is it always true that your answer is smaller than the multiplicand when you multiply by a common fraction?

Teacher: Test your ideas with these examples.

[Teacher wrote on board:]

$$\begin{array}{ccccc} 9 & 6 & 6 & 1\ 2 & 1\ 2 \\ \times\ \dfrac{1}{2} & \times\ 1 & \times\ \dfrac{1}{2} & \times\ 1 & \times\ \dfrac{1}{2} \\ \hline & & & & \end{array}$$

Mary: In $\frac{1}{2} \times 9$, your multiplier is $\frac{1}{2}$ as large as if it were 1. The product will be $\frac{1}{2}$ as large as 9. Nine divided by 2 equals $4\frac{1}{2}$.

Paul: In the next two examples, 1×6 and $\frac{1}{2} \times 6$, the multiplicands are the same. $\frac{1}{2} \times 6$ will be 3. All you need to do is to divide 6 by 2.

Beth: And in the next two examples, the same is true. $\frac{1}{2} \times 12$ is 6.

Teacher: We can also write the examples this way. Both ways are good, but you will use this way most of the time.

[Teacher wrote on the board:]

$$\begin{array}{c} 9 \\ \times \frac{1}{4} \\ \hline \end{array} \qquad \frac{1}{4} \times 9 \qquad \begin{array}{c} 8 \\ \times \frac{1}{3} \\ \hline \end{array} \qquad \frac{1}{3} \times 8$$

Jim: It is easier to see which is your dividend and which is your divisor when you write the numbers across. That way will be easy.

Teacher: You have made a good start. Let us end the lesson with your telling what you have discovered to be true about the multiplication of common fractions.

Connie: Multiplying a common fraction is different from multiplying by a whole number. You have to think about division too.

Susie: When you multiply by $\frac{1}{2}$, you really divide by 2. Multiplication turns out to be dividing.

Helen: When you multiply by $\frac{1}{4}$, you really divide by 4.

Bert: When you multiply by $\frac{1}{8}$, you really divide by 8.

Teacher: If we use L to stand for the value of any given number we want to use, what would the answer to this problem be?

[Teacher wrote on the board:]

$$L \times \frac{1}{2}$$

Bert: Your answer would be L divided by 2. But that doesn't seem like other work we've had.

Teacher: What would be the answer to that problem if the value of L is 10?

Gail: It would be 5. Ten divided by 2 is 5.

Teacher: What would be the answer if L equals 24?

The lesson continued with several other examples of generalizations concerning a whole number multiplied by a unit fraction.

Lesson 4
MULTIPLICATION OF COMMON FRACTIONS —
CANCELLATION
Grade Six Class

Purpose of lesson: To lead the children to interpret cancellation in multiplication of common fraction expressions.

Background of children: The children had an excellent background of concepts that are prerequisite for this lesson. These concepts are the following: (a) divisor-dividend-quotient relationships when the dividend and divisor are variable and the quotient is kept constant; (b) meaning of common fraction expressions; (c) concepts of multiplier-multiplicand-product relationships; and (d) understanding of multiplication of common fraction examples in which cancellation does not occur.

Lesson Procedure

Teacher: [Presented a brief review of types of examples that had been developed during the previous lesson. See Lesson 3.] As I write a set of examples on the blackboard, see how many things you can discover concerning them.
[Teacher wrote the following examples on the blackboard:]

$$\begin{array}{cccc}
\text{(a)} & \text{(b)} & \text{(c)} & \text{(d)} \\
2 & 2 & 2 & 2 \\
\hline
1)\ 2 & 2) & 4) &)\ 1\ 6
\end{array}$$

Connie: The quotients in the examples are constant, but the divisors and dividends change. You didn't finish the examples.
Teacher: I had a reason for not finishing! Look at Example (b). Its divisor is how many times as large in number value as that of Example (a)?
David: The divisor of Example (b) is twice as large as that of Example (a).
Connie: The dividend should be 4. The dividend of Example (b) is 2 times as large as that of Example (a).
Donald: When you make the divisor 2 times as large, you have to make the dividend 2 times as large.
Helen: Then the dividend of Example (c) has to be 8.
Marjorie: And the divisor of Example (d) should be 8.
Teacher: Compare Example (a) and Example (d).
Susie: The divisor of Example (a) is 8 times as small as the divisor of Example (d), and the dividend of Example (a) is 8 times as small as that of Example (d).
Bert: And the quotients are constant.
Teacher: Can you state the idea that underlies these examples?
Jack: When you want to keep the quotient constant, you can change the divisor and the dividend in the same way. When you make the dividend smaller, you have to make the divisor smaller in the same way; and when you increase the divisor, you have to increase the dividend in the same way.

Bert: We've had that in multiplication. You call it direct proportion when it changes in the same way.

Gene: If you continued making dividends and divisors 2 times as large, the quotient would always remain constant.

Teacher: How would the idea work in this problem? We want to keep the value of the quotient constant. [Teacher wrote on the blackboard:]

$$
20 \overline{) \,\, 40 \text{ cups of punch}}^{\,2 \text{ cups of punch}} \qquad 40 \overline{) \,\, \text{cups of punch}}^{\,2 \text{ cups of punch}}
$$

The divisor stands for the number of people who are going to share the punch represented by the dividend figure. The sharing is to be as nearly equal as possible.

David: You'll have to change the dividend in direct proportion with the divisor. The dividend will be 80 cups of punch.

Helen: It wouldn't be easy to share the punch equally. It would be difficult to measure that accurately.

Teacher: Can you think of any other examples in which the value of the quotient is kept constant and the divisor and the dividend vary? [The children were given a few minutes to think of examples. Some children used scratch paper and pencils in making up and figuring out their examples.]

Tommy: I have an example. [Tommy went to the blackboard and wrote his example and then explained it.]

$$
\text{number of people} \overline{) \,\, \text{cupcakes}}^{\,\text{number per person}}
$$

If we serve cupcakes when our mothers come to school, the more parents that come, the more cupcakes we'll need if we serve each parent one cupcake.

Jim: [Jim wrote his example on the blackboard and then explained it.]

$$
\text{speed of travel} \overline{) \,\, \text{distance traveled}}^{\,\text{time}}
$$

If I should go on a trip, I'd fly. If the speed of travel is twice as fast, I'd go twice as far in the same amount of time.

Susie: What if you go by bus instead of by plane? Then you decrease speed and decrease distance traveled if you keep time constant.

Jim: I prefer to fly — I could go faster and farther than if I travel by bus.

Helen: I'd rather go by bus, and take my time.

Eddie: [Eddie wrote his example on the blackboard and explained his idea.]

$$
2 \overline{) \,\, 2 \text{ ice cream bars}} \qquad 6 \overline{) \,\, 6 \text{ ice cream bars}}
$$

My mother gave me money for 2 ice cream bars for John and me. Before we started eating them, 4 friends joined us and we didn't want to eat and not give them any of our ice cream. My mother felt generous so she gave me money for 4 more ice cream bars, so we could keep the quotient constant. My mother isn't always that generous!

[There were other examples, and the teacher suggested that the children keep their scratch paper showing their illustrations and that during their mathematics period the next day they could write their examples for a bulletin board display.]

Teacher: You understand the idea very well. Now let us use that idea in multiplication of common fractions. Remember in a common fraction example such as

$\dfrac{3}{4}$ The 3 is the dividend.
The 4 is the divisor.

[Teacher wrote on the blackboard: $\dfrac{7}{8} \times 4$.]

Teacher: Who discovers something about how we could change the divisor and the dividend?

Jean: You can make the dividend 4 times as small and the divisor 4 times as small, just as we did with whole numbers.

Tommy: You could change the dividend and the divisor in direct proportion.

[Teacher showed procedure by crossing out the 4 and crossing out the 8 and writing a 2 under it, like this:]

$$\frac{7}{\cancel{8}_2} \times \cancel{4}^{\,1} \quad \frac{\text{dividend made 4 times as small}}{\text{divisor made 4 times as small}}$$

[The children completed the example.]

Teacher: How could we check to see if we are right?

John: We could multiply it out the long way. Then we would have 28 divided by 8 equals 3 and $\frac{4}{8}$. Three and four-eighths equal $3\frac{1}{2}$. That is a long way. The other way is much easier.

Teacher: When we take the short cut and change the dividend and the divisor in direct proportion, we say that we cancel. Do you think that canceling will save you work?

Bert: I should say so! Who would want to do it the long way?

Teacher: What is true in these examples?

[Teacher wrote on board:]

$$\frac{5}{12} \times 12$$

$$\frac{4}{15} \times 15$$

Gail: It would be a lot harder to multiply 5 by 12 and then divide it by 12 than to cancel. The answer is 5.

Gene: Twelve times 5 is 60, and 60 divided by 12 is 5. That is a harder way.

Jack: The answer to the next example is 15. You can cancel.

Gene: You mean the answer is 4. You cancel the 15s.

Jack: That's what I meant.

Dick: Would it work with this example?

[Dick wrote on board:]

$$\frac{2}{3} \times 10$$

Jack: Of course it wouldn't, Dick. Three won't go into 10 an even number of times, and it won't work.

Bert: It would work, wouldn't it? But it would be harder to do the multiplication.

Jack: Let's try it.

Teacher: Eugene is right. Unless the division comes out evenly, the multiplication would be difficult. We'll use cancellation only with examples in which the division is even. I suggest that you wait until you have had more work with multiplication of common fractions before you try out Eugene's idea.

The period ended with the children's working some examples such as the following:]

$$\frac{1}{3} \times 18 \qquad \frac{1}{4} \times 16 \qquad \frac{2}{3} \times \frac{6}{7} \qquad \frac{7}{8} \times 6$$

Several examples of this type were given to see if the children could generalize and find the common divisor when the common divisor was not apparent. They were able to proceed with very little help from the teacher.

Lesson 5
DIVISION OF COMMON FRACTIONS —
INTRODUCTORY LESSON
Grade Five Class

Purpose of lesson: To introduce division of common fractions and to lead the children to discover some of the main ideas underlying this unit of instruction.

Background of children: The children had developed fine concepts concerning divisor-dividend-quotient relationships and meaning of common fraction expressions. Their language kept pace with their concepts.

Lesson Procedure

[The following charts were pinned on the chalkboard at the beginning of the lesson:]

Chart 1

number of pupils) total number of examples incorrect

Chart 2

(a)	(b)	(c)	(d)	(e)
$8)\overline{\ 8\ }$ 1	$4)\overline{\ 8\ }$ 2	$2)\overline{\ 8\ }$ 4	$1)\overline{\ 8\ }$ 8	$\frac{1}{2})\overline{\ 8\ }$

Teacher: Looking at Chart 1, let us say that the dividend is constant. What would the quotient tell, and what is true concerning the relationship of the divisor, dividend, and quotient?

Joseph: The quotient tells the average number of examples incorrect for each pupil. If the dividend is constant, the more pupils there are, the fewer the errors for each pupil. The fewer the pupils, the bigger the number for each child.

David: Let's figure that problem for our class on the next test. Some pupils make no errors and others make many mistakes.

Teacher: Would you like to count the total number of examples incorrect and make a problem for the class to solve, David?

David: Yes.

[Arrangement was made for David to prepare his problem.]

Teacher: What can you tell about Chart 2?

Susanna: We've had examples like that before except that one with the $\frac{1}{2}$. The dividends are constant. When the divisors decrease, the quotients increase. When the divisors increase, the quotients decrease.

Matilda: When the divisor is made 2 times as small (in number value), the quotient is 2 times as large in value.

Kenneth: What about the $\frac{1}{2}$ as a divisor?

Paul: The quotient would have to be larger than if you divided by one (unit). The smaller the divisor, the larger the quotient if the dividend stays the same.

Eugene: I know the quotient. It would have to be 16. The divisor is $\frac{1}{2}$. One-half is twice as small in (number) value as 1, so the quotient would have to be twice as large as if you divided by 1.

Sara: Then if we kept making the divisor smaller and smaller, the quotient would keep getting larger and larger. What if you make the divisor one thousandth?

Tim: Then your quotient would be really large — 1000 times as large as if you divided by 1 (unit). Teacher, could such a thing be true?

Teacher: What do you think, Harold?

Harold: If the dividend stays the same, it would have to be true, but it surely seems funny to get such large answers.

Teacher: In these examples, I shall change the divisor, and we'll keep the dividend constant. See how many things you can discover concerning division by a common fraction.   •

[Teacher wrote examples on the chalkboard. In each case, he wrote the example using the unit 1 as a divisor, and then changed the divisor to a unit fraction. The children then interpreted the relationship and stated discoveries. The following are samples of the examples that were used:]

$$1)\overline{6}\quad \tfrac{1}{3})\overline{6}\qquad 6 \times 3\ =\ 18$$

$$1)\overline{9}\quad \tfrac{1}{7})\overline{9}\qquad 9 \times 7\ =\ 63$$

Susanna: When you make the divisor 3 times as small, the quotient must be made 3 times as large. When we divided by $\frac{1}{3}$, we really multiplied by 3.

Sara: And when we divided by $\frac{1}{7}$, all we did was multiply by 7. That's easy.

Harold: Do we need to show our work for such simple problems? We would just know the answer. If we had problems with dividing by $\frac{1}{8}$, we could just multiply by 8.

David: Yes, but how about dividing by $\frac{2}{3}$ and $\frac{3}{4}$ and harder divisors?

Teacher: That is a good question, David. Let us look at the example we have here on the board. [Teacher indicated the following example.]

$$\tfrac{1}{3})\ \overline{8}\qquad 8 \times 3$$

I shall leave the dividend as it is, but what have I done to the divisor? [Teacher then changed divisor from $\frac{1}{3}$ to $\frac{2}{3}$.]

David: You made the divisor twice as large, so the answer will be twice as small. The answer would have to be 12.

Teacher: Very good thinking, David. If we wanted to show what we have done, we could do it this way.

[Teacher illustrated with the following procedure and explained that we could show 8 × 3 divided by 2 by writing the 2 as a divisor under the 3.]

$$\tfrac{2}{3})\ \overline{8}\qquad \frac{8 \times 3}{2}$$

Teacher: What do you notice that is interesting about the example?

Dorothy: The divisor is upside down.

Frances: Yes. Two thirds as a divisor is $\frac{3}{2}$ as a multiplier.

Sara: That's nothing *new*. When we divided by $\frac{1}{3}$, we multiplied by 3.

Martha: And $\frac{1}{7}$ became 7 as a multiplier.

[Eugene and others commented concerning what happened to the divisor.]

Teacher: When we do examples with multiplication of common fractions, we'll write the examples this way most of the time.

[Teacher demonstrated, writing:]

$$8 \div \frac{2}{3} = \frac{\overset{4}{\cancel{8}} \times 3}{\underset{1}{\cancel{2}}} = 12$$

[Other examples were used to develop the procedure.]

The remainder of the period was used to let the children discuss and use scratch paper to work out division of common fraction examples in which a whole number was divided by a proper fraction. The examples were discussed, and each child checked his own work. The teacher noted the children's level of readiness for a written exercise in which the types of examples that had been taught would be used.

Lesson 6
DIVISION OF COMMON FRACTIONS
Grade Six Class

Background of children: Excellent background of concepts with regard for divisor-dividend-quotient relationships and with regard for common fraction expressions. The group had had several lessons with division of common fractions, but had not reached the stage of generalization planned for this lesson. Using letters to state generalizations was not new to the group, although they had not used letters extensively.

Lesson Procedure

[Teacher wrote on the blackboard:]

$$\frac{?}{\text{variable})\ \text{constant}}$$

Teacher: What can you tell concerning the symbols that I have written on the blackboard?

David: When the dividend is constant and the divisor variable, the quotient will be variable. The quotient will change in the opposite way from the divisor.

Evelyn: Yes. The divisor and quotient change in opposite directions. Inverse means opposite direction.

Donald: If the divisor gets larger, the quotient gets smaller.

Jack: If the divisor is made 8 times as large (in number value), the quotient will become 8 times as small (in number value) if the dividend is constant.

Susie: If the divisor is made 8 times as small (in number value), the quotient will be made 8 times as large (in number value) if the dividend is constant.

[Teacher wrote on the blackboard:]

$$1) \overline{R}$$

Teacher: What is true concerning any number divided by 1?

Dick: The quotient comes out the same as the dividend.

David: Equals itself.

Tommy: R divided by one equals R.

Teacher: I am going to change the divisor.

[Teacher changed the divisor to $\frac{1}{2}$ so that it was:]

$$\tfrac{1}{2}) \overline{R}$$

Marjorie: You made the divisor 2 times as small so the quotient will be made 2 times as large. Then the answer is $R \times 2$ or $R2$.

[Teacher wrote on the blackboard:]

$$1) \overline{S} \qquad \tfrac{1}{8}) \overline{S}$$

Paul: S divided by one equals S, and S divided by $\frac{1}{8}$ equals 8 S's. The smaller the divisor, the larger the quotient if the dividend is constant.

Teacher: What is the answer if S equals 8?

Peggy: The answer would be 64.

Teacher: If S equals 3?

Jack: 24.

Teacher: If S equals 20?

Susie: 160.

Teacher: If S equals 40?

Barbara: 320.

Teacher: What is true about any number divided by $\frac{1}{3}$?

Marvin: The quotient will be 3 times as large as the dividend.

[Teacher wrote on the blackboard:]

$$\tfrac{1}{3}) \overline{N} \qquad \tfrac{2}{3}) \overline{N}$$

Jerry: N divided by $\frac{2}{3}$. The divisor is 2 times as large as N divided by $\frac{1}{3}$.

Marvin: The quotient will be 2 times as small for N divided by $\frac{2}{3}$ as for N divided by $\frac{1}{3}$. [He showed work like this on the blackboard.]

$$\frac{N \times 3}{\frac{1}{3})\ N} \qquad \frac{\dfrac{N \times 3}{2}}{\frac{2}{3})\ N}$$

Teacher: [Not writing example on blackboard] What is the quotient if N equals 8?

Paul: 12. Because you multiply by 3 and divide by 2. That's just the same as if you multiplied by $1\frac{1}{2}$.

Dicky: N divided by $\frac{2}{3}$ equals $1\frac{1}{2}N$.

Helen: I got the answer by thinking 8 and 4. N equals 8, and $\frac{1}{2}N$ equals 4. Eight and 4 are 12.

Lois: I figured this way. I took 3 eights and divided by 2. N divided by $\frac{2}{3}$ equals N multiplied by 3 and divided by 2.

Shirley: How was that again, Lois?

[Lois went to the blackboard and explained her procedure.]

Teacher: N divided by $\frac{2}{3}$. What is the quotient if N equals 4?

Sharon: Six. Four and 2 are 6.

Teacher: If N equals 30?

Barbara: Forty.

Jack: No, it would be 45, Barbara, because 30 and 15 are 45.

Barbara: Yes. I added wrong.

Teacher: What has been true concerning examples in which the divisor was a proper fraction?

Donald: The quotient is larger than the dividend. That is always true if the fraction is less than 1 (unit).

Paul: Yes. You come out with more than you start with.

Class: This kind of arithmetic — like N divided by $\frac{1}{2}$ — is fun. Can we have some more work like that?

Teacher: Would you like to have some problems like the ones we did today on a written exercise later in the week?

Class: Yes, but let's do some more problems on the board first.

[These generalizations followed and were stated by the group:]

$$N \div \frac{2}{3} = 1\frac{1}{2}N$$

$$L \div \frac{2}{5} = 2\frac{1}{2}L$$

$$t \div \frac{3}{4} = 1\frac{1}{3}t$$

Discussion Questions

1.   In common language, a fraction may be referred to as "a part of something." How does such a connotation differ from the meaning of a fraction in number language expression?

2.   In what respects are fraction-number scales similar to the scale of whole numbers? How do they differ?

3.   How do the properties of the division operation apply in interpreting fraction numbers?

4.   Which of the terms "rational numbers," "fraction numbers," and "ratio numbers" do you think is preferable for the ideas of fractions? Why?

5.   In what ways does the transforming of values from one fraction scale to another resemble the transforming of number values from Roman notation to decimal notation?

6.   Should common fractions always be expressed in simplest form when they are answers to computation?

7.   In examples such as $7\frac{1}{4} - 4\frac{7}{8}$, regrouping the whole number has been shown to produce difficulty. Suggest ways to be alleviate the difficulty.

8.   Does the classifying of computational examples with fractions suggest anything relative to instruction? If so, what?

9.   Is it feasible to eliminate fraction numbers from mathematical behavior?

Suggested Readings

Banks, J. Houston, *Learning and Teaching Arithmetic*, 2d ed. Boston, Mass.: Allyn and Bacon, Inc., 1964, Chaps. 8–10.

Bell, Clifford, Clela D. Hammond, and Robert B. Herrera, *Fundamentals of Arithmetic for Teachers*. New York: John Wiley & Sons, Inc., 1962, Chap. 10.

Clark, John R., and Laura K. Eads, *Guiding Arithmetic Learning*. New York: Harcourt, Brace & World, Inc., 1954, Chap. 6.

Crumley, R. D., "Teaching Rate and Ratio in the Middle Grades," *School Science and Mathematics*, vol. 60 (February 1960), pp. 143–150.

Gibb, E. Glenadine, "Fractions," *Grade Teacher*, vol. 79 (April 1962), p. 54.

Grossnickle, Foster E., and Leo J. Brueckner, *Discovering Meanings in Elementary School Mathematics*. New York: Holt, Rinehart and Winston, Inc., 1963, Chaps. 10 and 11.

Gunderson, Ethel, "Fractions — Seven-Year-Olds Use Them," *The Arithmetic Teacher*, vol. 5 (November 1958), pp. 233–238.

Hall, Jack V., "A 'Self-Starter' Approach to Fractions," *The Mathematics Teacher*, vol. 43 (November, 1950), pp. 331–333.

Johnson, Harry C., "Division with Fractions, "*The Arithmetic Teacher*, vol. 12 (May 1965), pp. 362–368.

Johnson, J. T., "Are Ratios Fractions?" *Elementary School Journal*, vol. 48 (March 1948), pp. 374–378.

Mueller, Francis J., *Arithmetic: Its Structure and Concepts*. Englewood Cliffs, N. J.: Prentice-Hall, Inc., 1956, Chap. 5.

Mulholland, V., "Fifth Grade Children Discover Fractions," *School Science and Mathematics*, vol. 54 (January 1954), pp. 13–30.

National Council of Teachers of Mathematics, *Topics in Mathematics for Elementary School Teachers. Numeration Systems For The Rational Numbers*,

Booklet Number 7. Washington, D. C.: The National Council of Teachers of Mathematics, Inc., 1964.

National Council of Teachers of Mathematics, *Topics in Mathematics for Elementary School Teachers. The Rational Numbers*, Booklet Number 6. Washington, D. C.: The National Council of Teachers of Mathematics, Inc., 1964.

Niven, Ivan, *Numbers: Rational and Irrational*. New York: The L. W. Singer Company, 1961.

Polkinghorne, Ada R., "Young Children and Fractions," *Childhood Education*, vol. 11 (May 1935), pp. 354–358.

Sanders, Walter J., "The Use of Models in Mathematics Instruction," *The Arithmetic Teacher*, vol. 11 (March 1964), pp. 157–165.

Sauble, Irene, "Teaching Fractions, Decimals, and Per Cents: Practical Applications," *Arithmetic 1947*, Supplementary Education Monograph, No. 63. Chicago, Ill.: University of Chicago Press, 1947, pp. 33–48.

Smart, James R., *New Understanding in Arithmetic*. Boston, Mass.: Allyn and Bacon, Inc., 1963, Chap. 2.

Swenson, Esther J., *Teaching Arithmetic to Children*. New York: The Macmillan Company, 1964, Chaps. 15 and 16.

Trimble, H. C., "Fractions Are Ratios Too," *Elementary School Journal*, vol. 49 (January 1949), pp. 285–291.

10

Concepts Underlying Computation: Denominate Numbers

10.1 THE METRIC SYSTEM

"We're losing by inches, by feet, and by yards. We're handicapping our engineers, businessmen, and even our schoolchildren with our anti-quated way of measuring."[1] These are shocking statements that certainly deserve serious attention, since they were made by one of our leading scientists.

There is an urgent need at the present time for a serious consideration of our systems of weights and measures. The industrialization of the world demands that systems of measurement be used in common. The newer nations have the advantage of beginning their development with ideas, instruments, and techniques that have already been refined to serve modern needs. They, in turn, will expect those with whom they trade to supply materials and machines that are in accord with such measurements.

In the United States today, we are using two systems for measurement of volume, length, weight, and temperature. We inherited the English system of weights and measures, and tradition has fastened its tentacles around us. But, we also use the metric system, which was adopted by the Congress of the United States in 1866. The metric system is used extensively in chemistry and other sciences, engineering, medicine and pharmacy, athletics, and so forth.

The Roman system of notation was a handicap to trade and to engineers in its time. We may compare it with the cumbersome systems

[1] Edward Teller, "We're Losing by Inches, by Feet, and by Yards," *This Week Magazine*, May 15, 1960, pp. 6–7 and 34–35.

of measurement that handicap our society today. The decimal system
facilitated the expression of quantitative ideas, thus releasing men's
minds to concentrate upon the validity and effectiveness of ideas rather

It's easier to compute using grams, liters, and kilo than inches,
feet, ounces, pounds, and so forth.

than be burdened with difficulties of numerical orthography or with de-
ciphering unwieldy symbols. The metric system, which makes use of the
ideas of decimal notation, has many advantages over the English system.

THE MAIN ADVANTAGES OF THE METRIC SYSTEM

1. All measures of the metric system are calibrated in the decimal
scale. This facilitates computation and thinking with regard to the
relationships among the measures. The advantage of this is evident
when one considers decimalization of the inch, foot, and mile. If operations with common fractions and decimal fractions could be carried out
with the same base or radix that operates with decimals, the simplification would be very great. For example, compare the simplicity of
shifting a decimal point to multiply or to divide by 10, 100, 1000, and so
forth, with the computational feats needed to express 237 inches as
yards, feet, and inches.

2. Using the metric system, all measures of length are related to
the *meter*, all measures of weight to the *gram*, and all measures of capacity to the *liter*. In contrast, the multiplicity of English measures is

evident as we consider measures such as *inches, feet, yards, rods, miles, ounces, pounds, pints, quarts, gallons,* and *bushels.*

3. One of the greatest advantages of the metric system is the interrelationship between and among the measures of length, weight, and capacity. For example, the unit dimension of capacity can be converted to a corresponding unit of weight. A cubic centimeter of water weighs 1 gram. A corresponding unit of weight for a cubic foot of water is not related in a precise way. The nearest we come to it is to say that a cubic foot of water weighs 62.4 pounds. Much computation would be involved to find the weight of tanks filled with commodities when the dimensions are expressed in the English system.

The metric system uses only the three basic units — the liter, the gram, and the meter. All other units of measure are either multiples or subdivisions of the basic units. And, of even greater importance, they are convertible from one to another. The weight of one cubic centimeter of pure water is 1 gram; it is the basic measure of weight. One thousand cubic centimeters equal a liter, and a liter of pure water equals a kilogram.

TABLE 10.1

METRIC SYSTEM	ENGLISH SYSTEM
463 centimeters =	463 inches =
46.3 decimeters =	$38\frac{7}{12}$ feet =
4.63 meters =	$12\frac{31}{36}$ yards
Create a new numeral by relocating the decimal point.	To convert units, divide or multiply.

TEACHER AND PUPIL EDUCATION CONCERNING THE METRIC SYSTEM

It is important for teachers and pupils to know how the metric system works, to interpret the principles that underlie it, and to be able to evaluate its advantages. The metric measuring instruments that are on the market and the use of metric measures for canned goods, and so forth, make it almost impossible to be unaware of the use that is made of the system. The metric system also offers unlimited possibilities for application of the concepts that underlie the decimal system, both decimal integers and decimal fractions.

The main purpose of teaching the metric system is to help the learner interpret the system. Converting from English weights and measures to metric or from metric to English is not likely to contribute to the interpretation of the system, and the computational feats have little value in themselves. Computations should be made directly in the metric system. Charts showing the meter, the liter, and an idea of gram may be used. Or better yet, a metric ruler, a scale showing metric units, and a liter measure may be used. Weighing objects, measuring their length, and finding their capacity should be achieved through considering the metric measures. These acitivities combined with teaching the three basic units of liter, gram, and meter, and the commonly used suffixes and prefixes to express increase or decrease of the basic unit, can lead to significant interpretation. The following six prefixes are the main ones that are used.

DEKA	meaning ten	10
HECTO	meaning one hundred	100
KILO	meaning one thousand	1000
DECI	meaning one tenth	.1
CENTI	meaning one hundredth	.01
MILLI	meaning one thousandth	.001

In Table 10.2, one may see the application of the relationships of the decimal system in the pattern of metric measures.

TABLE 10.2

DECIMAL SYSTEM	METRIC SYSTEM
Thousands	Kilo
Hundreds	Hecto
Tens	Deka
Units	*Liter, Gram, Meter*
Tenths	Deci
Hundredths	Centi
Thousandths	Milli

Note that in the tables above a basic referent has been selected and that all other values are determined in their relationship to the referent. In the decimal system, the referent for determining positional value is the units' position. In the metric system, the basic referent for measuring length is the *meter*, the basic referent for weight is the *gram*, and the *liter* is the referent for measuring capacity. Surface measures are derived from the square of linear measures; volume measures are similarly derived from the cube based on linear units.

A meter is the basic unit of measure of length. A dekameter is equal to 10 meters, a hectometer is equal to 100 meters, a kilometer is equal to 1000 meters. A decimeter is equal to one-tenth meter, a centimeter to one-hundredth meter, and a millimeter is equal to one-thousandth meter. The same procedure operates with liter and with gram.

Teaching the system directly rather than relating it with the English system has many advantages. As brought out by J. T. Johnson concerning this point: "This has the same benefits as learning a language by the direct method. It is much better to learn to think in French than to first translate the French into English and then think in English. Likewise it is better to think in terms of centimeters and meters than to first translate these into inches and yards."[2]

Lesson 1 at the end of this chapter presents some ideas concerning the way a group of children developed concepts concerning the metric system.

10.2   THE ENGLISH SYSTEM of WEIGHTS and MEASURES (denominate numbers)

Denominate numbers are really not a different type of number. They are, more strictly speaking, elements of sets of measurements. Decimal numerals are used to designate how many of each measure are being considered in a denominate number, but, for the most part, the relationships among the groupings are not decimally scaled. For example, while such expressions as 325 or 3.25 or $\frac{5}{8}$ or $2\frac{3}{4}$ are commonly called "abstract" numbers, actually they express *names of particular number groupings*. "Three hundred twenty-five" consists of the names for 3 of the hundreds' grouping, 2 of the tens' grouping, 5 of ones' values. "Three AND twenty-five hundredths" denotes 3 of units' values AND 2 of the tenths' grouping, 5 of the hundredths' grouping. "Five eighths" similarly designates 5 of the eighths' grouping. And, in like manner, two and three-fourths names 2 of units' values, together with 3 of the fourths' grouping.

The grouping of number values into named categories is identical in principle to the designation of series of measures in the so-called denominate numbers. There is an inferential recognition of this fact in the common fraction notation terminology. The divisors in the fraction symbols are commonly called "denominators." Denominators are defined as the namers of the sizes of parts into which a whole is divided. In the discussion of the previous chapter, the point was made that the groupings of common fraction values into denominational categories is similar to the scheme used in decimal notation. This scheme makes possible the writing of large number values by means of only 10 digits. *Place value in decimal notation, size categories in common fraction notation,*

---

[2] J. T. Johnson, "A Survey on the Use of Metric Measures," *The Metric System of Weights and Measures*, National Council of Teachers of Mathematics, Twentieth Yearbook. New York: Bureau of Publications, Teachers College, Columbia University, 1948, p. 162.

and measure categories in denominate numbers are all expressions of a common idea. Consequently, techniques used in regrouping into categories of related values are similar for all these numbers. When the idea is understood with any of them, it is applicable with all.

In the preceding chapter, the decimal numbers and common fraction numbers were compared as to grouping categories. In this chapter, a similar comparison is made with some of the denominate numbers.

Decimal integers are a scale for measuring successive amounts of oneness. The scale is sectioned into groupings according to a standard or constant guide; that is, ten of the values in the space to the right equal one of the values in the space to its left. Liquid measure is similarly a scale for measuring successive amounts of liquid. For convenience, the scale in common use in our country is calibrated in divisions representing amounts commonly used. However, the relation of the divisions is not the same throughout the scale. See Table 10.3.

TABLE 10.3

DECIMAL INTEGERS		LIQUID MEASURE	
Thousands	Tens of hundreds of units	*Gallons*	4-quart grouping
Hundreds	Tens of tens of units	*Quarts*	2-pint grouping
Tens	Tens of units	*Pints*	4-gill grouping
Units	Ones in their primary sequence	*Gills*	Primary unitary measure

METRIC LINEAR MEASURE		ENGLISH LINEAR MEASURE	
Kilometer	Tens of hectometers	*Mile*	8 furlongs
Hectometer	Tens of decameters	*Furlong*	40 rods
Decameter	Tens of meters	*Rod*	$5\frac{1}{2}$ yards
Meter	Basic unit for length	*Yard*	3 feet
		Foot	12 inches
		Inch	Primary unit

10.3   COMPUTATIONAL TECHNIQUES with DENOMINATE NUMBERS

Difficulty with denominate numbers is likely to arise from the arbitrary and irregular relationships among the groupings in the various tables or scales. Learning the tables and making them recallable when needed is an onerous task. However, the use of denominate numbers presents nothing essentially new in the processes of computation. The grouping of values into higher categories on the scales is done just as it is done with decimal and common fraction numbers. Similarly, regrouping, changing a scale value from a higher to a lower category, is done in the same way as with the other numbers. The same principles govern the procedures. *Only terms within the same groupings or categories are added or subtracted.*

The following illustrations for denominate numbers were devised for the purpose of clarifying certain techniques and characteristics of computational processes. They are not necessarily proposed as devices or procedures for general use in elementary school instruction. Their purpose is to make the steps of the procedure evident and understood by the teacher. When a teacher thoroughly knows what she wishes the pupils to learn, she should then be free to select and to use such devices, illustrations, and procedures as will give the greatest potential to their learning.

ADDITION AND SUBTRACTION

The same techniques used with "abstract numbers" are applicable with "denominate numbers." The following examples illustrate these points with addition:

ADDITION

Decimal Numbers   *Mixed Numbers*   *Linear Measures*

tens units tenths		units thirds		yards	feet	inches
6 7.5		5 $\frac{2}{3}$		1	2	7
4 5.6		2 $\frac{2}{3}$		1	2	8
1 1	partial	1 $\frac{1}{3}$	partial		1	3	partial
1 2	sums	7	sums	1	1		sums
1 0		8 $\frac{1}{3}$		2		
1 1 3.1				3 yd. 2 ft. 3 in.		

The variable relationships among the positions in the denominate number make each grouping a special step. The sum of 7 inches and 8 inches is 15 inches. But 15 inches is more than 1 foot. Hence, the one-foot value of the sum was placed in the feet category and the 3 inches were represented in the inches' position. Similarly, 2 feet and 2 feet are 4 feet. But 4 feet is more than 1 yard. Therefore, that sum is expressed as 1 yard and 1 foot. The values were recorded in their respective positions. The sum of the yards' position is within the limits of value expressed in that position. It is written in its proper place. The separate values in the several respective groupings are then collected to make the final sum. In writing that sum, the label of each category (feet or inches) must be used, because the principle of place value is not expressed adequately otherwise.

Subtraction situations in which the minuend values in each grouping equal or exceed the values in the subtrahends offer little difficulty. However, the need for regrouping presents a potential source of difficulty, when the subtrahend value is greater than the minuend value in any grouping. The following examples require regrouping and illustrate how it is accomplished in three types of number language.

SUBTRACTION (Please note that the respective groupings in each number expression are identified. This was done in order to emphasize the application of the regrouping technique.)

Decimal Numbers		regrouped		Mixed Numbers		regrouped		Denominate Numbers		regrouped	
tens	units	tens	units	units	thirds	units	thirds	feet	inches	feet	inches
7	4	6	14	4	$\frac{1}{3}$	3	$\frac{4}{3}$	4	4	3	16
5	9	5	9	2	$\frac{2}{3}$	2	$\frac{2}{3}$	2	8	2	8
1	5	1	5	1	$\frac{1}{3}$	1	$\frac{2}{3}$	1 ft.	8 in.	1 ft.	8 in.

MULTIPLICATION

Multiplication with denominate numbers is a relatively simple operation. Only the multiplicand can be a denominate number. The multiplier is an "abstract" number. Consequently, multiplication with denominate numbers is similar to addition. The same techniques for expressing partial products (partial sums) can be used. The grouping of values in their proper positions within the number expression is required.

MULTIPLICATION

Decimal Numbers				Mixed Numbers				Denominate Numbers					
tens	units	tens	units	units	thirds	units	thirds	yards	feet	inches		feet	inches
4	8	4	8	2	$\frac{2}{3}$	2	$\frac{2}{3}$		2	7		2	7
	2	2	2	2		2	2			2		2	2
1	6	8	16	1	$\frac{1}{3}$	4	$\frac{4}{3}$		1	2		4	14
8				4				1	1				
9	6			5	$\frac{1}{3}$			1 yd.	2 ft.	2 in.			

The solutions for the examples above have been performed in two ways. The solution to the left under each number type was performed in extended form. The solution to the right in each case was performed with the number value categories separated. This was done to illustrate the sources of the partial products recorded in the more customary procedure. Multiplication is done with each group value separately. The products are recorded in their respective groupings according to each of the number types.

With the mixed number, a similar procedure is used. Two thirds taken 2 times make 4 thirds. That is a higher value than is properly expressed in the thirds' category. Hence, 4 thirds is regrouped as 1 unit and 1 third. Two units taken 2 times gives 4 units. Collecting the values in each grouping gives a total product of 5 units and 1 third.

With the denominate number, the same procedure is used. Seven inches taken 2 times gives 14 inches. That is a higher value than is commonly assigned to the inches' category. Hence, it is grouped as 1 foot, 2 inches. Those values are written in their respective positions. Two feet taken 2 times gives 4 feet. That is larger than the value assigned to the "feet category" in the system of linear measure. Hence, it is grouped as 1 yard, 1 foot. Those values are written in their proper positions. Collecting values in the respective groupings gives 1 yard, 2 feet, 2 inches. The names of these groupings must be indicated, because there is no other way to identify their values.

Denominate numbers are extensively used in designating dimensions in surface measure or volume measure. In order to work with such measures, one must regroup them to numbers of the same unit of measurement such as numbers of feet or numbers of inches. Then the number values are treated as abstract numbers. Their product is given the name of the comparable unit in surface or volume measure. If the dimensions were expressed in feet, the product would be square feet for surface measure and cubic feet for volume measure. Technically, a square foot is a unit of measurement for surface measure. It is not the product of 1 foot multiplied by 1 foot. It is a unit of measurement that has the dimensions of 1 foot in length and 1 foot in width. Only as a convenient technique is it permissible to say that "feet times feet gives square feet."

DIVISION

Division with denominate numbers is similar to subtraction when the regrouping of number values is involved. When the divisor of a denominate number is an abstract number, the division process is not unlike that followed with decimal numbers and with mixed numbers. For example, in each specimen that follows, the problem is to divide each of the number expressions by 2. The idea is illustrated as follows with decimal number symbols and denominate number symbols.

DIVISION

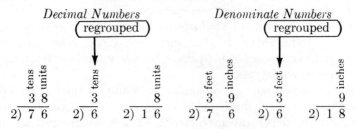

The examples were devised to require regrouping among the several value categories used. This was done in order to illustrate the major source of difficulty with this type of division. The process is similar when regrouping is not required, but it is less involved in number interpretation. Each example is solved twice. The solution to the left is in the customary form. The solution to the right is illustrative of the regrouping step which is not shown in the more customary solution form.

Sometimes it is more convenient to regroup all the values in the number expression in terms of one of the group categories. Then the division can be performed as it is with decimal numbers. For example, in $7\frac{1}{2} \div 2$, the mixed number $7\frac{1}{2}$ would be expressed as $\frac{15}{2}$. Fifteen halves divided by 2 gives $\frac{15}{4}$. When that expression is changed to its simplified form it is expressed as $3\frac{3}{4}$. Similarly, 7 feet 6 inches may be expressed as 90 inches. Ninety inches divided by 2 gives 45 inches. That amount grouped in simplified form yields 3 feet 9 inches.

Mathematical experiencing offers unlimited possibilities for developing social understanding and social competency. When a pupil understands basic mathematical concepts, he is in a position to use good sense concerning them. A questioning mind and a scientific approach should be the product of such thinking. This approach should lead the pupil to sense that new measures are needed and that better measures are likely to be available from time to time. Examples for such consideration are the world calendar, the 13-month calendar, the 24-hour clock, the metric system, and the improvement in standardization of weights and measures. The great strides that man has made with measurement are reflected in comparisons such as the following:

(a) Horse-and-buggy means of travel compared with orbiting satellites

(b) Smoke signals compared with Telestar

(c) Bows and arrows compared with atomic bombs

(d) Telling time by means of water clocks compared with methods of telling time that are accurate to a millionth of a second

(e) Measurements of weight using simple balances compared with modern scientific measurements on balances accurate to a millionth of a gram

Methods for teaching mathematics need to keep pace with the strides that man has made in the measurement of quantity. With the instructional unit of denominate numbers — as with other instructional units in mathematics — the emphasis should be upon the understanding of basic relationships. Computational techniques should be an outgrowth of interpretation of those relationships.

ILLUSTRATIVE LESSONS

The following illustrative lessons and lesson plans are presented in this chapter:

Lesson 1. The metric system
Lesson 2. Procedures for measuring
Lesson 3. Using known measurements as standards of reference for estimating other measurements
Lesson 4. Estimating and measuring capacity
Lesson 5. Estimating and measuring specific things to serve as standards of reference

Lesson 1
THE METRIC SYSTEM
Grade Six Class

Purpose of lesson: (a) To lead the children to extend their concepts concerning decimal notation through applying them to interpret the metric system, (b) to introduce the main units of the metric system, (c) to introduce the main prefixes used for metric measure, and (d) to do some simple problem solving using metric measures.

Materials for lesson: A meter stick, a liter measure, a yardstick, a quart container, and a chart showing metric measures compared with English weights and measures, and a bulletin-board display concerning the metric system.

Background of children: The children had a good background of understanding concerning the decimal system of notation including decimal fractions. They had a good background in computational work with decimal fractions and had developed some work with denominate numbers other than metric. They were aware of the metric system through observing labels of canned goods and rulers marked in metric units.

Lesson Procedure

Teacher: Some of you have noticed that most of the leading brands of canned goods are marked in metric units of measure in addition to being marked in English weights and measures. Today I brought a meter stick and a liter measure to class. I also brought this chart showing metric units as compared with the system of weights and measures that we commonly use.

John: The meter looks like a yard except that it is a little longer than a yard.

Alex: The liter looks like a quart.

Sue: A liter looks a little larger to me, but maybe it isn't.

Jean: The kilogram is heavier than a pound. On that chart, it shows a kilogram as $2\frac{2}{10}$ pounds.

Teacher: Would you like to measure and compare a quart and a liter and a meter and a yard?

Class: Yes. [Many volunteered to do the measuring.]

Janice: [Compared quart and liter by pouring water from liter measure into quart container.] A liter is a little more than a quart. It is not very much more. It is just this much more. [Indicated how much of liter was left over after quart was filled.]

Katherine: A liter is so much like a quart that we could use it easily.

Billy: [Compared meter with yardstick.] A meter is about $3\frac{1}{4}$ inches longer than a yard.

Katherine: I looked at the chart the teacher put up. It says that a meter is 39.37 inches, but that it can be rounded off to 40 inches.

Billy: It is closer to 39 inches than to 40 inches.

Katherine: But, it is easier to think of it as 40 inches.

Ina: It says on the chart that a kilogram is about $2\frac{2}{10}$ pounds. It would be easy to think of a half-kilo as about a pound. It (a half-kilo) would be just a tenth of a pound more than a pound.

Teacher: If we used metric units of measure, do you think that we would need to do much comparing with English weights and measures? Would we be able to think in terms of metric?

Paul: We could think in metric. It would be easy to buy a liter of milk instead of a quart. A half-liter would be about a pint.

Marjorie: It wouldn't be difficult to buy dress material by the meter. Your pattern that you use should tell you how many meters of cloth to buy.

Nadeene: I think that kilogram would be the hardest to get used to. I don't know how many kilograms I weigh, but I know how many pounds.

Ilse: And some things you buy cost a whole lot, and it would make a difference. You would have to get used to kilograms.

Kenneth: But why would we want to change? It would be a lot of bother.

Teacher: It would mean a great amount of changing, but let us see how the metric system works. There are many things that are very interesting about the metric system. Let's see what you think about the way it works. In the metric system, you wouldn't have to change inches to feet, feet to yards, yards to miles, pints to quarts, and so on.

Nadeene: But wouldn't the metric system be just as difficult? What would you change liters to? And meters? And kilograms?

Teacher: See if you can discover how this idea works. You multiply the base unit and divide the base unit in a way that is very simple. Through the use of six prefixes, you can increase and decrease the main unit. The following prefixes are the main ones.

[Teacher wrote the prefixes on the chalkboard.]

deka	meaning ten	10
hecto	meaning one hundred	100
kilo	meaning one thousand	1000
deci	meaning one-tenth	.1
centi	meaning one-hundredth	.01
milli	meaning one-thousandth	.001

Teacher: In another period, we shall see how these prefixes are used in many words. Do you notice something about how the prefixes work?

Janice: They go 10, 100, 1000, and one tenth, one hundredth, one thousandth. That is the way the number system works.

Teacher: Do you know how these prefixes work with using the base units — meter, liter, and gram?

Walter: Can't you say "dekameter" and mean 10 meters?

Teacher: That is true, Walter. What other words could you use with the term "meter"?

Ray: That's easy. You could use dekameter, hectometer, kilometer, decimeter, centimeter, and millimeter.

Lewis: Dekameter would be 10 meters, hectometer would be 100 meters, kilometer would be 1000 meters, decimeter would be one tenth of a meter, centimeter would be one hundredth of a meter, and millimeter would be one thousandth of a meter. That sounds very simple.

Geraldine: Would the same thing work with liters?

Katherine: Why wouldn't it? You would have . . . [listed the prefixes to the base liter, and explained the meaning of them.]

Darwin: Then it would be the same with kilogram, but kilogram already means a thousand grams, doesn't it?

Teacher: That is right.

Darwin: Then gram is the base word.

Larry: It seems almost too simple. What's the catch?

Ray: Maybe there isn't any catch.

Teacher: Would it take much work to regroup dekameters to meters and to regroup centimeters to millimeters?

Walter: A dekameter is 10 meters. That would be easy.

Ina: And how about centimeters and millimeters?

Larry: A centimeter is one hundredth of a meter. A millimeter is one thousandth of a meter.

Teacher: How many millimeters does it take to make a centimeter?

Marjorie: It would take 10. Isn't a thousandth 10 times as small as a hundredth?

Lewis: Then 10 millimeters equal 1 centimeter.

Teacher: To regroup kilometers to meters, what do you do?

Jean: That would be easy. Just multiply kilometers by 1000.

Ilse: If you multiply a whole number by 1000, just *suffix* 3 zeros.

Teacher: I'm glad that you said to suffix 3 zeros, Ilse. You aren't going to get caught just placing them any place, are you? *Direction* for affixing zeros does matter!

Kenneth: If you multiply a decimal fraction by 1000, you can just move the decimal point. You may have to suffix zeros, too.

Paul: This sounds too easy. Let's work some problems.

Sue: Decimal fractions are lots easier than common fractions.

Teacher: Let's see if you can do these problems. Express 173 centimeters as decimeters. Then express it as meters.

Alex: Wouldn't you just divide by 10 to change centimeters to decimeters? One hundred seventy-three centimeters would be 17.3 decimeters.

Katherine: And divide by 10 to change decimeters to meters — 17.3 decimeters would be 1.73 meters.

Teacher: Now express 173 inches as feet.

Darwin: We have to divide 12 into 173.

[Class figured and arrived at the correct answer, $14\frac{5}{12}$ feet.]

Teacher: Now express 173 inches as yards.

John: We could divide 173 by 36, or we could divide $14\frac{5}{12}$ by 3. I think it's easier to divide by 36.

[Class figured and arrived at the correct answer, $4\frac{29}{36}$ yards.]

Paul: That is a lot of work.

Katherine: It's a lot more work than moving a decimal point. When the metric is so easy, why is it that we don't use it? It would save people a lot of time, and it would make arithmetic a lot easier for us in school. We've studied inches, feet, and yards, and we've worked with pounds and ounces, and some of the work the teacher gave us was really hard.

Jean: You [the teacher] told us that the metric system has been legal in our country for a long time. Why don't we make everybody use it?

Teacher: To make the use of the metric system compulsory, there would need to be enough people to want it and vote for making it compulsory. Such a movement has been under way for some time. Perhaps in your lifetime the change will come about. However, what are some of the things that changing to metric would involve?

Nadeene: All measuring cups, rulers, scales, and cartons would have to be changed.

Billy: And machinery to make things would have to be changed.

Ilse: And signposts for highways.

Darwin: And we'd have to change, and be able to figure with metric.

Lewis: And our parents and our teachers and everybody that's grown up. It might be hard for some people to change.

Larry: I think it would be easy for boys and girls because they learn about the metric system in school.

Discussion of the issue continued. The brief instructional unit on the metric system included some computational work. It included, also, further development of the systematic pattern of ideas that operate to make work with the metric system facile.

Lesson 2
PROCEDURES FOR MEASURING
Grade Four Class

Purpose of lesson: To lead the children to formulate and organize their concepts with regard for procedures for measuring.

Background of children: The children had studied a short unit on measurement. They had brought many measuring devices and things to measure into their classroom. Through a process of problem solving, they had measured to determine relationships between units of measure, procedures for measuring, and so forth.

Lesson Procedure

Jamie: This measuring has surely been fun. I've learned a lot.

Marie: Mother says that I should make a good cook — I measure so accurately.

Larry: Yes, but being a good cook and measuring accurately doesn't always work. My mother doesn't measure very much, and she's a very good cook.

Teacher: Does your mother measure by taking just a pinch of salt and a cup "just so full" of flour, and by *knowing* how much of each to use?

Larry: Yes, that is the way she cooks. She doesn't need a cook book or a measuring cup.

Marie: But she measures! Remember how we discussed that early man may have done a better job of telling time than we do. He didn't have clocks, watches, and radio as we do, but he could tell time. Having clocks and watches doesn't mean that you will be on time.

Teacher: That's a very good point, Marie. Larry's mother probably measures more accurately than many people who follow a recipe carefully. She is probably so familiar with her recipes that she knows just how much of each ingredient is needed to make the delicious food that Larry eats. Is that true, Larry?

Larry: Yes, but she also knows how to mix the things she uses.

Teacher: This morning, let us talk about the procedures for measuring as accurately as we can. What things would you say are important to consider for you to do accurate measuring?

[After the question was asked, the teacher gave the children a short time to think about the problem.]

Page: One of the most important things is to use a good measuring stick or thing to measure with.

Natalie: Some of our rulers and yardsticks are not good. You can't tell where the very beginning point is on the ruler I have. We talked about buying some new rulers and yardsticks. I hope we do.

Jane: But no matter how good the measuring stick is, the measurement won't be accurate if you don't measure carefully.

Teacher: That is true, Jane. What things can *you* do to measure accurately?

Jane: Use the ruler or thing you use to measure with carefully. You should put your ruler down carefully and mark where the starting point is and the ending point.

Sandy: You have to know how to line up your ruler carefully. If you let it slip or be crooked, it won't be accurate.

Jamie: You should be very careful. When I measure too fast, I'm careless.

Teacher: Besides being careful, what else can you do, Jamie?

Jamie: I don't know.

Denny: I know. You can measure and then go back and measure again and check your first measuring. I did that when Daddy had me measure for a new bookcase we're going to build.

Susie: You can have somebody else check you, too. After I measured my desk, the teacher measured to check me.

Virgil: And you should read the measure carefully. When we read the thermometer in our room, some of us aren't very accurate. We don't look carefully.

Teacher: If you are writing down the measurement, what should you think about?

Helen: You should write it down carefully. If you write down the wrong things, you would be wrong. If you wrote down feet when you meant inches, or pints when you meant quarts, you would have the wrong answer.

Jamie: You should know how to use the measuring thing you use. If you use a ruler, you should know about inches and feet, and parts of inches. If you use a thermometer, you should know about degrees, and to measure water, you should know about cups and pints and quarts, and . . ..

Teacher: Can you measure all things that you know about with the same accuracy?

Peter: It's harder to measure some things than other things. It's easy to measure my desk, but it isn't easy for us to measure how high our school building is.

Susie: It's harder to weigh my baby brother than to weigh me. I stay still; he doesn't. Mother surely has a hard time to weigh him.

Marie: It would be hard to measure how thick this piece of paper is. We couldn't do it using a ruler. You [the teacher] said that there are good ways to measure things like the thickness of this paper. I'd like to see them.

Teacher: I'll have to borrow the measuring instruments that I told you about, Marie, but I'll bring them to class soon.

Denny: It was much harder to measure that odd-shaped box we brought to school than to measure that other box.

Patricia: It is much easier to measure around squares. If you find one side, you don't need to measure the other sides. You can multiply by 4. That's easy.

Denny: It is easier to measure medium-sized things than things that are very large or things that are very small. Maybe it would be easy to measure very small things if we had the right things to measure with, but we don't have.

Teacher: Which do you think we usually measure more carefully — very valuable things or things that aren't so valuable?

Jerry: Very valuable things. Gold and silver and things like that are measured very carefully. Things that aren't worth so much are not measured so carefully.

Patricia: The grocer weighs things carefully. Sometimes he doesn't weigh them after Mother has weighed them, but usually he does. My mother watches the scales when the butcher weighs meat. It costs a lot of money, and my mother is careful and watches the butcher so he won't overcharge her.

Virgil: My mother knows the butcher won't cheat her. She doesn't pay any attention to the scales.

Teacher: Is it more important to weigh a small thing carefully than something very large?

Denny: That all depends. Sometimes a very big thing is just as important as something little. The big thing might contain gold bricks.

Jerry: Or precious stones for jewelry.

Marie: Or an atom bomb.

Teacher: What you have said is true. However, let us think about which is more important to weigh carefully. Would it matter as much if you were 2 pounds off when you were weighing a large load of hay as it would if you were 2 pounds off in weighing Susie's baby brother?

Susie: It would make a lot of difference with my baby brother. He weighs only 9 pounds, and 2 pounds make a lot of difference.

Helen: A large load of hay weighs very much. A few pounds wouldn't make much difference.

Jerry: And hay doesn't cost so much by the pound. We buy hay for my horse. We buy it by the ton, and a few pounds isn't much.

Helen: How much is a ton?

Jerry: My daddy says it is 2000 pounds, but he doesn't buy exactly 2000 pounds. The hay is in bales.

Teacher: Do you think that we measure the distance to the moon and to the stars so that we know exactly the number of miles?

Class: No. Of course not!

Denny: How do we measure the distance to the stars?

Teacher: That is a splendid question. Let's discuss it tomorrow. See what you can find out about it before tomorrow. Also be thinking about the smallest thing and the largest thing that you have ever measured. After we discuss the things that you have measured, would you like to discuss the things that man has measured — the smallest things and the largest things?

The following day, the teacher had some charts ready for the children to complete. The title of one chart was "How to Measure Accurately." The children listed procedures and filled in the chart. "Smallest Amounts That Man Has Measured" was the title of another chart, and another was "Largest Amounts That Man Has Measured." These charts were developed during the following week when the children discussed these topics.

Lesson 3
USING KNOWN MEASUREMENTS AS STANDARDS
OF REFERENCE FOR ESTIMATING OTHER
MEASUREMENTS
Grade Four Class

This grade four class had measured many things in their environment. The following list tells some of the things that they had measured and used as standards of reference for estimation of other quantities.

Height of classroom door — 6' 8"
Width of classroom door — 3'
Height of classroom (floor to ceiling) — 11'
Length of classroom — 26'
Height of ledge near windows — 2' 6"
Height of their teacher — 5' 2"
Distance from school to main avenue — about 1 mile
Sizes of paper — $8\frac{1}{2}$" × 11" (scratch paper for doing schoolwork)
$\qquad\qquad$ 18" × 24" and 12" × 18" (paper for art work)
$\qquad\qquad$ 6" × 9" (scratch paper for doing schoolwork)
Cards for making book reports — 5" × 8"
$\qquad\qquad\qquad\qquad\qquad\quad$ 3" × 5"
Height of school building — 35'
Span — distance from end of thumb to end of little finger when hand
$\qquad$ is stretched out. Each child had measured his span and knew
$\qquad$ about how many inches it was.

Lesson 4
ESTIMATING AND MEASURING CAPACITY
Grade One Class

Purpose of lesson: To lead the group of children to estimate capacity and to compare measurements of quart, pint, and half-pint.

Background of children: Several discussions had taken place concerning measuring things they used.

Materials used: Bucket of water and quart, pint, and half-pint cartons.

Lesson Procedure

Teacher: Many of you have brought milk cartons to show how we measure milk. Which is the largest carton that you brought?
[The children classified the cartons that hold a quart as the largest they brought, the pint size as the middle-sized, and the half-pint size as the smallest.]

Teacher: Do you know what we call the amount that this largest carton holds?

Norma: I think that you call it a quart. That's what my daddy calls it.

Teacher: Yes, that is right. It is called a quart.

Dean: And the middle-sized carton holds a pint.

Richard: What does the smallest carton hold?

Christina: It is smaller than a pint. Is it called a small pint?

Craig: It is called a half-pint. We buy a half-pint of milk for a lunch. The carton is just like that one. [Craig pointed to half-pint size.]

Teacher: Craig is right. The smallest carton holds a half-pint. . . . Did we decide that we wanted to use water and measure how many times as much water this carton (quart-size) holds as this one (pint-size), and how many times as much the quart-size holds as this one (half-pint)?

Class: Yes. Let's see now.

Teacher: Before we measure, let us decide how we should do the measuring.

Christina: We can fill the half-pint size and pour it in (into) the quart size. Then we can fill it again, and pour it in (into) the quart size. We can keep doing that until the quart is full.

Teacher: How many times do you think that we will need to fill the half-pint size and pour it into the quart to fill the carton that holds a quart?

Dean: I think that we'll have to fill that one (half-pint size) 3 times to fill the quart size.

Ruth: I think that it will take 2 of the small ones.

Jean: I think that it will take 4.

[The estimates ranged from 2 through 4, but the most frequent responses were "three" and "four."]

Paul: May I fill the small carton?

Teacher: Shall we watch while Paul measures how many times he needs to fill the half-pint carton and empty it into the quart carton to fill the quart? We'll leave the cartons on your table where you keep your things to do measuring, and anyone who wants to may measure later in the day.

[Paul counted how many times he needed to fill the half-pint carton and empty it into the quart carton to fill the quart carton. He decided that it took 4 half-pints to make a quart.]

[The children had observed that cartons usually are not filled to the very top of the carton. The teacher had measured to determine how "full" the cartons should be.]

[Each child evaluated his own estimate.]

Teacher: We have this carton which holds a quart of water. If we pour the water from this carton (quart size) into pint-sized cartons, how many pint-sized cartons will it fill?

[The children's estimates were "two," a "bit over two," "three," "a little less than three," and "almost two." The most frequent response was "two."]

[The children measured by pouring the water from the quart carton into two pint-sized cartons.]

Craig: I was quite sure that the quart would fill 2 pints.

Christina: You can almost see that the larger one (quart size) holds 2 times as much as the smaller one (pint size). You can tell by just looking at them.

Jim: I guessed right. And I bet that it will take 2 of the smallest carton (half-pint size) to fill the carton that holds a pint. May I measure? [There was general agreement that it would take 2 half-pints to make 1 pint. Jim measured and confirmed their estimates.]

Richard: We have a milk bottle — not a carton — at home that holds more than any of these cartons. I'll bring it tomorrow, and may we measure how many of each of these it takes to fill the large bottle?

Teacher: Would you like Richard to bring his large bottle?

Class: Yes. [Various children chimed in, "I'll bring one that is larger than Richard's," "We have a very large carton," and so forth.]

Teacher: Shall we leave these cartons on your table where you keep things to show how we measure?

Children: Yes. And pretty soon our table will be full of things.

Lesson 5
ESTIMATING AND MEASURING SPECIFIC THINGS TO SERVE AS STANDARDS OF REFERENCE

Purpose of lesson: to use the classroom as a laboratory in which pupils experiment with (a) estimating length, width, and height; and (b) measuring some specific things that may serve as standards of reference for further estimating.

Materials used: Cards (3″ × 5″ and 5″ × 8″), tongue depressors, pieces of paper 8½″ × 11″ and 18″ × 24″), sheets of paper with the sample record form for recording estimates and measurements shown in Fig. 10.1.

Lesson Procedure

Have each child estimate the things indicated on the record form. After he has estimated all of the objects, he should use a foot ruler and a yardstick and measure the given things within a precision of ½ inch.

Part 1. Each child will estimate and record his estimate of each thing listed on the record form.

Part 2. Using foot rulers and yardsticks each child will measure the things listed on the record form.

Part 3. Discuss the actual measurements arrived at and have each child evaluate his work. Discuss procedures for improving one's estimation. The following are some anticipated points for discussion:

(a) How close were your estimations to the actual measurement?

(b) How did you formulate your estimation?

(c) The children who were consistently close in their estimations will try to identify their method and show why it obtained good results.

THING TO BE MEASURED		ESTIMATE	MEASUREMENT
SMALL CARD	width		3"
	length		5"
LARGER CARD	width		5"
	length		8"
TONGUE DEPRESSOR	width		¾"
	length		6"
PIECE OF PAPER	width		8½"
	length		11"
PIECE OF PAPER	width		18"
	length		24"
DOOR IN CLASSROOM	height		
	width		
CHALKBOARD (FRONT OF ROOM)	width		
	length		
	height from floor		
DOOR KNOB	height from floor		
MY DESK	length		
	width		
	height		

Fig. 10.1

(d) The children who were consistently far removed from the actual measurement will try to identify why they were far removed.

(e) Procedures for estimation, such as comparing the height of the classroom door with the teacher's height, comparing the height of the room with the height of the door, judging how many yards will go into the length of the chalkboard, and trying to visualize a foot, a yard, and other measures.

Discussion Questions

1. List some uses of metric measures that you have observed. You may include news clippings, labels from canned goods, and so on.
2. What effect is world trade likely to have on our systems of weights and measures?
3. Should mathematical instruction attempt to lead our nation to use metric measurements?
4. In what ways are subgroupings in the whole-number scale, the scaling of fraction numbers, and the subgroupings in the systems of weights and measures alike? How do they differ?
5. Are the techniques for computing with whole numbers applicable for computing with "denominate numbers"?
6. Does the name "denominator" as used in identifying a term in a common fraction numeral have a similar meaning to that of "denominate" in the expression "denominate number"?
7. Is there a comparable relationship between errors made by projecting phonetic principles into nonphonetic word patterns and those made by projecting decimal techniques into nondecimal computations? Give illustrations.
8. What advantages or disadvantages would come from measuring our day on a 24-hour scale rather than on a 12-hour scale?
9. What advantages or disadvantages would come from measuring a year in terms of 4 weeks or 28-day units instead of the irregular monthly increments now commonly used?
10. Suppose we should be able to land on Mars or on Venus, will our Earth measures be applicable?

Suggested Readings

Arnold, C. J., "An Answer to 'Arguments against Universal Adoption of the Metric System,'" *School Science and Mathematics*, vol. 51 (April 1951), pp. 310–315.

Banks, J. Houston, *Learning and Teaching Arithmetic*, 2d ed. Boston, Mass.: Allyn and Bacon, Inc., 1964, Chaps. 12 and 13.

Bendick, Jeanne, *How Much and How Many: The Story of Weights and Measures*. New York: Whittlesey House, McGraw-Hill Book Company, Inc., 1947.

Billingham, G. Harold, "Metric, a Post-War Aid?" *Education*, vol. 69 (February 1949), pp. 383–385.

Bowles, D. Richard, "The Metric System in Grade Six," *The Arithmetic Teacher*, vol. 11 (January 1964), pp. 36–38.

Bullock, William E., "Why the Metric System Didn't Work As a System," *Education*, vol. 71 (April 1951), pp. 528–530.

Burchenal, Joyce M., "A Device for Measuring Understanding of the Meaning of Units of Measure," *School Science and Mathematics*, vol. 58 (November 1958), pp. 601–604.

Committee on the Metric System of the National Council of Teachers of Mathematics (J. T. Johnson, chairman), Twentieth Yearbook, *The Metric System of Weights and Measures*. New York: Bureau of Publications, Teachers College, Columbia University, 1948.

Committee on Space Science Oriented Mathematics, *What's Up There*. 1964. For sale by the Superintendent of Documents, U.S. Printing Office, Washington, D.C.

Davis, O. L., Jr., and Carolyn Crigler, "The Growth of Pre-School Children's Familiarity with Measurement," *The Arithmetic Teacher*, vol. 6 (October 1959), pp. 186–190.

Eddy, Claire Frances, "What Weights and Measures Should be Taught in the Elementary School?" *Education*, vol. 71 (April 1951), pp. 483–487.

Johnson, J. T.: "The Metric System," *School Science and Mathematics*, vol. 44, (November 1944), pp. 717–721.

MacLatchy, Josephine H., "The Pre-School Child's Familiarity with Measurement," *Education*, vol. 71 (April 1951), pp. 479–482.

Parker, Helen C., "Teaching Measurement in a Meaningful Way," *The Arithmetic Teacher*, vol. 7 (April 1960), pp. 194–198.

Payne, Joseph N., and Robert C. Seber, "Measurement and Approximation," *The Growth of Mathematical Ideas, Grades K–12*, National Council of Teachers of Mathematics, Twenty-fourth Yearbook. Washington, D.C.: The Council, 1959, pp. 182–228.

Rappaport, David, "Units in Measurement Should Be Meaningful," *School Science and Mathematics*, vol. 60 (March 1960), pp. 202–206.

Read, Cecil B., "Arguments against Universal Adoption of the Metric System," *School Science and Mathematics*, vol. 50 (April 1950), pp. 297–306.

Smart, James R., *New Understanding in Arithmetic*. Boston, Mass.: Allyn and Bacon, Inc., 1963, Chap. 5.

Spitzer, Herbert F., *The Teaching of Arithmetic*. Boston, Mass.: Houghton Mifflin Company, 1961.

Swain, Robert L., *Understanding Arithmetic*. New York: Holt, Rinehart and Winston, Inc., 1957, Chap. 11.

The World Calendar. New York: The World Calendar Association, Inc.

Ward, Morgan, and Clarence E. Hardgrove, *Modern Elementary Mathematics*. Reading, Mass.: Addison-Wesley Publishing Company, Inc., 1964, Chap. 14.

Wheat, Harry Grove, *How To Teach Arithmetic*. New York: Harper & Row, Publishers, 1951, Chap. 12.

Wray, D. Eileen, "You and the Metric System," *The Arithmetic Teacher*, vol. 11 (December 1964), pp. 576–580.

Yorke, Gertrude Cushing, "Weights and Measures in South America," *Education* vol. 71 (April 1951), pp. 514–527.

11

Algebra: A Way
of Mathematicking

"Understanding is thinking things together."

Thorndike

Most of us are aware that it is easier to take things apart than it is to put them back together. However, parts must be reassembled to form wholes in order that they may again operate effectively. The "reduction of parts to a whole" or the "reunion of broken parts" is the generic meaning of the term *algebra*. Algebra, as a term, was derived from an Arabic expression "al-jabr," literally referring to "setting bones."

To infer is human. We constantly generalize from our experience and project what we have learned regarding specific things to guide our observations and our responses to things in general. That inferential procedure is a way of mathematicking that produces our algebra.

"Algebra is the best language for thinking about laws. Algebra puts the law into small space. The formula is shorter to write, easier to read, quicker to say, and simpler to understand than the corresponding sentence in ordinary English."[1]

11.1 ALGEBRA as an EXTENSION of ARITHMETIC

There is no sharp or definitive boundary line between arithmetic and algebra. Arithmetic behavior is initially concerned with measuring and

[1] W. W. Sawyer, *What Is Calculus About?* The L. W. Singer Company, A Division of Random House for the Monograph Project of the School Mathematics Study Group, 1961, p. 7.

classifying specific concrete entities, but inevitably this leads to our making generalizations regarding such things. For example, the counting-number scale originates from tangible collections of specific items. The scale readily lends itself to extension by generalization, making feasible the symbolizing of quantities that are rarely if ever concretely experienced — billions of dollars, for instance.

11.2   DIRECTIONAL COUNTING: an ALGEBRAIC GENERALIZATION

Having devised a scale for measuring successive aggregates of one-ness, we readily sense that such a scale may be used either to "count-in" *to* a larger grouping (add) or to "count-out" *from* such a grouping, (subtract). Addition and subtraction are *directional opposites*. Hence, each may be used as a check of the accuracy of the other.

Also, there are some characteristics of addition situations that may readily be observed and generalized. For example, in finding the sum of two numbers, the order in which they are added does not alter the result: $3 + 5 = 5 + 3$. This is known as the *commutative property of addition*. "Commutative" means that the operation works both ways, that is, its elements are interchangeable. Later, the idea may be generalized that $a + b = b + a$ when a and b are symbols representing any whole number.

Furthermore, when a series of sets or groups is to be totaled, the groups may be "counted-in" in any stated order without changing the value of their sum. For example,

$$(2 + 4) + 6 = 2 + (4 + 6)$$
$$6 + 6 = 2 + 10$$
$$12 = 12$$

This is known as the *associative property of addition*. Later, the idea may be generalized to $(a + b) + c = a + (b + c)$ when a, b, and c are counting numbers.

In its initial form, multiplication may be a special case of addition. For example, 4×5 is a short way of expressing $5 + 5 + 5 + 5$. Since $4 \times 5 = 5 \times 4$, the order of the terms does not affect the value of the product and the *commutative property applies in multiplication*. $a \times b = b \times a$ when a and b are whole numbers.

In like manner, when one performs a series of multiplications, he may perform them in any stated order. For example,

$$(3 \times 5) \times 4 = 3 \times (5 \times 4)$$
$$15 \times 4 = 3 \times 20$$
$$60 = 60$$

Hence, the *associative property* applies in multiplication. When a, b, and c are whole numbers, we may say that $(a \times b) \times c = a \times (b \times c)$.

If a series of numbers is to be multiplied by the same multiplier, they may be added and their sum multiplied by the multiplier, or they may be multiplied individually and their respective products added to secure the final sum. For example,

$$3 \times (2 + 5) = (3 \times 2) + (3 \times 5)$$
$$3 \times 7 = 6 + 15$$
$$21 = 21$$

This illustrates the *distributive property of multiplication* with respect to addition. The distributive property is commonly used when one multiplies by a number having two or more digits.

$$
\begin{array}{l}
2\ 5 \\
\underline{\times\ 3}
\end{array}
\qquad
\begin{array}{l}
3 \times 25 = (3 \times 20) + (3 \times 5) \\
75 = 60 + 15 \\
75 = 75
\end{array}
$$

The concept may be generalized in the following example: $a \times (b + c) = (a \times b) + (a \times c)$ where a, b, and c are whole numbers.

11.3   COUNTING-NUMBER SCALE APPLIED DIRECTIONALLY [2]

The counting-number scale implies a measurement of deviation from zero as a basal reference point. We have observed that counting *outward* toward a larger grouping (addition) is directionally opposed to counting *inward* toward a smaller grouping (subtraction). However, on such a scale the beginning of outward counting and the terminus of inward counting is the "not any" or "zero" point. If the "not any" or zero reference point were absolute, such measurements would be adequate, but we often experience situations wherein the zero designates only an arbitrary or selected point of reference, deviations from which extend in opposite directions. For example, in terms of time, we identify the *present* but recognize that there are both *past* and *future* deviations from it. In positional measurements we may select a "bench mark" or base reference and make directional measurements to the *right* and to the *left*, *upward* and *downward*, *forward* and *backward*. As such measurements are quantified, we use the number scale and name the *direction* of its application, for example, *above* sea level or *below* sea level, *east* or *west*, in the *past* or in the *future*.

Naming the direction of our regard is satisfactory for ordinary ref-

---

[2] Zero is not always recognized as a counting number. We have used it in this regard because it is needed as a point of reference and to designate "not any" on a scale measuring "someness."

erence, but it does not serve well for expressions in the number languages. Consequently, as with numerals, a more succinct symbol needs to be devised.

11.4   A DIRECTIONAL-NUMBER SCALE

By inference the counting-number line may be extended to make a directional-number scale. By the simple device of extending the number line on through the zero point and giving it directional scaling, *its usefulness is more than doubled.* Surely, this is no mean accomplishment!

The parts of the scale on the respective sides of the zero or base point are comparable in every respect. Their calibrations are the same, but they need to be directionally identified. Custom has decreed that measures toward the *right* be considered as "positive" and those toward the *left* are designated as "negative." The number symbols representing those measures bear those respective identifying signs. Hence, such numerals represent "signed numbers" or "directional numbers."

PLUS AND MINUS SIGNS MAY SYMBOLIZE EITHER VERBS OR ADJECTIVES

It may be unfortunate that the plus (+) and minus (−) signs are used both as verbs signifying operations and as adjectives indicating which part of the number scale is being considered. However, having knowledge of their dual usage and using reasonable care in reading should materially reduce a tendency to confuse them. The verb plus (+) indicates that a *sum* is to be considered, while the verb minus (−) signifies that two amounts are to be compared and their *difference* considered. When the positive or negative sign is an integral part of the number symbol, it serves as an *adjective* modifier identifying which "directional number" is being considered. The authors recommend that, in teaching children, the negative and positive signs be written higher than those for showing minus and plus, that is, $^-7$ (negative 7) and $^+7$ (positive 7).

11.5   DIRECTIONAL NUMBERS USED in COMPUTATION

Signed or directional numbers may be used in computation. In computing with directional numbers, care must be taken to interpret their directional cues correctly. By charting a few specimen cases on the directional-number line, cues of some important generalizations may be observed. Segments are extended to the right to represent positive measures and to the left to represent negative measures. Simple number situations which can be readily checked are all that are needed to illustrate the points under consideration.

ADDITION OPERATION WITH DIRECTIONAL NUMBER

What is the sum of two or more numbers having the *same directional sign?* In order to study this question, number values equivalent to the respective numerals may be laid off along a number line by means of line segments or vectors having lengths equal to the measures they respectively represent. The "tail" of a segment is its beginning point. The "head" is its terminal point. The vector reaching from the "tail" of the first to the "head" of the second shows the sum of the two vectors.[3]

The following four examples are illustrated below:

Example a $(+2) + (+3) = ?$
Example b $(-2) + (-3) = ?$

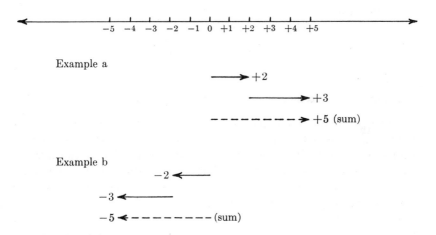

DIRECTIONAL-NUMBER LINE

Example a

$\longrightarrow +2$

$\longrightarrow +3$

$-------\rightarrow +5$ (sum)

Example b

$-2 \longleftarrow$

$-3 \longleftarrow$

$-5 \longleftarrow ------ $ (sum)

Generalization

As should have been anticipated, if we were reading the directional signs correctly, *the sum of two addends having like signs is their arithmetic sum with the same sign as the addends. Positive numbers added give a positive sum. Negative numbers added produce a negative sum.*

What is the sum of two unlike directional addends? The solution for this problem may be pictured as was done previously, *but,* care

---

[3] National Council of Teachers of Mathematics, *The Growth of Mathematical Ideas, Grades K–12,* Twenty-Fourth Yearbook. Washington, D.C.: The Council, 1959, p. 48.

must be taken to construct the addend vectors in conformance with their directional cues. The following examples are to be solved:

Example c $(+2) + (-4) = ?$
Example d $(-2) + (+4) = ?$

DIRECTIONAL-NUMBER LINE

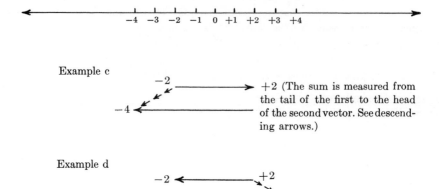

Example c

-2 → $+2$ (The sum is measured from the tail of the first to the head of the second vector. See descending arrows.)

-4

Example d

-2 $+2$

$+4$

Summary of Preceding Number Lines

As the illustrations show, the *sum* of two addends having unlike directional signs is equal to the *difference* between their arithmetic number values (their absolute values) given the directional sign of the addend having the larger number value. This generalization needs to be given careful consideration, because it uses familiar terms in an unfamiliar manner: the *sum* equals the *difference*.

These examples illustrate all of the situations involved in the addition of directional numbers. The simple illustrations upon the number line should assist in clarifying the directional relationships and in the recall of the generalizations concerning the nature of the respective sums.

SUBTRACTION OPERATION WITH DIRECTIONAL NUMBER

The operation of subtraction is directionally opposite to that of addition. In the addition operation, we were concerned with combining the values of the addends. In subtraction, we are concerned with determining *the amount of difference between them*. Hence, in charting the vectors on the directional number line we shall be measuring the distance *from* the head of the second vector (the relatum that is the subtrahend vector) *to* the head of the first vector (the referent that is the minuend vector).

The examples to be solved are:

$$(+6) - (+3) = ?$$
$$(+6) - (-3) = ?$$
$$(-6) - (-3) = ?$$
$$(-6) - (+3) = ?$$

If we chart each of these examples on the directional-number line, we get the following:

Positive six minus positive three $(+6) - (+3)$

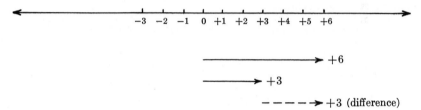

The difference is measured by the vector extending from the head of the subtrahend vector to the head of the minuend vector.

Positive six minus a negative three $(+6) - (-3)$

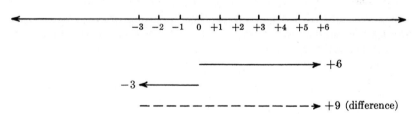

Negative six minus negative three $(-6) - (-3)$

Negative six minus positive three $(-6) - (+3)$

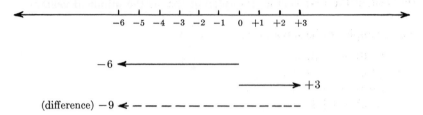

Summary of Preceding Number Lines

If we observe the amount and the direction of the difference vector in these respective solutions, an interesting and apparently consistent characteristic is revealed.

The Situation as Presented	*The Situation as Solved*
$(+6) - (+3) = ?$	$(+6) + (-3) = +3$
$(+6) - (-3) = ?$	$(+6) + (+3) = +9$
$(-6) - (-3) = ?$	$(-6) + (+3) = -3$
$(-6) - (+3) = ?$	$(-6) + (-3) = -9$

In every instance the solution was achieved by adding the inverse of the subtrahend to the minuend. *Subtraction was achieved by adding!*
Subtractions are solved by adding the inverse of the subtrahend.

The inverse of a number of the directional-number scale is its corresponding value on the other side of the zero or base point. For example, the inverse of negative two is positive two, and vice versa.

Operationally then, when subtracting, *we change the sign of the subtrahend and add that value to the minuend.* The basis for this is known as *the additive inverse principle.*

THERE ARE FOUR TYPES OF SITUATIONS REGARDING THE SIGNS OF THE TERMS IN MULTIPLICATION

In multiplication examples as in subtraction, there are four possible arrangements of directional numbers as factors: both terms may be (1) positive or (2) both may be negative, or (3) the multiplicand may be positive and the multiplier negative or (4) vice versa.

Situations wherein both terms are positive are familiar, because that is the type of number with which usual arithmetic multiplications have been performed. Since multiplication is developed in arithmetic as a special case of addition, the multiplicand being the addend value that is repeated, no difficulty is encountered with situations wherein the multiplicand is a negative number and the multiplier is positive. This merely indicates that the negative value is to be added as indicated, and the sign of the sum or product will be the same as that of the addends — negative.

However, there may be difficulty in visualizing the effect of a negative sign in the multiplier. But, by recalling and applying the *commutative property* for multiplication, this situation becomes the same as the one just discussed.

Hence, we infer that *the product of two numbers having unlike signs is a negative number*. This is a basic characteristic that needs to be thoroughly understood and consistently applied. The situation in which both the multiplicand and the multiplier are negative numbers needs some special consideration.

A double negative makes a positive. This observation is commonly expressed. It serves as a guide for interpreting statements such as, "It is not underweight" or "anti-anti-communist," and so forth. To demonstrate its applicability in multiplication of directional numbers calls for inferential reasoning, since it is difficult to visualize concretely the effect of the negative directional character of the multiplier. By inference we may reason from known relationships to determine the probable state of those that are unknown. For example, $(+3) + (-3) = 0$. By definition, opposite directional-number values balance or cancel. Further, $(-3)(0) = 0$. Hence, by substituting the first of these statements for its equivalent in the second statement we have $(-3)[(+3) + (-3)] = 0$. By applying the *distributive principle* of multiplication we secure the following: $[(-3)(+3)] + [(-3)(-3)] = 0$. Since we know that $(-3)(+3) = -9$ (the product of unlike directional numbers being negative), we infer that $(-3)(-3) = +9$, because it takes a positive 9 to cancel or balance a negative 9.

If our reasoning has been correct, we may infer that *the multiplication of two neagtive numbers produces a positive number*. Since the product of two positive numbers is likewise positive, we may generalize the characteristics of the multiplication of directional numbers as follows: *the multiplication of factors having like signs produces a positive product. The multiplication of factors having unlike signs produces a negative product.* These are important generalizations which need to be conceived and understood by everyone who uses numbers from both sides of the directional-number scale.

DIVISION OF SIGNED OR DIRECTIONAL NUMBERS: the inverse of multiplication

Multiplication is a procedure for finding the product of two known factors. Division, in contrast, is a procedure for finding one of the factors when the product and one of the factors are known. The dividend in division corresponds to the product in multiplication. The divisor and the quotient are the factors. Hence, we may readily infer that the same characteristics of signs for the numbers apply in division as were found to apply in multiplication. *If the dividend is positive, the divisor and quotient have the same directional sign. If the dividend is negative, the divisor and quotient have unlike directional signs.*

11.6   MEASUREMENTS on a TWO-DIMENSIONAL SCALE

The directional-number scale may be applied in any direction. It may be used to measure deviations from a reference point in the vertical or horizontal or oblique directions. As was pointed out above, extending the counting-number line through zero, thus giving its measures a directional meaning, more than doubled its usefulness. In like manner, combining a horizontal directional-number line with a vertical directional-number line probably more than doubles its usefulness. This amounts to approximately a fourfold increase in the usefulness of the primary-number scale by merely extending and applying it with directional reference. Surely, this justifies our mathematicking through inferential reasoning.

By combining the vertical and horizontal positions of the directional-number scales and using a common zero or reference point, we secure a device for measuring positions in space (see Fig. 11.1). The vertical scale measures deviation *only in a vertical direction.* The horizontal scale

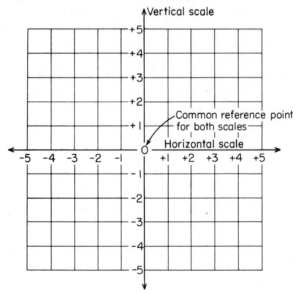

Fig. 11.1

measures deviation *only in a sidewise direction*. But, together they provide a means for measuring deviations both vertically and horizontally.

The type of measurement shown in Fig. 11.1 is facilitated by constructing supplemental lines both vertical and horizontal through the scaled points as illustrated in Fig. 11.2. The vertical line through the

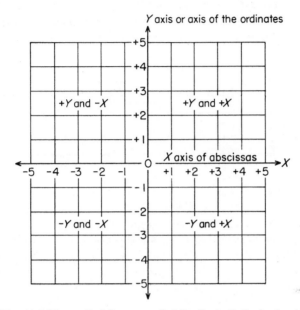

Fig. 11.2 The vertical lines are called "ordinates"; the horizontal lines are abscissas or "cutters."

zero point is called the axis of the ordinates or Y axis. The horizontal line through the zero point is designated as the X axis or axis of the "abscissas." The horizontal lines are termed abscissas because they abscise or cut across the vertical lines. Any point on the figure can be located by indicating the amount and the direction of its deviation as measured on both of the "coordinate" axes.

11.7   THE MANY USES of the COORDINATE CHART

The schema of two-dimensional measurement is essentially what one uses to locate things in space. For example, the directional references "in front of," "behind," "to the right," "to the left," which are commonly used by everyone, are the same ideas that are depicted by the coordinate chart.

Two-dimensional measurement is used in making the grid of lines of longitude (ordinates) and those of latitude (abscissas) used in determining location on the globe map of the world. It is also used in describing surface shapes and in calculating areas.

The coordinate chart serves a very important function when it is used to depict the relationship between two variable measures. For example, the variation in sunrise time at latitude 45 degrees north latitude is reported for weekly intervals from November 17, 1961, through February 16, 1962, both as a table of numerals and in graphic form. This is the period just preceding and following the winter solstice.

TABLE 11.1

DAY	SUNRISE TIME	DAY	SUNRISE TIME
Nov. 17	7:00 a.m.	Jan. 5	7:38 a.m.
24	7:09	12	7:36
Dec. 1	7:18	19	7:33
8	7:25	26	7:27
15	7:31	Feb. 2	7:19
22	7:35	9	7:10
29	7:38	16	7:00

The ordinates or vertical lines on the chart scale the sunrise time. The abscissas or horizontal lines scale the passage of weekly intervals.

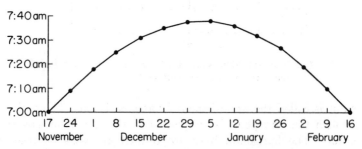

Fig. 11.3 Chart of sunrise during winter solstice period from Nov. 17 to Feb. 16 (after *World Almanac*, 1963).

While the reverse trend is discernible as one reads the table of numerals, it is *strikingly* illustrated by Fig. 11.3. This is one of the advantages of using this type of algebraic language.

11.8   PRONUMERALS

In our illustrations we have used numerals to represent the number relationships. However, the relationships being considered were not dependent upon the particular numerals. The relationships are characteristic of all the numbers of the types considered.

One of the contributions of algebraic language is that of using letters or other symbols as *"pronumerals,"* just as pronouns are used in ordinary language to designate persons instead of using their specific names. The need for some such mode of representation is readily experienced in working with number-language expressions just as it is in working with the common language. For example, the word *what* in the following sentence is symbolized by a question mark, by a "frame," and by a letter in the parallel expressions in number-language form:

VERNACULAR LANGUAGE FORM	NUMBER-LANGUAGE FORMS
What is the product of five threes?	$5 \times 3 = ?$ $5 \times 3 = \square$ $5 \times 3 = n$

THE USE OF LETTERS AS PRONUMERALS SIMPLIFIES MATHEMATICAL EXPRESSIONS

Consider these specific arithmetical factual statements as compared with the general statement that characterizes all of them:

VERNACULAR LANGUAGE	NUMBER LANGUAGE
Three threes is one larger than two fours.	$3 \times 3 = 1 + (2 \times 4)$
Four fours is one larger than three fives.	$4 \times 4 = 1 + (3 \times 5)$
Five fives is one larger than four sixes.	$5 \times 5 = 1 + (4 \times 6)$
Six sixes is one larger than five sevens.	$6 \times 6 = 1 + (5 \times 7)$
	$n^2 = 1 + (n - 1)(n + 1)$

The sequential nature of these sentences should be noted. There is consistency in pattern. Each sentence states that the product of a number multiplied by itself is equal to one more than the product of the number which precedes it on the number scale multiplied by the number which follows it on the scale. Based on this observation, we generalize that $n \times n = 1 + (n - 1)(n + 1)$. The arithmetic statements refer to specific facts. The generalization states a characteristic that is true of *any* such number situation.

In like manner, if we compare the paired items in the two series of data as given, a *consistent relationship* or *common property* is revealed:

      Series A   0 1 2 3 4 5
      Series B   0 2 4 6 8 10

Each item in Series B is 2 times its respective counterpart in Series A. Such a relationship may be expressed as $B = 2A$.

A similar relationship having a somewhat different *property* is characteristic of the following paired series:

      Series A   0 1 2 3 4
      Series B   0 3 12 27 48

In this instance each item in Series B is 3 times as large in number value as the square of the corresponding item in Series A. This relationship is more succinctly expressed in algebraic terms as $B = 3A^2$. It can also be depicted on the coordinate chart as shown in Fig. 11.4.

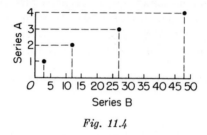

Fig. 11.4

The values of Series A are shown on the ordinate or Y axis. Those for Series B are shown on the abscissa or X axis.

OTHER SYMBOLS MAY BE USED AS PRONUMERALS

Another technique for succinctly representing mathematical ideas consists in the use of Greek letters to denote them. For example, the relationship of the length of the circumference of a circle to the diameter is conceived to be the same for all circles regardless of their size. It is interesting to note, though, that we have no numeral that *exactly* expresses that relationship.[4] Approximate measurements varying in accuracy between 3.14*1* and 3.14*2* are usually adequate for practical purposes, however. That number idea is commonly expressed by a mixed numeral, $3\frac{1}{7}$, or by the mixed decimal numeral, 3.1416, or it may be designated by the pronumeral which is the small form of the Greek letter pi (π). Since π symbolizes the length of the circumference as compared to that of the diameter, the relationships may be expressed as $C/D = \pi$ or $\pi D = C$ or $C/\pi = D$.

11.9   THE USE of EXPONENTS

An *exponent* is a symbol written above and on the right of another symbol called the *base*. The exponent denotes how many times the base is repeated as a factor. For example, 5^2 symbolizes 5 multiplied by 5, and 2^4 indicates the product of $2 \times 2 \times 2 \times 2$.

The exponent is merely a special technique for spelling certain number symbols. It makes possible the writing of more succinct symbols; for example, our federal government has an annual budget of approxi-

[4] *Science Newsletter* for September 9, 1961 reports a calculation of that ratio carried out to *one hundred thousand digit spaces* without terminating.

mately one hundred billions of dollars. As a customary numeral this is written as \$100,000,000,000, but exponentially it is merely 10^{11}, signifying that 10 is used as a factor 11 times to produce that value.

The product of a number multiplied by itself represents a *power* of that number. For example, 2 multiplied by 2 is said to be "squared" or "raised to the second power." Likewise, 5 multiplied by 5 and again multiplied by 5 is said to be "cubed" or "raised to the third power." The 10 used in the symbol for the annual federal budget was raised to its "eleventh power."

The root of any given number is a quantity which multiplied by itself a specified number of times produces the given number. For example, 9 may be produced by multiplying 3 by 3. We say that 3 is the *square root* of 9. And 2 is the *cube root* of 8 ($2 \times 2 \times 2 = 8$). The procedures for determining the root of a number are special cases of division.

Since we have shown that for every number in our primary counting-number series there is an *equal* but *directionally opposite* number, we anticipate that either of those numbers may be used as a base or as an exponent in constructing number symbols. For example, we may use -2 as the base and 3 as the exponent for spelling the symbol $(-2)^3$. The symbol indicates the product of $-2 \times -2 \times -2$. Or we may express $+2$ as the base and -3 as an exponent as 2^{-3}, which represents the reciprocal of the value 2^3. The reciprocal of a number is a number such that the product of the two numbers is one. Hence, the reciprocal of a number can be determined by dividing one by the number; for instance, the reciprocal of 2^3 is $1/2^3$ or $1/8$ or it may be expressed as 2^{-3}.

As should be anticipated, not only the directional whole numbers may be used as roots or as exponents, but fraction numbers may be so used as well. However, a fraction used as an exponent indicates the *root* rather than the *power* of the base number in the symbol. For example, the cube root of 8 may be indicated by the symbol $8^{1/3}$ (eight to the one-third power) or by a different type of symbol $\sqrt[3]{8}$. In either case, the number value expressed by the symbol is 2.

Negative or fractional exponents are not likely to be needed for mathematical expressions in the elementary school. They are mentioned in this connection to point out how the use of numbers is readily extended and applied to serve functions that may not have been the ones for which they were originally devised. This characteristic of evolution or emergence and extension of simple basic ideas and modes of expression so that they also serve in less obvious and more complex situations is the very essence of mathematicking. The genius of man's intellect can be illustrated no more clearly than by revealing the essential simplicity, and yet evident aptness, of his ways of solving mathematical problems.

ILLUSTRATIVE LESSONS

The following illustrative lessons and lesson plans are presented in this chapter.

Lesson 1. Generalizing concerning commutativity for addition
Lesson 2. A game involving reward and penalty that uses signed numbers
Lesson 3. Playing shuffleboard (using directional or signed numbers)
Lesson 4. Where am I? (a game using a coordinate plan)
Lesson 5. An original skit presenting ideas of coordinate measurements

Lesson 1
GENERALIZING CONCERNING COMMUTATIVITY FOR ADDITION

Lesson Procedure

The children had learned combinations such as the ones presented here. Miss Zit, their teacher, wanted to lead them to sense some of the properties of the addition operation. She gave each child a copy of the duplicated material.

Add	Add
$4 + 2 =$	$2 + 4 =$
$5 + 3 =$	$3 + 5 =$
$6 + 1 =$	$1 + 6 =$
$7 + 2 =$	$2 + 7 =$
$4 + 3 =$	$3 + 4 =$

[After the answers had been written, there was a discussion period.]
    Miss Zit: What did you notice about the examples today?
    Jack: They were too easy.
    Mary: They were in pairs.
    Miss Zit: What do you mean, Mary?
    Mary: Each example was given in two ways. $4 + 2$ is the same as $2 + 4$.
    Miss Zit: Did all of you notice that each fact was given in two ways? Since the two ways of stating the fact give the same answer, would it be correct to say $4 + 2 = 2 + 4$?
    Bill: Yes. But that still doesn't say how much it is.
    Alice: We could write the answer. (Alice went to the board and wrote $4 + 2 = 2 + 4 = 6$.)
    Miss Zit: That is an interesting number sentence, Alice. Now, can

someone tell us something that he thinks is always true about adding two numbers?

Tom: I think that it doesn't make any difference which one you *choose to add to.* The result is the same either way you add them.

Miss Zit: Do you all agree with Tom's idea? Can any one think of any reason why it might be wrong?

[The class agreed that Tom's idea "made sense."]

Miss Zit: Then I wonder who can tell what this equals? [She wrote on the board:]

$$\triangle + \square$$

[Tom wrote:]

$$= \square + \triangle$$

Tom: "But, we still don't know how much it is."

Miss Zit: That is a good point, Tom. The sentence we've written may be true or it may be false. We can't know unless we tell what we mean by the symbols. If the $\square$ and the $\triangle$ each stand for a number such as 0, 1, 2, 3, and so forth, then what can you say? Let's say

$$\square = 5 \quad \text{and} \quad \triangle = 3$$

Tom: I could let $\square$ stand for 5 and $\triangle$ stand for 3, and then the sentence would be true.

[Tom wrote $5 + 3 = 3 + 5$.]

Mary: I'd have $\square$ stand for 75 and $\triangle$ stand for 25, and $75 + 25 = 25 + 75$. It's 100.

Joe: Those are fun. May I write a new one? [Joe wrote:]

$$\triangleleft + \square = \square + \triangleleft$$

Joe: I'll have $\triangleleft = 3$ and $\square = 1$.

Miss Zit: Today we had easy number facts to work, but we found out by looking at them carefully that we could learn something that may be true with all sorts of additions. This is a good way to learn. We need to use what we know to help us find out about things that we don't know. Would you like to make some examples as Joe did?

The class was ready to make examples, and the following illustrate the type of examples they shared at the end of the class period.

$$\cap + \square = \square + \cap \qquad \cap = 7$$
$$7 + 9 = 9 + 7 \qquad \square = 9$$
$$\odot + \oslash = \oslash + \odot \qquad \odot = 15$$
$$15 + 7 = 7 + 15 \qquad \oslash = 7$$
$$\odot + \oslash = \oslash + \odot \qquad \odot = 8$$
$$8 + 2 = 2 + 8 \qquad \oslash = 2$$

Lesson 2

A GAME INVOLVING REWARD AND PENALTY THAT USES SIGNED NUMBERS

Mr. Smith devised a game of Bean Bag Toss to introduce simple ideas concerning positive and negative numbers. The target was a piece of plyboard with holes cut in it, with positive and negative scores assigned to the holes. The pupils tossed bean bags trying to put them through the positive holes. If the bag fell through a negative hole, that counted against one's score. The pupils played in pairs. Each player was allowed 3 tosses. Each totaled his score, adding the positive values and subtracting the negative values. For example:

Sue and Jane played Bean Bag Toss. Sue threw a bag through the −5 hole; another went through the +2 hole; and the last went through the +3 hole. What was Sue's final score? (See Fig. 11.5.)

Jane threw her first bag through the +5 hole; her second went through

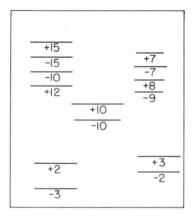

Fig. 11.5

the −3 hole; and her third toss went through the +2 hole. What was Jane's score?

Jane gave Sue another throw to see if she could beat her score. Through what hole must Sue's bag go in order for her to beat Jane's score? Through what hole must it go to equal Jane's score?

Lesson 3

PLAYING SHUFFLEBOARD (USING SIGNED NUMBERS)

Bill and Ned played shuffleboard. Each boy had 4 disks and tried to make as high a score as he could. The disks that landed on the area marked with + were added to make a total score. All disks that were in the −10 were subtracted from the total score. All disks that were knocked off the board were counted as "dead." No score was recorded for "dead" disks.

Bill played first and had a disk in +10. Ned played next and knocked Bill's disk off the board, and Ned's disk stayed on +10. Bill's second shot landed on −10, and Ned's on +8. Bill's third shot knocked Ned's +10 off the board, and his own went off with it. Bill's fourth shot landed on

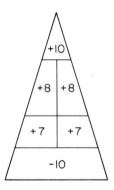

Fig. 11.6

+7. Ned tried to knock Bill's disk off. He didn't succeed, but he landed on +7. (See Fig. 11.6.)

When the game ended, Bill had one disk on −10, one on +7, and two disks were off the board. What was Bill's score?

Ned had one disk on +8, one on −10, and one on +7, and one was off the board. What was Ned's score?

How much does Bill need in order to bring his score up to 0? How much does he need in order to equal Ned's score?

Lesson 4

WHERE AM I? (A GAME USING A COORDINATE PLAN)

In Mr. Hill's room, there were 35 desk-chair units for pupils. Mr. Hill made a sketch similar to that shown in Fig. 11.7, but he used no labels. The children, with their teacher's help, invented a game called, "Where Am I?" They discussed ways that each child could tell someone where he sat in the classroom. They talked about locating a given desk in terms of the front of the room, rear of the room, window side of the room, and side opposite the windows. They decided that using two positions would be a good way to tell their location. They labeled the positions as in Fig. 11.7. They decided upon using *W* for window side and *R* for rear of the room.

[Bill's desk is located 3 rows from the rear and 4 rows from the windows.]

Bill: My desk is $4R3W$.

[The teacher had him mark X on the chart to show his location.]

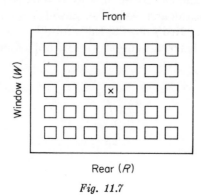

Fig. 11.7

Susie: My desk is $2R1W$. I could find it even if I didn't know where it was!

Jane: I am $5R1W$. That's easy to find. But, we could locate any seat in the room if we used R and W and told the numeral that goes with each.

Peggy: That wouldn't work for the teacher's desk! To tell where his desk is, we'd need to move it into the rows with our desks.

Each child was given a sketch similar to that pictured above. He wrote questions concerning, "Where Am I?" and called upon a pupil by his locational name, such as $2R2W$, to answer the question. If the person recognized himself by his "locational name" and answered correctly, he was the next one to ask a question.

The following are examples of questions that were asked:

"I am at the highest elevation in the United States. Tell where I am, $3R5W$."

"I am weightless. Where could I be? $4W3R$."

"I am a point on a number scale. I'm in the middle between 4 and 5. I am a fraction numeral, and my divisor is 1000. Who am I? $2R3W$.

Lesson 5
AN ORIGINAL SKIT PRESENTING IDEAS
OF COORDINATE MEASUREMENTS

The sixth grade had been studying coordinate measurements. They decided to give a report of their findings in the form of a program for the Parent-Teachers' Association. They proceeded as follows: (1) the chairs in the assembly hall were placed so that they made a coordinate pattern. The middle aisle was labeled *axis of ordinates*. The cross aisle was labeled *axis of the abscissa*. The seats in the rows were numbered each way from the axis of ordinates, *plus* to designate "to the right" and *minus* to designate "to the left." The seats in the columns were likewise numbered each way from the axis of the abscissa, *plus* desig-

Can you locate $x - 3$, $y + 4$, and so on?

nating toward the front and *minus* toward the rear. Tickets were prepared, giving the location of each seat as $x - 4$, $y + 4$, and so forth. Each member of the PTA drew from a box a ticket that designated his seat for the performance. They were expected to find their seats by themselves, but ushers from the class were available to assist them when requested.

Programs were printed with a regional map of the area showing the school as located by "ordinate" and "abscissa" streets. The program was as follows:

1. Prelude — Melody from "Around the World in 80 Days."

2. Where in the World Are You?

This was a skit using a large globe marked clearly with lines of longitude and latitude. Students representing each of the quadrants turned the globe so that their homelands faced the audience, and then pointed out where the countries were and gave brief accounts of their locations coordinately speaking.

3. Watching the Sun Go Down

The children used a large coordinate chart on which they had numbered the days from November 17 to the following January 1. The scale on the ordinate was the time of sunset, which was read off by one child and plotted on the chart with large red-headed pins. A string was strung from the November 17 pin, touching each of the other pins, to the January 1 pin. Then the question was asked, "Where will it go from here?"

Discussion Questions

1. Some sets of actions obey the commutative principle and some do not. For example, sugar + water = water + sugar. It doesn't matter which one is the augend (thing added to). But, in putting on socks and shoes, does it make any difference which action you do first? Write a list of actions that obey the commutative principle.

2. Write a list of actions that do not obey the commutative principle.

3. Write a list of actions that obey the associative principle.

4. Show how the distributive principle operates in the following example: Mary wanted 100 cards that were 3 inches × 3 inches and 100 cards that were 3 inches × 5 inches. There was a sale on packages of 100 cards each that were 3 inches × 8 inches. Describe how Mary may have applied the distributive principle and used a package of 100 cards that were 3 inches × 8 inches.

5. Write other illustrations that show the use of the distributive principle in problem solving. Make a sketch to illustrate the idea for one of your examples.

6. Give some illustrations in a problem-solving setting that show the meaning of examples such as $(-3) + (-4) = -7$.

7. Distinguish between the terms *number, numeral,* and *pronumeral.*

8. Since the term algebra refers to the "reduction of parts to a whole," may an assembly line in industry properly be considered as an algebraic operation?

9. Do you agree that "to infer is human"? Are all inferences true? How can the truth of an inference be determined?

10. In what respects are "directional counting" and "directional measurement" alike?

11. Since the numeral 5 is easier to use in computing than is the verbal counterpart, five, does it follow that -5 is likewise easier to use than its verbal counterparts, five below zero, five blocks to the west, five dollars in the hole, and so forth?

12. How may one tell whether the $-$ or $+$ signs are *verbs* indicating operations or merely *adjectives* identifying which directional number is being considered?

13. How would you make clear the statement that the *sum* of two numbers having unlike signs is equal to their *difference,* given the sign of the larger number value?

14. Is it true that the *difference* between two number values is measured by what needs *to be added* to the lesser to make it equal to the greater?

15. Explain how the commutative principle as applied with multiplication helps in deriving the generalization that "the product of two factors having unlike signs will be negative."

16. Show that the common statement that "a double negative makes a positive" is illustrated by the subtraction of a negative quantity as well as the multiplication of two negative factors.

17. In what respects are the verbal statements, "upper right-hand corner," "south-southwest," and "three rows from the windows and four rows from the front," comparable to locations on a coordinate chart?

18. Construct a coordinate graph of the sunrise times for a month prior to, and a month following, the summer solstice. (The *World Almanac* presents the needed data. It also contains many other bits of information that may be graphically depicted.)

19. Compare "pronumerals" with pronouns as to their respective uses in communicating general ideas.

20. In what ways do the orthographic techniques used with algebraic expressions simplify communication?

Suggested Readings

Banks, J. Houston, *Elements of Mathematics*. Boston, Mass.: Allyn and Bacon, Inc., 1956, Chap. 7.

Davis, Robert B., and others, *Supplementary Modern Mathematics, For Grades 1 through 9*. St. Louis, Mo.: Webster College (Madison Project).

Davis, Robert B., "Algebra in Grades Four, Five, and Six," *Grade Teacher*, vol. 79 (April 1962), pp. 57, 106–109.

Driscoll, Lucy E., "Ordered Pairs, Patterns, and Graphs in Fourth Grade," *The Arithmetic Teacher*, vol. 8 (March 1961), pp. 127–130.

Hogben, Lancelot, *Mathematics for the Million*. New York: W. W. Norton & Company, Inc., 1941, Chaps. 3 and 7.

Johnson, Donovan A., and William H. Glenn, "*Adventures in Graphing*. St. Louis, Mo.: Webster Publishing Division, McGraw-Hill Book Company, Inc., 1961.

Lansdown, Brenda, "Exploring Rate Graphs with Gifted Ten-year-olds," *The Arithmetic Teacher*, vol. 11 (March 1964), pp. 146–149.

Meserve, Bruce E., and Max A. Sobel, *Introduction to Mathematics*. Englewood Cliffs, N. J.: Prentice-Hall, Inc., 1964, Chap. 8.

Mueller, Francis J., "Building Algebra Readiness in Grades Seven and Eight," *The Arithmetic Teacher*, vol. 6 (November 1959), pp. 269–273.

Page, David A., "Number Lines for the Orbiting Atomic Teacher," *Grade Teacher*, vol. 79 (April 1962), pp. 53, 100–103.

Parsons, Cynthia, "Algebra in the Fourth Grade," *The Arithmetic Teacher*, vol. 7 (February 1960), pp. 77–79.

Sawyer, W.W., "Algebra in Grade Five," *The Arithmetic Teacher*, vol. 7 (January 1960), pp. 25–27.

12

Geometry: Measurement
of Space and Time

"I keep six honest serving-men.
(They taught me all I knew);
Their names are *what* and *why* and *when*,
And *how* and *where* and *who*."

Rudyard Kipling

12.1 MEASUREMENT of SPACE and TIME

READING THE SPACE ENVIRONMENT

We all have need for "honest serving men" to aid us in reading our environment. Everyone experiences phenomena of space and time. The answers to the perennial questions, *where, when, in what direction, how far, how long, what shape, how much,* and so forth, involve us in space-time discriminations. But space and time, as such, are difficult to identify and to pin down and define. They appear to be continuous and intrinsically unstructured. Hence, they are identified only by objects or events that occur within them and that offer cues for structuring and measurement.

GEOMETRY AND CHRONOMETRY: IMPORTANT
AREAS FOR MATHEMATICKING

The term *geometry* is a combined form of the Greek term *ge* meaning "earth" + *metrein* meaning "to measure." Geometry implies *earth measurement*. However, little in the study of what is called geometry in the elementary school curriculum has direct reference to measurement of the earth. It is more commonly concerned with the identification and measurement of other forms in space. Hence, the term "spacometry" might well be used. The concern is mainly with points, lines, surfaces, solids, angles, distances, directions, and so forth.

How many sides?

The word *chronometry* is a combined form of the term *chron* referring to *"time"* + *metrein* meaning "to measure." Chronometry implies *time measurement*. The structuring of space and time is initially simple to accomplish and everyone achieves it to a considerable degree. However, as concern extends beyond such immediate experiences, measurement becomes less obvious and more difficult.

THE MANY TERMS REFERRING TO SPACE
AND TIME MEASUREMENTS

The fact that our common language is replete with terms that symbolize ideas regarding space, time, and form indicates the prevalence and the importance of mathematicking with such notions. Some idea of the commonness of experiences with space and time can be derived from noting the terms that are used to refer to position or to identify and to quantify specific portions of those phenomena. For example, in order to answer the simple question "Where?" the terms range all the way from such immediate references as "here," "there," "near," "far," "before," "behind," "above," "below," and so on, to references concerned with location anywhere on the earth and even in outer space. In like manner, answers to the question "When?" may range from simple statements such as "right now" or "sometime" to a very precise and exacting point or interval in the time-line sequence. These may refer to such diverse measures as milleniums and milliseconds. Measurements of space and of time are prevalent in everyone's experience. They are important matters for mathematical instruction.

SPACE AND TIME STRUCTURED BY OBJECTS AND EVENTS

The process of structuring the continua of space and of time is basically intuitive and simple in nature. Objects that occur in space offer primary cues for its structuring. As objects are identified, they are sensed in positional relationship. Some thing is chosen as a referent and other things are then located directionally in relation to it. For example, with the individual using himself as a referent, he may perceive other things (relatums) as being near at hand, far away, above him or below, to the right of him or to the left, in front of him or behind. This personalized referent-relatum relationship becomes separated from the individual and is applied to other selected objects in other situations. It finally becomes abstracted so that the referent may be an imaginary "point" in space, and directional cues may be used to locate other things in relation to it.

The structuring of time is somewhat less complicated than is the structuring of space. Time is a continuum with only linear or straight-line dimension. "Time marches on," but it does not extend sideways or depthwise. Hence, by selecting any event as a referent point, time can be described in reference to that event as preceding it, following it, or occurring simultaneously. A time line can be symbolized as is done by a number line extending bidirectionally from some designated point or reference. For example, the day is measured from the zenith position of the sun. The portion of the day prior to that positional event is termed ante meridian (before the sun is above the meridian) and the portion of the day that follows the noon or zenith position is termed post meridian (afternoon). In like manner, the chronology of years is measured from some event such as birth or other important events, and the periods before and after the selected events are designated. Everyone experiences this procedure in relation to his own birthday and in the use of a clock.

QUANTIFYING SPACE AND TIME—A MORE DIFFICULT TASK THAN MERELY STRUCTURING THEM POSITIONALLY

Determining "where" and "when" is not the same as determining "how much." Time may be measured intuitively by observing the recurrence of events. For example, the regular recurrence of sunrise and sunset, the sequential appearance of the moon, and the periodic change of season are ready-made reference points for the construction of time-measurement units.

Space measurement is more involved than is the measurement of time. While time measurement is concerned mainly with sequential or linear measurement, the measurement of space must deal with linear distance and direction, surface coverage, and depth or volume. Space measurement is further complicated by our need to identify and to quantify particular objects, such as particular forms and shapes. In addition to these, there is the matter of angular measurement to be considered.

Initially all of these measurements are performed more or less intuitively in simple mathematical behavior, but as extension and refinement are required the intuitive procedures are insufficient. They need to be modified, implemented, developed, and standardized in order that they may become adequate for personal needs and effective for social communication. A major function of instruction in mathematics in the primary and secondary schools is that of stimulating and directing the discovery, extension, and refinement of the student's ideas and practices regarding the measurement of space and of time. The manner in which this function is served is a matter of considerable importance. Two aspects of the developmental process need to be considered. The first aspect has to do with conceiving and refining the ideas that constitute the body of knowledge concerning space and time. The second is concerned with achieving competence with the expression and communication of the ideas. In general, the conception of the ideas should precede attempts to master the technical language. Reversing that sequence frequently leads to mere verbalization with little or no understanding of the terms which are used.

12.2 SPACE: CONCRETE REALITY and ABSTRACT PERCEPTION

The immediate spatial environment is replete with figures that give it discernible characteristics. We readily perceive objects in locational relationship. The relationships have characteristics of position, direction, and distance. The objects have characteristics of shape and size.

Everyone experiences immediate spatial phenomena and reacts with regard to them. From this behavior, ideas of location, direction, distance, form, and so forth, are conceived. However, as one's environmental horizon expands, ideas need to be modified, extended, and refined. For example, the clear sky presents an entirely different type of spatial situation than does the immediate earth-bound terrain. Structuring space without concrete guides as to location, direction, distance, form, and so forth, such as conceiving of a clear sky, calls for imaginative abstraction. Such ideas are quite different from those that serve so readily for the highly structured immediate earth environment.

Just as the physicist and chemist find it necessary to delve more deeply into the nature of things than is necessary for those who deal only with the immediate physical and chemical substances, so also does the student of space need to conceive of some simpler structure that is basic for resolving his field. For the physicist and chemist, atoms and atomic behavior serve this purpose. For the student of space, a similar, simple structural unit is the idea of a point. The idea that space is an infinite, universal set of points and that every figure in space is essentially a subset of points is currently serving that purpose for the student of space. It fits well with the theory of sets and with the terminology that has been developed in connection with sets. (See Chapter 3.) However, the ideas are extremely abstract concepts for pupils of primary grade to comprehend. There is danger that ideas of space will be presented in a "tell-and-do" fashion. Students may learn the definitions, but they are not likely to conceive of the concrete space phenomena being described by them.

There are divergent points of view concerning the nature of space. One may be termed "static." Points, as the elemental structures of space, are conceived to be positionally fixed and immutable. All of the figures in space, according to this point of view, are specific sets of points permanently situated and available to be identified. A technique for making the identification is a primary requirement.

Differing from this conception is an idea of dynamics. According to this point of view, points, lines, and all other figures in space are conceived to be movable. Their motion identifies other figures and offers potential descriptions of spatial phenomena. For example, a point in motion describes a line. This is comparable to the concrete experience that one has as he moves the "point" of a pencil on the surface of a sheet of paper. The "line" records the path of the pencil, and it may also symbolize an idea. Since, in so far as is known, the cosmic universe is constantly in motion and undergoing change, it seems reasonable to incorporate these functions within ideas of space. Meaningful conceptions are achieved through experience. Concrete experiences of the spatial

environment must provide the basis for the comprehension for generalized ideas. In the discussions that follow, both static and dynamic
descriptions are considered.

12.3 POINTS and LINES

Points are locative devices without dimension. A point has no size.
It is smaller than any dot that you can see. Points are abstract mental
creations which serve as positional referents in much the same manner
that concrete objects serve in our intuitive structuring of space.

Space is sometimes described as a universal, infinite set of points.
However, such identifications fail to distinguish the characteristics of
dimension, direction, distance, form, size, and so forth, that are necessary
for the comprehension of spatial phenomena. For example, since a point
does not occupy space, how can a set of points acquire properties of
dimension that are essential for spatial structuring? It appears that each
spatial figure must have characteristic properties which distinguish it
and which are necessary for its identification and interpretation. These
properties must be included along with the idea of a set of points and
the definition of the figure.

Lines are sets of points having a single dimension — length. As
mentioned above, in dynamic terms, a line may be thought of as the
path identified by a point in motion. The points that are members of
the set of points which compose the line should be described as being
IN the line. They are not ON the line.

Lines are conceived as extending in both directions without end.
Symbols such as the ones in Fig. 12.1 may be used to represent a line.

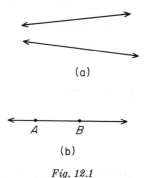

(a)

(b)

Fig. 12.1

The arrowheads at each end of the symbol indicate that the line extends
continuously in two directions. A line may be named by any two of
its points. The line in Fig. 12.1(b) may be called "line AB" and is
symbolized as $\overleftrightarrow{AB}$.

When we identify a particular portion of a line that joins any two of its points, we are talking about a *line segment*. Figure 12.2(a) represents a line segment. Points A and C and the set of points between

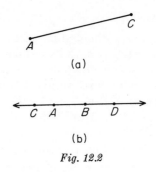

(a)

(b)

Fig. 12.2

them in the line compose a line segment. A line segment is symbolized by naming its terminal points with a bar placed over them, $\overline{AC}$.

Any line contains an infinite number of line segments. Name some of the line segments that are indicated for $\overleftrightarrow{CD}$ in Fig. 12.2(b).

If concern is with a portion of a line that begins at a specified point and extends continuously in only one direction, the term *ray* is used. In Fig. 12.3(b), the point A and the set of points to the right of A are called ray AC which may be written $\overrightarrow{AC}$. The arrow is used to show

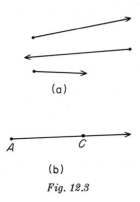

(a)

(b)

Fig. 12.3

that the ray continues endlessly in the direction indicated. A ray has only one endpoint. However, a given endpoint in a line may serve for two rays. Since there are only two directions in a line, only two rays in the same line have a single, common endpoint. However, there are infinitely many rays in a line, since each point in a line may serve as the endpoint for two rays.

Not all lines maintain a constant direction. Some are irregular or broken. Some are curved, that is, they are not irregular but they have a common starting point and ending point: they enclose a portion of space, forming a surface figure.

12.4   SURFACES as an AID in STRUCTURING SPACE

Many types of surfaces are experienced as we deal with the concrete things in our spatial environment. Floors, walls, ceilings, doors, table tops, and other flat surfaces suggest the idea that space be structured by surfaces having characteristic properties of length and breadth. (See Fig. 12.4.) Hence, a plane may be conceived as "a particular set

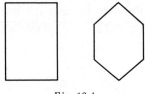

Fig. 12.4

of points which can be thought of as the extension of a flat surface such as a table."[1] A plane surface may also be identified in static terms by any three points that are not in the same line. Or, it may be described in dynamic terms as the path that would be generated by a line moving sideways.

Much of our mathematical experience is related to identifying and quantifying figures and objects that are observed as plane figures. This part of mathematics is sometimes referred to as "plane geometry." Since many of the tasks with which it is concerned are not directly related with earth measurement, the term "planometry" (the measurement of planes) may be more clearly representative of the activities involved.

PLANE GEOMETRY OR PLANOMETRY:
THE MEASUREMENT OF PLANE FIGURES

Plane geometry consists in identifying particular sets of points within a plane surface and then describing certain of the relationships that are observed among them. The simplest of the figures within a plane are points and line segments. Linear measurement consists in selecting some suitable unit of linear distance and then applying it to the line segment

---

[1] School Mathematics Study Group, *Studies in Mathematics*, vol. 9. Stanford, Calif.: Stanford University, 1963, p. 466.

to determine the ratio of their relationship. Everyone makes such measurements intuitively, but the process and the units of measure are also refined and standardized — for example, the English and metric systems of linear measurement. (See Chapter 10.) Linear measurement is the simplest and most basic form of space measurement. The tasks of making the process understood and developing competence with the systems used are important parts of mathematical instruction.

ANGLES AND THEIR MEASUREMENT

Everyone experiences *corners*, which commonly occur in spatial configurations. The term *angle* symbolizes the idea of corners. One concept of a plane angle identifies it in static terms as a set of points composed of the union of the sets of points in two rays having a common point of origin. For example, the angle for Fig. 12.5(c) may be described as $\overrightarrow{BA} \cup \overrightarrow{BC}$. Since both $\overrightarrow{BA}$ and $\overrightarrow{BC}$ are infinite sets of points, their union

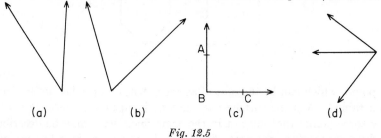

(a)   (b)   (c)   (d)

Fig. 12.5

is equivalent to two infinite sets of points minus one point which is the endpoint common to both sets. Such identification offers no cues for differentiating among angles, nor does it suggest any application for measurement of angles. Differentiating among angles and measuring angles are important aspects of common experience with angular phenomena.

A plane angle may also be conceived as a *portion of a plane* that is identified by two rays having a common endpoint. According to this conception, angles differ in relation to the portion of the plane that lies between their sides. Hence, angular measurement consists in quantifying that plane surface. Since that surface is not limited, it is not amenable to areal measurement, such as may be made with enclosed areas. The measurement of an angle is a measure of the slope of its sides. By using the concept of the primary elements of a plane, that is, a point and a ray extending from that point, we can devise a useful description of an angle. For example, an angle may be described by a ray rotating about its point of origin. The path identified by the rotation symbolizes the angle.

The line of sight directly in front of a person as he pivots about a fixed position is a personal illustration of such rotational phenomena. The portion of the complete turn that has been accomplished at any moment of concern is the measure of the angle formed between the starting point (referent position) of the ray and its present position. Hence, angular measurement is a measure of rotation.

When a ray makes a complete rotation about its point of origin, it describes what is termed a perigon or "round angle." *Perigon* is derived from a combination of Greek terms: *peri* meaning "all around," and *gonia* meaning "angle." A complete rotation is the mathematical phenomenon to be scaled. Since this differs from other measurements, it requires a special scaling. A unit referent of the same type of thing to be scaled needs to be selected. Since rotational movement is limited in extent, it calls for a finite, modular system of scaling.

The complete rotation has been arbitrarily scaled into 360 equal segments (unit measures), called *degrees*. The selection of this number for the segmentation of the perigon illustrates how mathematics utilizes the common experiences of peoples to resolve problems. Three hundred sixty was chosen for the number of divisions because, at the time this measure was developed, it was thought that a year was composed of 360 days as units of time measurement. The annual time cycle was likened to the rotation of a pivoting act. Recently the rotation has been scaled in a thousand equal units which are called mills.

Angles are classified according to the number of degrees of rotation between their sides. An angle measuring 90 degrees or $\frac{1}{4}$ of a full rotation

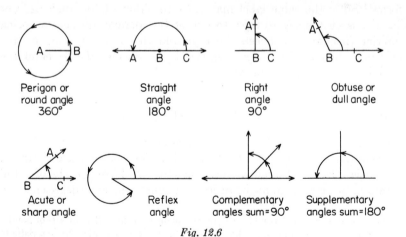

Fig. 12.6

is called a *right angle*. An angle having 180 degrees between its sides looks like a straight line. It is called a *straight angle*. If an angle contains less than 90 degrees it is termed *acute*, that is, sharp. If it measures more than 90 but less than 180 degrees, it is called *obtuse*, meaning dull or blunt. An angle greater than 180 degrees but less than 360 degrees is termed a *reflex angle*. And, an angle containing 360 degrees is referred to as a perigon or *round angle*.

Space measurement has many types of angles, several of which are shown in Fig. 12.6.

In mathematical language an angle is symbolized by the simple sign ∠. The plural of that symbol is ∠ˢ. When reference is made to a particular angle, it is commonly identified by naming the rays that form its sides. Since the rays have one point in common, that point is designated as the vertex or pivotal point of the angle. For example, the rays *BA* and *BC* intersect at point *B*:

$$B \diagup^{A} C$$

Hence, they form an angle which is designated as

$$\angle ABC \quad \text{or} \quad \angle CBA \quad \text{or} \quad \angle B$$

In constructing such a symbol for naming angles, the vertex or pivotal point is named between the other points that identify the sides (rays).

Any angular form divides space into two segments. Just as any line divides a plane into two parts, an angular form other than a perigon divides the rotational area into two parts, or actually into two angular forms.[2] Since the same label may refer to either of the angles ∠ or ∠, it is customary to refer to one of the angular surfaces as being interior (inside) or between the rays and the other as lying on the exterior (outside). The usual practice is to consider the lesser of the angular surfaces: those "inside."

A MEASUREMENT SCALE FOR ANGLES

As mentioned previously, the basic angular rotation, the round angle (perigon), has been scaled into 360 equal sections called degrees. Hence, the basic referent of angular measurement is 1 degree or $\frac{1}{360}$ of a full rotation. Since measurements of lesser amounts than one degree need to

---

[2] Some writers assert that a line separates a plane into three disjoint sets of points: the line and the two half planes. This appears to attribute a spatial characteristic to the line. Hence, we prefer to think of the line merely as a symbol indicating where one spatial entity terminates and another begins.

be made, the basic referent is divided or scaled into 60 equal units called minutes. Minutes are similarly scaled into 60 smaller units called seconds. These scalings are comparable to the scaling of the rotational movement of the hands of a clock, except that the complete rotation for the clock-hand is divided into 12 or into 24 equal segments which are called hours.

A protractor is used to measure angles. Just as a calibrated ruler is used to measure linear distance, a comparable instrument adapted to circular measurement is used to measure angular forms. The most common type of protractor consists of a calibrated semicircle. However, a full circle or round angle calibrated to give directional bearings is also extensively used. These instruments (see Fig. 12.7) illustrate the two

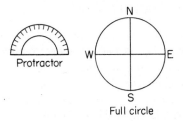

Fig. 12.7 Instruments for angular measurement.

major uses of angular measurement: (1) to quantify the measurement of the angle, or (2) to identify a directional relationship between the sides of an angle when one side is used as a basal referent.

12.5   PLANE FIGURES

In addition to identifying particular points, lines, angles, and directional characteristics of space there is concern for identifying and quantifying particular portions of space which may be enclosed by line segments. Figures are commonly identified by the character of the lines that surround them or by the number or character of the angles formed by their boundary lines. For example, a circle has only one side and one angle. It may be described as a portion of a plane surrounded by a closed curved line all points of which are equally distant from a point within the enclosure. Other common plane figures which are bounded wholly or in part by curved lines are the semicircle, the quadrant (quarter circle), and the oval or ellipse. Each of these has special properties and special uses that need to be developed. However, the major concern for elementary school experience is with the circle and with plane figures which are bounded by straight-line segments. Figures enclosed by three or more than three line segments are called *polygons*.

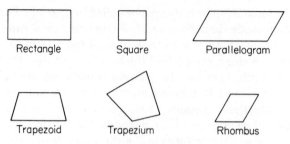

Fig. 12.8 Plane figures.

PLANE FIGURES CLASSIFIED ACCORDING TO THE NUMBER OF SIDES OR ANGLES

Plane figures may be classified according to the *number of sides or angles*. They may also be described as being *regular* (having sides that are equal in length) or *irregular* (sides unequal). Trigonal or triangular figures classified under this schema are (1) equilateral (all sides having the same length); (2) isosceles, two sides equal in length (*iso*, meaning *equal* + *skelos*, meaning *legs*); and (3) scalene (unequal sides).

TABLE 12.1

NUMBER OF SIDES	NAME OF FIGURE
one	perigon or round angle
two	gonia or angle
three	trigon or triangle
four	"quadrigon," quadrangle, or quadrilateral
five	pentagon
six	hexagon
seven	heptagon
eight	octagon
nine	nonagon
ten	decagon
.	.
.	.
.	.

Quadrilateral or four-sided figures are classified according to several criteria: (1) the comparative length of the sides, (2) the character of the corners or angles, and (3) the parallelism of the sides. If the sides are equal and the angles are equal, the figure is a square. If the sides are equal but the angles are unequal, the figure is a rhombus. If no two sides are parallel, the figure is a trapezium (Greek term meaning "little table"). If only two sides are parallel, the figure is called a trapezoid. If both pairs of opposite sides are parallel, the figure is called a parallelogram, that is, it is written or drawn by parallel lines. A parallelogram having right angles is called a rectangle (*rect* meaning *right*). Fewer classifications are made among the figures having five or more sides.

MEASUREMENT OF PLANE FIGURES

Measurements of the plane figures are of several types: (1) linear or length measure of the sides, (2) perimeter or distance around, (3) diagonal (*dia* + *gonal*) meaning "across the angles," (4) altitude (*alti*, meaning "high" + *tude*, a suffix meaning "ness" or height, and (5) surface coverage or area. Except for the measurement of area, these are all linear measures. Linear measurement consists in selecting a suitable unit of length and then determining how many such units are needed to equal the particular distance with which we are concerned.

The measurement of the area of a plane figure calls for the selection of a unit for measurement. Do you see how a square unit (see Fig. 12.9)

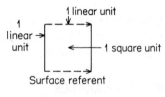

Fig. 12.9

may be used as a referent for surface measurement in the same manner that the linear unit is used as a referent for distance measurement? When it is so used, it may properly be termed a "unit of surface measure" or a surface unit.

A SQUARE UNIT OR SURFACE UNIT SERVING AS A REFERENT FOR SURFACE MEASUREMENT

The fact that the surface unit is rectangular makes its application to the measurement of rectangular figures direct and simple. For example,

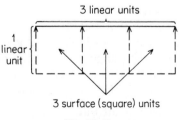

Fig. 12.10

a rectangular figure that is 3 linear units in length and 1 linear unit wide contains 3 square units of surface (Fig. 12.10). Whatever linear unit is selected — inches, feet, yards, meters, and so forth — the surface unit will be a square having that unit for its side. It is evident that, if the rectangular figure is 3 of such units in length and 2 of the units in width, it will contain 2 tiers of 3 square units each making 6 square units in

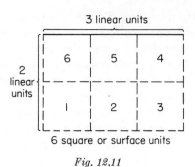

Fig. 12.11

all (Fig. 12.11). Hence, *the number of square units in a rectangular figure is equal to the product of the number of linear units in its length multiplied by the number of such linear units in its width.*

12.6   MEASUREMENT of TRIANGLES

SURFACE MEASUREMENT OF RIGHT TRIANGLES (TRIGONS) DERIVED FROM THAT OF RECTANGLES

The measurement of triangles is properly termed *trigonometry* (*trigon* + *metry*). The study of this field of mathematics emerges naturally from 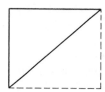 the study of rectangles, since one form of triangle has one angle that is a right angle (measures 90 degrees). Because of this characteristic, such triangles are classed as "right triangles." By constructing a rectangle using the sides of the right angle for its length and width, respectively, it is readily observed that the rectangle contains two congruent (identical) right triangles. Hence, the area of a right triangle is shown to be equal to one half of the area of a rectangle having the same linear measurements as the sides of the right angle, namely, the product of the length and width divided by two. This is commonly expressed as base (B) multiplied by altitude (A) divided by 2, or more simply as

$$\frac{BA}{2} \quad \text{or} \quad \text{area} = \frac{\text{base} \times \text{altitude}}{2}$$

MEASUREMENT OF OTHER TRIANGLES INFERRED FROM THE MEASUREMENT OF RIGHT TRIANGLES

Just as the measurement of the right triangle is inferred from the measurement of the rectangle, the measurement of other types of triangles may be inferred from the measurement of the right triangle. For example, an isosceles or an equilateral triangular surface may be resolved into two congruent right triangles by constructing a straight-line segment from the vertex of the angle formed by two equal sides and forming right angles with the side opposite. (This can be illustrated by folding illustrations of such surfaces so that the two equal sides coincide.) Such a line cuts the surfaces into two congruent right tri-

angles, and it also represents the altitude measure of the respective triangles. Since the surface measure of each of the right triangles is equal to one half of the product of its base and altitude, the area of the original triangles is the sum of the areas of the respective right triangles formed from it. Thus, it also must be equal to one half the product of its base and altitude.

The case of the scalene triangle (a triangle having no two sides equal in length) may be attacked in a comparable manner (see Fig. 12.12). For example, in a figure such as triangle ABC, if a perpendicular

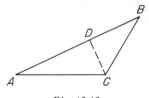

Fig. 12.12

is drawn from the vertex C to the side AB it divides triangle ABC into two right triangles, ADC and BDC, respectively. The area of each of these has been shown to equal one half of the product of its base multiplied by its altitude. Using DC as the altitude in both instances, we find that the area of triangle ADC is equal to

$$\frac{(DC)(AD)}{2}$$

and that the area of triangle BDC is equal to

$$\frac{(DC)(BD)}{2}$$

Now since triangle ABC is made up of triangles ADC and BDC, we can combine the measures of their areas and we find the area of triangle ABC equal to

$$\frac{(DC)(AD) + (DC)(BD)}{2}$$

By applying the distributive principle of multiplication, we simplify that expression to read

$$\frac{(DC)(AD + BD)}{2}$$

Since $AD + BD$ is equal to AB, the expression can be written

$$\frac{(DC)(AB)}{2}$$

Once again we find that the area of a triangle is equal to one half of the product of its base multiplied by its altitudes.

THE AREA OF A PLANE TRIANGLE (TRIGON): EQUAL TO ONE HALF OF THE PRODUCT OF ITS BASE AND ITS ALTITUDE

The preceding discussion illustrates how surface measurements based upon the idea of a simple square unit of measure can be applied to determine the surface measure of any type of plane triangle. However, there are other aspects of trigonometry (triangular measurement) which a study of the right triangle may also reveal.

OTHER TRIGONOMETRIC FUNCTIONS

Relationships of Dependency

Relationships of dependency or function are characteristic of right triangles. Actually the act of mathematicking is the observing and quantifying of relationships in general. For example, since one of the angles of a right triangle is a right angle, the sum of the other two angles must be 90 degrees. Hence, when the measure of either of the acute angles is established, that determines the measure of the other acute angle. This is a property used in calculating some of the other properties of the right triangle, which we shall point out later.

The sides of the right angle may be extended indefinitely. Thus, it is evident that the length of the side opposite the right angle (the hypotenuse) will be determined by the lengths given to the sides of the right angle. That this relationship is constant has been known since very early times. It is the subject of the Pythagorean theorem, which states that the length of the hypotenuse of a right triangle is equal to the square root of the sum of the squares of the lengths of the sides of the right angle. It is variously stated, but a common version is *the square of the hypotenuse equals the sum of the squares of the legs of a right triangle*. The idea may be illustrated by constructing a right triangle that has sides of its right angle 3 inches and 4 inches, respectively (Fig. 12.13). The long side or hypotenuse will measure 5 inches.

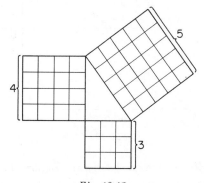

Fig. 12.13

Squares constructed upon the respective sides will indicate the relationship.

Further study of the relationships among the parts of the right triangle suggests the possibility of dependency on the size of an acute angle and the sides opposite and adjacent to it. That the amount of spread between the sides of an acute angle will affect the length of the side opposite it should be obvious. And since that side must make a right angle with one side of the acute angle, the length of the other side of that acute angle will also be determined.

The Six Trigonometric Ratios or Functions

There are six ways in which two sides of a right angle triangle may be compared. For each of the acute angles, the side opposite the angle may be compared with the hypotenuse in length, and the side adjacent to the angle may also be compared with the hypotenuse in length, and the side opposite may be compared with the side adjacent. Each of these comparisons may be made with either member used as the referent.

Each of these comparisons has been given a name. The ratio of the side opposite to the hypotenuse is called the *sine* of the angle. The ratio of the side adjacent to the hypotenuse is called the *cosine* of the angle. In like manner, the ratio of the hypotenuse to the side adjacent is called the *secant* of the angle, and the hypotenuse to the side opposite is termed the *cosecant*. The ratio of the side opposite to the side adjacent is named the *tangent*. And the ratio of the side adjacent

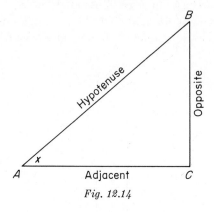

Fig. 12.14

to the side opposite is named *cotangent*. Figure 12.14 may help to clarify the references of these terms. For X, the six ratios are the following:

$$Sine \text{ ratio is } \frac{BC}{AB} = \frac{\text{side opposite the angle}}{\text{hypotenuse}}$$

$$Cosine \text{ ratio is } \frac{AC}{AB} = \frac{\text{side adjacent the angle}}{\text{hypotenuse}}$$

$$Tangent \text{ ratio is } \frac{BC}{AC} = \frac{\text{side opposite the angle}}{\text{side adjacent to the angle}}$$

$$Cotangent \text{ ratio is } \frac{AC}{BC} = \frac{\text{side adjacent to angle}}{\text{side opposite the angle}}$$

$$Secant \text{ ratio is } \frac{AB}{AC} = \frac{\text{hypotenuse}}{\text{side adjacent the angle}}$$

$$Cosecant \text{ ratio is } \frac{AB}{BC} = \frac{\text{hypotenuse}}{\text{side opposite the angle}}$$

It is not expected that these six trigonometric functions should be directly presented as part of the elementary school curriculum. However, it is important for teachers to interpret them, and certain pupils may be led to investigate the possibilities of such relationships.

12.7   MEASUREMENT of NONRECTANGULAR QUADRILATERALS

PARALLELOGRAMS STRUCTURED INTO TRIANGLES

Parallelograms that are not rectangles may also be structured into two congruent triangles merely by means of a diagonal line from opposite vertices (Fig. 12.15). Then, if a perpendicular is erected to the parallel

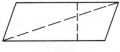

Fig. 12.15

lines serving as the bases for the triangles it will serve as an altitude for both of the triangles. Since the triangles are congruent, and since the area of the parallelogram is equal to the sum of the respective triangles, it is evident that the area of the parallelogram is measured by the product of the linear measure of one of its sides multiplied by the altitude erected to that side.

TRAPEZOIDS STRUCTURED INTO TRIANGLES

Deriving a procedure for finding the area of a trapezoid (figure with only two sides parallel) presents a somewhat different problem because the diagonal does not produce congruent triangles. However, a perpendicular erected between the two parallel sides serves as an

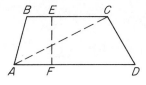

Fig. 12.16

altitude for both triangles. This makes possible the following calculations as illustrated in Fig. 12.16. S stands for surface area.

$$S \text{ of triangle } ABC = \frac{(BC)(EF)}{2}$$

$$S \text{ of triangle } ADC = \frac{(AD)(EF)}{2}$$

Hence, the sum of the two triangles is equal to

$$\frac{(BC)(EF) + (AD)(EF)}{2}$$

Simplifying by using the distributive property of multiplication this becomes

$$\frac{(BC + AD)(EF)}{2}$$

This may be verbally stated: *The area of a trapezoid is measured by one half of the sum of its parallel sides multiplied by the altitude between those sides.*

A TRAPEZIUM STRUCTURED INTO TRIANGLES

In like manner, the area of a trapezium (a figure with no sides parallel) may also be determined by dividing it into triangles by means of a diagonal, and then erecting perpendiculars from that diagonal used as a

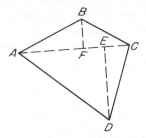

Fig. 12.17

base to the vertices of the respective triangles. (See Fig. 12.17.) Then the areas of the triangles may be calculated:

$$\text{area of triangle } ABC = \frac{(AC)(BF)}{2}$$

$$\text{area of triangle } ADC = \frac{(AC)(ED)}{2}$$

Hence, the area of the trapezium

$$ABCD = \frac{(AC)(BF) + (AC)(ED)}{2}$$

By applying the distributive property this becomes

$$\frac{(AC)(BF + ED)}{2}$$

The area of a trapezium is measured by one half of the product of its diagonal multiplied by the sum of the altitudes from the diagonal to the respective vertices opposite it.

12.8   MEASUREMENT of CIRCULAR SURFACES

The complete rotation of a line segment about one of its endpoints serving as a pivot illustrates a round angle. It also describes a surface that is called a *circle*. The endpoint opposite the pivot forms a line which is called the *circumference of the circle*. The pivotal point of the rotation is called the *center of the circle*. The line segment extending from the center to the circumference is termed a *radius*. Since the radius is the same as the line segment that by rotating describes the circle, all radii of a given circle are equal in length. A straight-line segment extending through the center of a circle and terminating at the circumference is called a *diameter of the circle* (*dia* meaning "across" + *metron* meaning "measure"). The diameter is equal to twice the length of the radius.

That there is a relationship between the diameter and the circumference of a circle is apparent. What the relationship may be and whether it is the same for all circles is not so apparent. However, it is not difficult to make approximate measurements of the diameters and circumferences of a considerable number of circular forms of various sizes such as wheels, cans, and so on, and then compare the findings. See Lesson 1 at the end of this chapter. The children's conclusion that the circumference "is a bit more than 3 times the diameter" in length is a good mathematical generalization. Having arrived at that conclusion, the children may be told that a number which represents the ratio of the circumference to the diameter is $3\frac{1}{7}$ or 3.1416. The ratio is commonly referred to as "pi." Its symbol is π.

It is interesting to note that our system of notation cannot produce a numeral which exactly symbolizes the value of the circumference-diameter ratio. By the use of an electric computer, the numeral has been calculated to 100,000 digit places[3] without finding an even division. Hence, this number idea is said to be "irrational." This should not imply that it is "unreasonable," because the idea that there is a constant relationship between the length of the circumference and the length of its diameter appears to be very *reasonable*. The term "irrational" as used in this connection implies that the numerical value of this ratio cannot be computed exactly by means of our system of notation.

The generalized statements that the length of the circumference (C) is equal to the diameter (D) multiplied by pi $(3.1416\ldots)$ namely, $C = \pi D$, or $C = 2\pi R$, needs to be formulated and made clear and readily recallable. They are used extensively in dealing with circular figures.

[3] *Science News Letter*, vol. 80, September 9, 1961, p. 167

CIRCULAR AREA APPROXIMATED FROM TRIANGULAR MEASUREMENTS

The measurement of the area of circular figures offers further opportunity for the application of the properties of the right triangle. See Lesson 8. This may not be readily evident because of the curved boundary of the circular figure. However, an approximate measurement is sufficient for bringing out a basic relationship.

The observation that the area of a circle is approximately three times the square of its radius is an important generalization. The fact that this relationship is similar to that of the diameter and its circumference measurements should aid in its being conceived and made easy to recall. The general formula for finding the surface area (S) of a circle, $S = \pi R^2$, needs to be developed in such a manner that the student clearly understands how it is derived and how it can be utilized.

There are, of course, other plane figures that will need to have some consideration. Those discussed above are the more common ones, and their treatment offers clues for the treatment of other types.

12.9   THE THIRD DIMENSION of SPACE

Everyone experiences the characteristic of depth in the space around him. However, the matter of devising ways for describing depth and for quantifying it, both as a general characteristic and as a special property of identified figures in space, presents a problem. Mathematicking with space and with objects in space can be interesting and profitable. Essentially the task of structuring space in a third dimension can be conceived in much the same manner as structuring in terms of the second dimension was accomplished.

Points, lines, and planes are still basic matters of concern, but they now are associated with three-dimensional constructs. A plane was identified as a portion of space described by a straight line moving sideways. In like manner, the depth dimension of space may be thought of as being described by a plane moving vertically to its surface or as rotating about a line on its surface.

Just as a line rotating about a point describes a plane angle, a plane rotating about a line describes a three-dimensional angle, that is, an angle, the sides of which have depth.

Angles having planes for their sides are called *hedra*, because they resemble the form of a *chair*. "Hedra" is a Greek term for "chair." The two-sided angle is called *dihedral* (see Fig. 12.18). A three-sided one is called *tri-hedral*. Others are named in a similar manner using a prefix to designate the number of sides. Dihedral angles are classified as right dihedrals, acute, obtuse, and so forth, in the same manner that plane angles were classified.

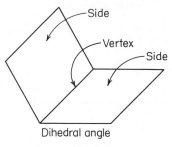

Fig. 12.18

Everyone experiences dihedral angles very often. They occur whenever two plane surfaces intersect, for example, where walls meet, where walls and ceilings join, or where walls and floors come together, or when one opens a hinged door. They are found at the edges of squared boards. Dihedral angles, that is, angles formed by two planes intersecting, are common.

Trihedral angles, those formed by three planes intersecting at a point, are also commonly experienced. They are illustrated by the common intersection of the two walls and the floor or ceiling at the corner of a rectangular room. It is evident that they differ materially from dihedral angles, because their vertex is a point and not a line. The sides of trihedral angles form dihedral angles as they intersect.

Other types of tridimensional angles occur, but they are not so common in ordinary experience. They can be illustrated, however, and named by the pupils as an aid in fixating the labels for such figures.

Most of the concern in this realm of mathematics is with figures that bound three-dimensional portions of space: figures that have the characteristic of volume. In plane figures, our major concern was with the measurement of surface area. With three-dimensional figures, both surface area and volume are of concern. Hence, there is need for devising a unit to measure volume, that is, a volume-measure referent.

Since measurement is made in terms of some selected unit of the type of measurement that is desired, a sensible procedure would be to develop a volume-measurement unit from other measurement units with which one is familiar. Hence, following the same procedure used to create a unit of surface measure based upon the unit of linear measure, we think of the unit of surface measure as moving vertically to its plane for a distance equal to the length of its side. This describes a three-dimensional figure having each of its dimensions equal to the original linear unit. Such a figure is called a *cube* (Fig. 12.19). Measurement using the cubic unit is called *cubic or volume measurement*.

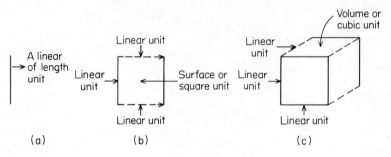

Fig. 12.19

Of course, other units of volume measurement may be used if they serve as well. For example, any container such as a cup, a teaspoon, a bushel, or other volume unit may be used as the referent and certain measurements may be made.

Solids may be identified by planes moving vertically to their surfaces. Such movement suggests that the figures on the plane will structure space accordingly. Hence, all the plane figures may take on the characteristic of the dimension of depth, thus forming new figures that are called *solids*.

The measurement of solids commonly involves finding the surface measure of the base of the figure and then transforming that into volume measurements. This is accomplished by multiplying the surface measure by the linear measure of the altitude or depth of the figure (see Fig. 12.20).

The common solid figures in some respects resemble the common plane figures. Plane figures bounded by straight lines when moved

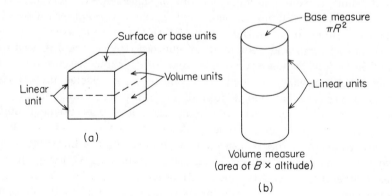

Fig. 12.20

vertically or slantingly produce solid figures called *prisms*. Prisms are classified as being triangular, quadrangular, and so forth, according to the shape of their base or generating figure. Circular figures when moved vertically or slantingly produce figures called *cylinders*. However, if a circle is rotated about its diameter it describes a unique figure which is called a *sphere*. The sphere is, of course, familiar — many balls are spherical in shape.

The geometry or space measurement pertinent for elementary school consideration deals largely with things that are readily and commonly experienced by the pupils. The inductive procedure of reading specific things carefully and noting their properties and relationships is significant in this experience. However, an important aspect is that of formulating apt generalizations and then testing them for their validity and utility. The main purpose of this instruction is to lead the learners to become competent readers of their environments insofar as ideas of space and the figures that structure space are concerned. It is not the purpose merely to develop a vocabulary of terms and a body of factual knowledge having little or no real significance for the learners. Later, more advanced instruction in mathematics should build upon this initial learning, in a manner that encourages individual interest, initiative, and purpose.

ILLUSTRATIVE LESSONS

The following illustrative lessons and lesson plans are presented in this chapter:

Lesson 1. Measuring the relationship of diameter and circumference
Lesson 2. Area of rectangular and of triangular regions
Lesson 3. Reasons and decisions in determining relationships
Lesson 4. Deriving relationships concerning the volume of right circular cylinders and right circular cones
Lesson 5. Weight
Lesson 6. Volume-shape relationship
Lesson 7. Finding the area of a circle
Lesson 8. Right triangles

Lesson 1 illustrates the nature of problem solving as it develops in experimenting with mathematical relationships. The group of children refined their concept with regard to the diameter-circumference relationship as far as was desirable for the given period of time. However, in another lesson concerning procedures for measuring, the children experimented with the other ways that had been suggested — that of using a piece of paper and that of drawing a chalk line around the can. In this lesson, which consumed approximately a 20-minute period of time, the children evolved a relationship that is frequently developed as a rule. Often the rule is accompanied by little understanding of the basic relationship. In fact, in this specific lesson, a student teacher (a college senior) who observed the lesson, gasped and said, "Gosh, 'pi *r* squared,' and I never really discovered it until today. I merely memorized the rule and accepted it because it was in a book!" *That she really had merely memorized the rule and accepted it can be readily discerned by her use of the incorrect formula for this relationship.*

Lesson 2 indicates a type of problem-solving exercise in which children can formulate basic mathematical relationships concerning the measurement of area. It is the type of lesson that lends itself to individual or to group activity.

The other lessons indicate the nature of children's sensing, hypothesizing, and formulating concepts about area and volume.

Lesson 1
MEASURING THE RELATIONSHIP OF CIRCUMFERENCE
AND DIAMETER
Grade Two Class

Purpose of lesson: To have the children discover the relationship between the distance around a circle (circumference) and the dis-

Measuring circumference-diameter.

tance across a circle (diameter). The goal was not to lead the children to express the formula as such. The two main goals for the lesson were: (a) to challenge thinking concerning procedures for measuring; and (b) to evolve the diameter-circumference relationship with language and refinement of concept that fit the development level of the given group of children.

Background of children: The group of children had been having a unit on measuring, and they had experimented with many types of measuring.

Materials used for lesson: Many cans, jars, and boxes were in the classroom. The children had brought them for their experiments with measuring. The teacher selected for this given lesson some of the jars, cans, and boxes that were cylindrical.

Lesson Procedure

[The group of children were discussing things that they had measured. One of the cans was the topic of discussion. A question was raised concerning how many times as far it was around the top of the can as it was across the top of it. The children were asked to estimate the distance around as compared with the distance across. Their estimates ranged from "about 2 times as far around" through "about 4 times as far around" as across. However, the estimate that was given by the greatest number of children was "about 3 times as far around."]

Teacher: How could we find out which children are the nearest to the correct answer?

Marilyn: We could measure with our hands like this. [Demonstrated what she meant.]

Harry: We could use a piece of paper to measure how far it is around and then measure how far it is across the can.

Peter: We could use a string. That would be easier than using a ruler.

Irene: We could use a piece of chalk to make a heavy line around the can, and then we can put the can down and see how many times it fits into the line.

Peter: I think that string would be the best to use.

[Since string was handy, it was used to measure the distance around the can. The children then suggested that we could find out how many times that amount of string would go across the top. The children, after careful measuring, discovered that it was "a bit over 3 times as far around the can as it was across the top of it."]

Kenneth: Let's see how it works with this jar. I bet it will be the same as with the can.

Mary Ann: I don't know. Let's see. Let me measure the distance around the jar.

[A number of jars, cans, and boxes (all cylindrical) were measured, and in each case the children discovered that it was "a bit over 3 times as far around as it was across." After several cans had been measured, these comments were made:]

Keith: We can measure all the jars and cans here, and it will come out the same way. We will find it is a bit over 3 times as far around as it is across.

Louis: But the bit left over is not a half of the distance across.

June: And it isn't even a quarter.

Emily: It's just a little bit.

Lesson 2

AREA OF RECTANGULAR AND OF TRIANGULAR REGIONS[4]

Grade Five Class

Purpose of lesson: To have the children evolve procedures for finding the area of rectangles and of triangles.

Background of children: The children had evolved many basic mathematical relationships through problem solving. Thus, the problem-solving setting of this lesson was not new to them.

Materials used for lesson: Cards one inch square and rectangles and triangles cut out of cardboard.

Lesson Procedure

[The teacher had a number of squares, rectangles other than squares, and many cards that were one inch square on his desk.]

Teacher: If we wanted to tell about the size of the surface of my desk, how could we describe it?

Michael: We could say that it is large in comparison with my desk.

Phillip: It is small in comparison with the size of our dining-room table.

Deanne: We could measure it and tell how many inches wide it is and how many inches long.

Patty: We could measure how many feet long and how many feet wide it is.

Teacher: [Held up a square inch.] What do you call this figure that I'm holding?

Class: It is a square.

Page: I think that it is 1 inch by 1 inch.

Patty: Don't you call it a square inch?

[4] Adapted from an unpublished lesson plan by Bob Koskinen, student teacher.

Teacher: That is right, Patty. How could you use this square inch to measure this larger square?

Gail: You have a stack of square-inch cards. We could place them on the larger square and see how many it takes. I'll show you.

[Gail placed the cards that were an inch square on the larger square.]

Gail: It took 25 of the squares.

Page: But you didn't need to put all the cards down, Gail. You could have put down 5 at the top of the larger square and 5 at the side. Then you could have multiplied 5 × 5.

Millie: But the teacher said that it was a square. You could have used just 5 of the square-inch cards. If you put them across the top, you know that it will take the same number down as across. You needed to measure only one side.

Page: But what if the teacher fooled us? Maybe the large piece isn't a square.

Teacher: When you find how many of the cards 1 inch square fit into the larger square, you term your result the area. We say that the area is 25 square inches, meaning that the unit of 1 square inch fits into the larger square 25 times.

Here are some rectangles. Some of the rectangles are squares and some are not. Using these square-inch cards, find the areas of the rectangles. Write your answer in the upper right-hand corner and then give your rectangle to another child to check. We'll see how accurately you can measure.

[The children measured the various rectangles and wrote their answers in the proper place; each measurement was checked by a second pupil. The children experimented by placing the cards over the entire surface and then by using only the unit squares at the top and bottom of the figure.]

Trixi: This is very simple. If you want to find the area of a square, all you need to do is find how many of the cards an inch square fit on one side. Then you can multiply. If the side is 6 inches, then the area is 6 × 6 square inches.

Teacher: Can you tell that by writing it out?

[Teacher wrote on the board:]

area of a square =

Trixi: That is easy. [Wrote: "side times side."]

Gary: It is also easy to tell about the area of an oblong. You can say length times width. I'll write it.

[Gary wrote on the board:]

area of an oblong = length × width

Teacher: Would it matter whether you measured both the length and the width by the same unit such as an inch? Would it matter if you used a foot to measure one side?

Carl: That wouldn't work. You would have to use the same thing for one as for the other. You could use a square foot, but you would have to use it both ways. Otherwise, it would be like adding 1 inch and 1 foot and calling it 2 feet. It wouldn't make sense.

Clyde: I figured it would take 144 square inches to make a square foot. You could have 12 cards each a square inch across, and 12 down. 12 × 12 equals 144.

Teacher: I cut this square into 2 parts that are equal — as much so as I could make them! What do you call the figures I cut?

Alice: You cut the square into 2 triangles. A triangle has 3 sides. Those 2 triangles can fit together and make a square.

Gary: But you could cut any oblong into triangles. You can cut two of them that are just alike out of any oblong.

Teacher: How would you go about finding the area of a triangle?

Millie: You could measure around the triangle.

Michael: That would not help very much. It would be like the area of the rectangle except it would be only half as much, but I don't know how you would find out.

Measuring triangles and rectangles.

Teacher: Let's look at what we wrote about how to find the area of a rectangle.

Michael: We wrote that the area equals length × width. The area of a triangle would equal length × width divided by 2, but I don't know which is the length.

Teacher: The base of the triangle is the side on which it is supposed to stand or rest. Instead of length, it is termed "base." The word height is used to express width.

[Teacher showed what was meant by height by drawing black lines on the triangles that he had cut the square into.]

Carl: Then the area of a triangle would equal base × height divided by 2. If you took the base × height, it would be the area of the rectangle made by two triangles that are just alike.

Page: Can we make some problems about the areas of triangles? I have some I'd like to figure.

Teacher: You may use the remainder of this period to experiment with these figures and to make some problems for us to discuss tomorrow.

Introduction to Lessons 3 and 4

Lessons 3 and 4 concerned with right circular cylinders and right circular cones.

Cylindrical forms are used for many things. Tin cans for canned goods, cylindrical pipes, tanks, tunnels, silos, and so forth, are examples of right circular cylindrical forms that children see frequently.

There are cylindrical forms that are not right circular cylinders, but they were not discussed in these lessons. Figure 12.21(a) shows a right circular cylinder. If the lateral surface is cut perpendicular to its

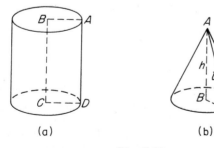

(a)   (b)

Fig. 12.21

bases and stretched out, it forms a rectangle. The diagram (b) of Fig. 12.21 illustrates a right circular cone. Only these cones were considered.

Lesson 3
REASONS AND DECISIONS IN DETERMINING RELATIONSHIPS
Primary Grade Level

Purpose of lesson: To challenge the children to solve problems concerning the relationship of the diameter-circumference of a circle, and to interpret ideas of volume of right circular cylinders and right circular cones.

Background of children: The class had developed a good background of general mathematical understanding. They were released to ask questions and to explore meanings. Extensive use was made of the bulletin board to challenge interest, and the table set aside for mathematics was a center of special interest in the classroom.

Lesson Procedure

To start the discussion and to stimulate the children to do problem solving, the teacher brought in cylindrical containers — boxes, cans, and jars. These were arranged on the table. String, scissors, colored paper, sticks, and rulers were available to use for problem solving.

The teacher, Miss Rose, started the discussion: "We have been measuring many things. On our table, we have some containers. [Miss Rose held up a cylindrical oatmeal box and asked the children to tell some of the things that they could measure about the box.]

The following ideas were brought out by the children:
"We could measure how much it holds."
"We could weigh it."
"We could measure how tall it is."
"We could measure how far across the top it is."

The teacher held up a second container that was "tall and skinny." The children's comments indicate the children's thinking:

"The fatter it (the container) is, the more it can hold."
"When they (referring to the containers) are skinny, they can't hold very much. Even when they are tall and skinny, they don't hold much."

When the children were asked to measure things about the oatmeal box (cylindrical), the idea of the distance around compared with the distance across was mentioned. The children were asked to compare the distance around with the distance across. Their estimates ranged from "a little more than 2" through "a little more than 4."

Most of the estimates were $2\frac{1}{2}$ times as far around as across. They were asked to suggest ways to measure and find out the answer to the problem. Included in the problem was the idea of using only the materials available on the table — string, paper, scissors, containers. The following responses indicate the nature of the thinking:

"I can find out how many times the string that I put around the box will fit across the box." The pupil used a pencil to mark his place on the string and then marked each time he put the string across the top. The class watched the measuring and agreed that for the given box that it was a "little more than 3 times as far around as it was across."

The children were asked to make an estimate of diameter-circumference for another cylindrical container. The estimates were similar to the preceding ones. The measurement was carried out. The children did not generalize at this stage.

The teacher said that all of the things that had been discussed would be left in the room and suggested that the children see if they could figure out other ways to measure how many times as far it is around containers as it is across. The children were stimulated to explore; the quest for problem solving was at a high point.

The next discussion period took place after a week end, which had given time for problem solving. There was electricity in the air! The children could hardly wait to tell the many things that they had discovered.

"I found a new way to find out how many times as far around these (meaning cylindrical containers) it is as across them." The child took a sheet of paper and an oatmeal box lid that had the rim cut off; he demonstrated how he had marked the lid on the side, rolled the lid to the place where the mark was, and then completed the measurement by seeing how many times the diameter measurement would fit into the circumference line.

Another child had cut the rim off the lid, unrolled it, and cut a piece of paper to match the length of the circumference. He showed how he had measured to solve the problem.

A number of ways had been developed, and the children were confident that they did not need to measure additional circles because it will always be "a little more than 3 times."

Miss Rose: Now I am going to ask you something harder. [Teacher showed two circular cylindrical containers — one with a diameter of 1 inch and another with a 2-inch diameter. The height of the two containers was constant (see Fig. 12.22).] "What do you see that is the same about these two containers?

Bill: They look like they are alike in tallness. [Pupils measured and agreed that they were the same height.]

Miss Rose: What do you think will be true about how much this one will hold as compared with this one? [Teacher had the children compare the smaller container with the larger.]

A Pupil: The fat one will hold a lot more.

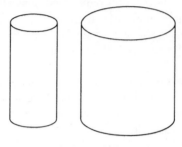

Fig. 12.22

Miss Rose: If these were filled with orange juice, think about how many times as much orange juice you would get if you chose this one (larger one) than if you chose this one (smaller one).

[The children wrote their estimates on a piece of paper, and the lesson continued.]

Miss Rose: How could we find out how many times as much this one (larger one) holds as this one (smaller one)? [Water and pitcher were available.]

Sue: We could fill the little one with water and pour the water into the big one and count how many times it takes to fill it.

Two children carried out the activity, and agreed that it took 4 "small" ones to fill the "large" one. However, they said that it was not exact because the two containers weren't exactly the same in "fullness"!

The next comparisons were of two cylinders — constant in height — one with a diameter of 2 inches and another with a diameter of 4 inches. The children again estimated (measured) and made judgments concerning how much the larger container would hold as compared with the smaller one. Again, they wrote their estimates.

Their estimates were "3" and "4" times, but the answer "4 times" was the general agreement. A question was raised concerning comparing the volume of the cylinder whose diameter was 1 inch as compared with the cylinder whose diameter was 4 inches. Two or three of the children — usually there are those two or three who stand out in almost any class — "hit the nail on its head" after considerable turning of cogs that it could almost be detected as the thought process operated.

Miss Rose had a right circular cone and a right circular cylinder that were the same height and same diameter (as in Fig. 12.23). The children handled the models for the cylinder and cone whose diameter and height were the same. They were asked to estimate how many times they would

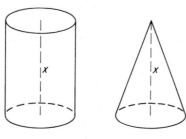

Fig. 12.23

need to fill the cone with water and put it into the cylinder in order to fill the cylinder. The estimates were written on their tablet that they had with them.

The estimates were good. The range was from 2 through $3\frac{1}{2}$.

The measurement was carried out, and the children again examined the models and tried fitting the cone into the cylinder and reasoning why the measurement came out as it did.

The ideas of measuring continued with estimating and formulating procedures for determining the volume of other containers.

Lesson 4
DERIVING RELATIONSHIPS CONCERNING THE
VOLUME OF RIGHT CIRCULAR CYLINDERS AND
RIGHT CIRCULAR CONES
Intermediate Grades

Background of children: The children had developed ideas and vocabulary concerning diameter, circumference, cylinder, ratio, and pi.

Lesson Procedure

Mr. Poe had the children generalize the relationship of height to volume when the diameter was constant. He showed the class a model of a right circular cylinder that was 4 inches high and 1 inch in diameter.

Mr. Poe: Let us think about things that we shall keep constant and things that will be variable. Let's say that we shall keep the diameter of this container constant. To make a container that would hold 100 times as much as this one (pointed to a 4-inch-high container), how many inches tall would it need to be?

Dick: A hundred times as tall, so it would have to be 400 inches tall.

Mr. Poe: Would it fit into this classroom?

Pupils: Computed — that would be $33\frac{1}{3}$ feet, and it would fit into the length of the room with some space left over. [The pupils felt sure that the statement was true, although they did not know the length of the room, they were confident that it was greater than 35 feet.]

Mr. Poe: Last week you talked about another idea. Some of you made posters for our bulletin board to show another relationship about right circular cylinders. The relationship we talked about was the one that exists when the height of the container is constant and we vary the diameter. Sarah made a poster for the title of our bulletin board. [Mr. Poe held up the poster on which was written:]

Right Circular Cylinders

constant: height of cylinders
variable: diameter of cylinders
variable: volume of cylinders

Mr. Poe: Jim made a poster that illustrated Cylinder *A* and *B* (Fig. 12.24). [Mr. Poe held up Jim's poster.]

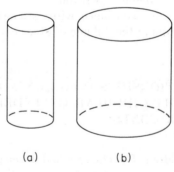

(a)   (b)

Fig. 12.24

The height of Cylinder *A* and Cylinder *B* are the same. The diameter of *B* is 2 times as great as the diameter of *A*. Cylinder *A* holds 4 times as much as Cylinder *B*.

[Mr. Poe held up Jill's poster (Fig. 12.25).]

The diameter of Cylinder *J* is 4 times as great as the diameter of Cylinder *K*. The two cylinders are the same height. Cylinder *J* holds 16 times as much as Cylinder *K*.

The children had generalized the volume of a cylinder equals pi times its radius squared times its height: $\pi r^2 h$.

Mr. Poe: The bulletin board that you arranged is very fine. You

have made an excellent exhibit. Now I have a problem for you that may
be difficult.

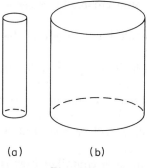

(a)   (b)

Fig. 12.25

We looked at this model that was 4 inches high and 1 inch in diameter.
You stated that it would take a container that is 100 times as tall
as this one to hold 100 times as much. That would be a very long container to keep in our room. What is another way that we could solve

Wrapping paper around a right circular cylinder to find out
relationships.

the problem if we wish to make a container that will hold 100 times as much as this one?

Jim: We could increase the diameter. It seems to me that would be much more sensible because volume increases very fast as you increase the diameter.

Mary: Our constant could be the height of the cylinder — the way we illustrated on our chart.

Dick: That should be a simple problem. When we made the diameter 2 times as great, the volume became 4 times as great. When we made the diameter 4 times as great, the volume was 16 times as great.

Susan: It's easier than that. All we need to think about is what number multiplied by itself will produce 100. That's 10. Ten times 10 equals 100.

Jerry: Then, if we'd make a container that is 10 inches in diameter and keep the height constant, it would hold as much as a container that was 100 times as tall in which the diameter was kept constant.

Mary: What if we wanted the container to hold 1000 times as much?

The children continued with their problem solving — the idea was a very exciting one. It led them ahead to many concepts of volume.

Later, the children refined their concepts and derived formulas which they stated in more precise mathematical language. For example, they wrapped paper around the right circular cylinder, and then rolled the paper out so that they could visualize the rectangular sheet of paper. In the example below, the height of the cylinder was 4 inches and the radius was 2 inches. Figure 12.26 indicates the procedure that they used.

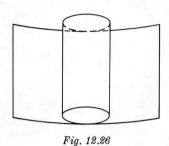

Fig. 12.26

Lesson 5
WEIGHT
Nursery School Children

[The children were building with blocks.]

David: This isn't safe — too heavy at the top.

Sally: You'd better sit down or you'll fall out of the wagon when we turn if you stand.

These children indicated their concept concerning the relationship between position, base area, and stability. The more weight that one puts in an elevated position, the more stable the base must be. In pyramid construction, they sensed the need for distribution of weight. It is easier to move the same weight if it is flat rather than upright.

Lesson 6
VOLUME-SHAPE RELATIONSHIP
Grade One Class

Connie: This holds a pint.
Ronnie: So does this, but this pint doesn't look like yours. Let's see. [Ronnie took Connie's measure to compare with his.] Mine is taller and skinnier. Yours is fatter and shorter.
Marie: This holds the same as that. [Held up 2 containers, a measuring cup and a half-pint carton.] This is round and this is straight across.
Judy: One is round and one is straight.

The preceding statements indicate the grade-one children's awarenes[s] that capacity can be constant while the shape of a container may vary·

Grade Two Class

Many cylindrical cans, boxes, and jars were available for comparing capacity. Two cans were the same distance across (diameter), but one of the cans was about $2\frac{1}{2}$ times as tall as the other one.
Freddie: If the cans are the same (distance) across, the higher the can, the more it holds.
Michael: And the short cans hold less.
Irene: I bet I know something. If the can is 2 times as tall, I bet it holds a lot more. Let's measure and see.
Teacher: But is the tall can 2 times as tall as the short one?
Irene: No. We could measure . . . .
Teacher: Here is a pencil. How can you mark the tall can to show where two of the short cans will come?
Irene: You can do it like this . . . . [Irene measured one short can by holding the short can against the tall one. She placed a mark with her pencil. She then measured another short can's distance and marked the place where two short cans came on the tall can.]
[Measuring by filling the shorter can with water and pouring it into the larger can was then carried out, and the generalization formulated.]

Irene: It is 2 times as tall. It holds 2 times as much. That is what I thought. I bet if the can were 4 times as tall as the short one it would be 4 times as much.

Michael: Yes, but I don't think that would work if the can is twice as wide. The wider it is across, the more it holds, but . . . .

[Michael, with the help of his teacher, located two cans to compare. One can was twice as wide as the other one. (This situation had been planned by the teacher. The two cans didn't just happen to be the given diameters.) Michael measured the distance across the two cans.]

Michael: This can is twice as wide as this one. Now I can measure how much they hold. I bet the wide one holds more than twice as much as the other one.

[Michael measured a constant height for the two cans so that capacity could be compared in terms of width of the containers. Michael then poured water from the less wide to the wider container.]

Michael: I can't tell exactly. I think this one that is twice as wide holds 4 times as much. I knew that when the can got wider, it held more than if it just got taller.

The measuring of the relationship of width of container to volume continued through letting the children experiment and formulate their generalizations.

Lesson 7
FINDING THE AREA OF A CIRCLE
Grade Six Class

The class had been finding the areas of different plane figures. The following discussion occurred.

Jerry: We have found out how to find the area of a lot of figures that have straight lines for their sides, but how can we find the area of a circle?

Alice: I've wondered about that, too. Curved lines make a difference. Miss McGee, how can we find the area of a circle?

Teacher: How did you go about finding the area of the other figures?

Thomas: First we made up an idea as to what a unit of surface measurement would be like. It is a square, but a square will not fit a circle.

Teacher: That's right, Thomas. A square doesn't fit a circle. But neither does it fit a triangle. Didn't you find the area of a triangle by using a square?

Bill: We used the idea of a right triangle a lot of times in working out how to find the surface measures of other figures.

Maria: Can't we use it again to find the area of a circle?

Mike: Circles have curved sides, Maria.

Maria: Sure, I know that, but maybe we don't need to bother about the curved part.

George: Say! That's an idea! Suppose we draw 2 diameters at right angles within a circle. Then, if we join their ends, we'll have right triangles inside the circle area.

Teacher: That's a good idea, George. Will you please make the drawing on the chalkboard?

George drew a circle with diameters as in Fig. 12.27.]

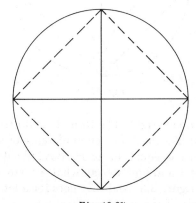

Fig. 12.27

Teacher: Now, who can tell us what the area of the square inside the circle is?

Bill: There are 4 right triangles. They are equal because their legs are radii of the circle. One of the legs is the altitude and the other is the base of each triangle. The area of each triangle is then $r \times r/2$ or $r^2/2$.

Maria: But, Bill, there are four such triangles. So the area of all of them would be $4r^2/2$. That is the same as $2r^2$.

Connie: That's keen! The area of the square is 2 times the square of the radius. But that doesn't measure the part of the circle that is outside of the square.

Pedro: I've an idea. Suppose we fold the parts of the circle that are outside the square over the sides of the square to see how much of the square they cover.

Maria: You can't fold a drawing on a chalkboard, you know.

Pedro: Sure, I know that. But we can make one like it on paper. (This was done by several children independently. See Fig. 12.28.

Bill: I'd say that the parts of the circle that were outside were equal to about one half of the area of the square.

Tom: Say! That would make the whole area of the circle equal to about 3 times the radius squared. That is $3r^2$ about. Is that anywhere near correct, Miss McGee?

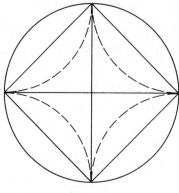

Fig. 12.28

Teacher: That is about right. The formula is 3.1416 times r^2 or *pi* r^2.

Bill: How do you like that! The circumference of a circle is equal to *pi·r·*2, and the area is equal to *pi·r*^{2}. Boy! We'd better be careful where we write that *2* and how we say what we wrote!

Teacher: That is right, Bill. And that goes for a lot of things that one writes with numerals. The correct numeral written in its proper place can be very helpful.

Mona: This looks okay for the particular circle, but how do we know that it fits any other circle?

Alice: It will fit any circle, Mona. We were not really working with a particular circle. The diameter of the circle George drew on the chalkboard was not the same as the diameters of the circles we drew on paper. We didn't use any exact measurements. We used only measures of relationship as we were working.

Teacher: You did very well, class. Tomorrow we will try out what we learned by working with some circles whose dimensions we know. I hope that everyone will remember how to use the 2 that Bill told us about.

Lesson 8
RIGHT TRIANGLES
Grade Seven Class

The pupils were studying right triangles. Tom asked, "What happens if one leg of the right angle is changed in length and the other leg is left unchanged?" The following discussion took place:

Mary: The right angle would not be changed, so the triangle would still be a right triangle.

Joe: If the leg were shorter, the acute angle opposite that leg would be made smaller, I think.

Alice: Why do you think that, Joe?

Joe: Because shortening the leg would move the hypotenuse in toward the vertex of the right angle.

Pearl: Is there a relationship between the lengths of the legs of the right triangle and the size of the acute angles?

Tom: There must be, Pearl. If the legs are equal in length, the triangle is isosceles. Then the acute angles would be equal in size. If the legs are not equal in length, the angles are not equal in their measure either. There must be a relationship between the length of the legs and the sizes of the angles.

Pearl: How can we find what it is?

Teacher: Why not construct some right triangles having different lengths of legs and measure the angles?

Tom: Let's do that! I have an idea how we could do it easily!

Teacher: How is that, Tom?

Tom: Let's make a right triangle using measuring sticks for its legs and then take another measuring stick to use for the hypotenuse. Then we can measure the lengths of the sides and we can also measure the acute angles. That way we can see what happens.

This was done, and Tom's original question was answered as Joe had hypothesized. As a leg was shortened and the other leg was unchanged in length, the acute angle opposite the shortened leg became more acute. This observation then provoked further study of the relationship of sides and angles in the right triangle.

Continuation of the Previous Lesson

The device constructed for the preceding lesson suggested that a study be made of what happens when the hypotenuse line is rotated about one end as a pivot. Figure 12.29 pictures such a device and its application for a further study of the size of the angle as related to the length of the sides.

In the triangles in Fig. 12.29, the angle at point B is constant in its measure. It is a right angle which determines the directions of its sides. These directions are constant, also. The hypotenuse of a right triangle is the line that joins points on the respective sides of the right angle.

The facts that the sum of the measures of the interior angles of any triangle equals 180 degrees and the right angles measure 90 degrees determine that the sum of the measures of the other two angles will also be 90 degrees. Hence, as one of those angles varies in its measure, the other must vary in inverse measure. Likewise as the size of the

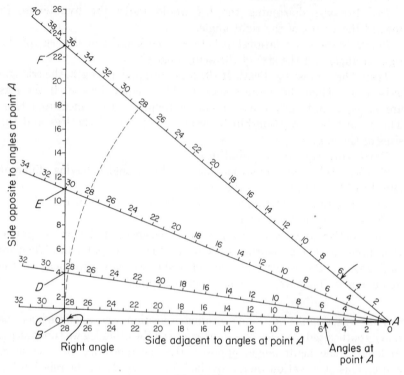

Fig. 12.29

angular spread changes, the length of the side of the triangle opposite it changes correspondingly. Consequently, the length of the hypotenuse also varies. These properties are readily shown by means of the calibrated scalings of the respective lines in Fig. 12.29. The curve that has been drawn with the side AB as its radius and the point A as its center shows clearly how the hypotenuse increases in length as the size of the angle at point A increases.

There are six possible comparisons of pairs of the three sides of such a triangle. Each side may be used as the referent and the other sides may be used respectively as relatums in such comparisons. These ratios are known as *trigonometric functions*. The trigonometric functions of the four triangles in Fig. 12.29 are shown in Table 12.2.

TABLE 12.2

TRIGONOMETRIC RELATIONS	TRIANGLES ABC	ABD	ABE	ABF
Sine (side opp : hypotenuse)	1 : 28+	4 : 28+	11 : 30+	23 : 36+
Cosine (side adj : hypotenuse)	28 : 28+	28 : 28+	28 : 30+	28 : 36+
Secant (hypotenuse : side adj)	28+ : 28	28+ : 28	30+ : 28	36+ : 28
Cosecant (hyp : side opp)	28 : 1	28 : 4	30 : 11	36 : 23
Tangent (side opp : side adj)	1 : 28	4 : 28	11 : 28	23 : 28
Cotangent (side adj : side opp)	28 : 1	28 : 4	28 : 11	28 : 23

The plus sign is designed to indicate that the measure is greater than the integer but less than the next integer. Measurement was approximate. When such ratios are computed to determine their value and the measure of the angle that produced them is known, it is possible to calculate the length of one side if the length of the other is known.

Discussion Questions

1. How would you identify or define space?
2. Is position a primary inherent property or is it a matter of a relationship?
3. How does the idea of a point compare with an actual object occurring in space?
4. How does motion enter into the structuring of space?
5. What is meant by rotational motion?
6. Four types of measurement occur in space measurement: linear, surface, solid, and angular. Give illustrations of each in ordinary life experiencing.
7. Trigonometry implies measurement of triangles. Indicate how the surface measurement of a triangle may be computed.
8. The trigonometry of right triangles reveals a constant relationship between the hypotenuse and the sides. What is the nature of that relationship?
9. The trigonometry of right triangles includes varied relationships between the sides as determined by the size of the acute angles. State how these relationships are identified.

Suggested Readings

Abbott, E. A., *Flatland*. Boston, Mass.: Little, Brown, & Company.

Banks, J. Houston, *Elements of Mathematics*. Boston, Mass.: Allyn and Bacon, Inc., 1956, Chap. 8.

Bell, Clifford, Clela D. Hammond, and Robert B. Herrera, *Fundamentals of Arithmetic for Teachers*. New York: John Wiley & Sons, Inc., 1962, Chap. 21.

Brumfiel, Charles F., Robert E. Eicholz, and Merrill E. Shanks, *Fundamental Concepts of Elementary Mathematics*. Reading, Mass.: Addison-Wesley Publishing Company, Inc., 1962, Chap. 21, 22, 23, and 24.

Brune, Irvin H., "Geometry in the Grades," *The Arithmetic Teacher*, vol. 8 (May 1961), pp. 210–220.

Felder, Virginia, "Geometry Concepts in Grades K–3," *The Arithmetic Teacher*, vol. 12 (May 1965), pp. 356–358.

Glenn, William H., and Donovan A. Johnson, *The Pythagorean Theorem*. St. Louis, Mo.: Webster Publishing Division, McGraw-Hill Book Company, Inc., 1960.

Hawley, Newton S., "Geometry for Primary Grades," *The Arithmetic Teacher*, vol. 8 (December 1961), pp. 374–376.

Hogben, Lancelot, *Mathematics for the Million*. New York: W. W. Norton & Company, Inc., 1941, Chap. 4.

Johnson, Donovan A., "Geometry for the Primary," *Grade Teacher*, vol. 79 (April 1962), pp. 52, 92–96.

Kasner, Edward, and James Newman, *Mathematics and the Imagination*. New York: Simon and Schuster, Inc., 1940).

Luchins, A. S., and E. H. Luchins, "A Structural Approach to the Teaching of the Concept of Area in Intuitive Geometry," *Journal of Educational Research*, vol. 40 (March 1947), pp. 528–533.

Marks, John L., C. Richard Purdy, and Lucien B. Kinney, *Teaching Arithmetic for Understanding*. New York: McGraw-Hill Book Company, Inc., 1958, Chap. 11.

Morton, Robert Lee, *Teaching Children Arithmetic*. Morristown, N. J.: Silver Burdett Company, 1953, Chap. 10.

Olander, C., "A Model for Visualizing the Formula for the Area of a Circle," *The Mathematics Teacher*, vol. 47 (April 1955), pp. 245–246.

Ravielli, Anthony, *An Adventure in Geometry*. New York: The Viking Press, Inc., 1958.

Rutland, L., and M. Hosier, "Some Basic Geometric Ideas for the Elementary Teacher," *The Arithmetic Teacher*, vol. 8 (November 1961), pp. 357–362.

University of Illinois Committee on School Mathematics (U. I. C. S. M.), University of Illinois, Urbana, Ill. Information may be obtained by writing to Max Beberman.

Ward, Morgan, and Clarence E. Hardgrove, *Modern Elementary Mathematics*. Reading, Mass.: Addison-Wesley Publishing Company, Inc., 1964, Chap. 8.

Weaver, J. Fred, "The School Mathematics Group Project in Elementary School Mathematics, a Progress Report," *The Arithmetic Teacher*, vol. 8 (December 1961), pp. 436–439. Also available from School Mathematics Study Group, Stanford University, Stanford, Calif.

13

Problem Solving

13.1 INTRODUCTION

In a very real sense, the process of mathematicking is one of problem sensing and problem solving. It seems axiomatic that problem-solving behavior occurs only when one is confronted with a problem that he wills to solve. Hence, the first concern with the development of problem-solving abilities is that of leading the student to sense a problem and to desire to find a way to cope with it.

"Thus, a teacher of mathematics has a great opportunity. If he fills his allotted time with drilling his students in routine operations, he kills their interest, hampers their intellectual development, and misuses his opportunity. But, if he challenges the curiosity of his students by setting them problems proportionate to their knowledge, and helps them to solve their problems with stimulating questions, he may give them a taste for, and some means of, independent thinking."[1]

Of course, not all problems will be sensed under teacher direction. The creation of our heritage of mathematical concepts, as well as the devices and procedures for applying them, has come about largely as a product of personal initiative on the parts of persons or groups who have sensed problems and sought their solutions. A teacher leading his pupils to recreate for themselves that heritage of ideas and procedures has a somewhat different set of conditions than did those who originated that heritage. It is important that this difference be recognized. Mathematical development need not be confined to teacher-directed activities. Personal curiosity and personal initiative are probably as prevalent today as they ever were. They need to be recognized and utilized.

---

[1] G. Polya, *How To Solve It*. New York: Doubleday Anchor Books, 1957, p. v.

13.2   CONCEIVING IDEAS for PROBLEM SOLVING

The ideas that are the foundation of the system of mathematical concepts are probably known to everyone. It would be difficult to find a normal person of school age or older who does not distinguish between the quantitative states of "no" thing and "some" thing, or who would not differentiate among simple groupings or sets of things. Likewise, it seems probable that everyone has conceived simple ideas of quantity, size, and order. Everyone has experienced determining how much, how many, where, when, and in what order. Ideas concerning such problems are products of simple intuitive perceptive processes of noting things and comparing them in many ways. These are foundational, but they are far from the entire structure of mathematical knowledge. The process of deriving the superstructure is the essence of problem solving.

The processes of freeing perception from dealing only with specific concrete experiences and of stimulating the making of inferences and of generalizations are basic to the building of a system of concepts. One cannot possibly experience concretely all of the groupings that are symbolized by decimal numerals, but one can experience directly the scaling of the simpler groupings and from that experience he can extend and project similar scaling ideologically without limit. This constitutes one form of mathematical problem solving.

13.3   DEVISING WAYS for PROBLEM SOLVING

"If to do were as easy as to know what were good to be done . . . ," aptly states a common problem situation that needs very much to be recognized and dealt with effectively. Sensing a situation and knowing what needs to be done regarding it, but not knowing how to use what one knows, presents a very real problem. It seems probable that this situation will be frequently experienced in the course of mathematical learning. There are many instances wherein the conceiving of an idea is likely to be easier to accomplish than is the procedure for expressing it in the technical languages used for that purpose. For example, it seems unlikely that anyone would not have ideas concerning fractions, but possessing facility with the special forms for expressing the ideas in the technical language for fractions, or skill in the use of the algorisms with fraction computation may not have been achieved.

13.4   SOLVING PROBLEMS

"From what we know about learning, there is only one way students can learn to solve problems — by solving problems and studying the process."[2] Studying the process of problem solving involves the two following aspects: (1) how one senses a problem to be solved, and (2) how one goes about creating a solution for the problems that he senses. Sensing a problem is the first step toward the solution. There are different ways in which problems are sensed. Perhaps the most evident way is to have the problem pointed out by the teacher. There is a hazard in this procedure, however, because the problem situation as sensed by the student may not be the problem situation that the teacher has in mind for him to solve. The student may be incorporating the teacher within the situation and be predominately concerned with doing what he thinks the teacher wants rather than attending directly to the problem situation the teacher tried to present. A somewhat different procedure is to present situations such that the pupil becomes aware of his need for new learning. This, of course, is still teacher-directed, but it is more subtle and less likely to produce extraneous attention to "what teacher wants."

A very different way of sensing problems is through the process of personal curiosity and inquisitiveness on the part of the student. In some respects this is the most productive procedure. It is the procedure by which our heritage of knowledge has been created. The innate curiosity of the human mind is recognized in the adage, "The fool can ask questions which the wise man cannot answer." As mentioned earlier in this volume, the IQ as depicting an "inner quest" needs as much educational consideration as does the IQ as a symbol of intellectual ability.

What is the problem? A clear formulation of the problem to be solved, together with an acceptance of responsibility to seek out a suitable solution, constitutes the beginnings of problem solving. The actual procedures for problem solving in mathematics vary substantially depending upon what is formulated as the problem to be solved. For example, if the situation calls merely for the choice and performance of a known numerical operation, finding a solution consists simply in performing the algorism accurately. The answer is assured because the operation is designed to serve that purpose.

However, if the problem situation calls for the creation of a new idea or a new procedure, a somewhat different attack will need to be used. As Dr. Polya says, "Solving a problem means finding a way out of a difficulty, a way around an obstacle, attaining an aim that

---

[2] Kenneth B. Henderson and Robert E. Pingry, "Problem-solving in Mathematics," *The Learning of Mathematics Its Theory and Practice*, The National Council of Teachers of Mathematics, Twenty-first Yearbook. Washington, D. C.: The National Council of Teachers of Mathematics, 1953, p. 233.

was not immediately attainable."[3] This calls for a careful reading of the situation as sensed to determine what is known about it and to ascertain which of the reader's present competencies appear to be applicable. On the basis of this, what is unknown can be structured out and judgments can be made regarding it. "Provisional tries" at behavioral responses can be made and observed as to their pertinency and adequacy. By means of such trial runs, a clearer idea of the situation should be evolved. One's experiential background will be tapped for cues regarding similar situations and one will need to utilize what has been termed "creative imagination." This procedure is sometimes referred to as heuristic. In somewhat less academic parlance, it is what is meant by the expression "using one's head."

Problem solving involves more than merely finding solutions for the verbal problems presented in the textbooks. The tendency to associate problem-solving activity only with the verbal problems presented in the textbooks needs to be corrected. For the most part, such problems are of the type that call merely for the selection and application of an algorism which assures an adequate solution if the task is properly performed. There is little real intellectual challenge in such behavior. Characteristically the problems as presented appear to be designed mainly for the application of computational processes that have previously been presented. As such, they are principally exercises in transforming statements presented in verbal language terms into equivalent statements expressed in number language sentences, and then in performing the operations indicated by the number language. Frequently, there is little or no relationship among the problems presented for solution. Each of them refers to a specific situation. There is little challenge for inferential reasoning from having solved them.

Other aspects of mathematical experience offer more and better opportunities for problem-solving activities than are presented by the customary types of verbal problems. The current emphasis upon personal derivation and understanding of mathematical ideas and procedures presumes problem-solving experiences. It was by such experiences that the ideas and procedures were originally conceived, and they can best be reconstructed from comparable source material. For example, initial concrete experiences of grouping objects need to be used to give the basic ideas of a calibrated number scale. But, this must readily be extended by the process of inferential reasoning so that the scale may be perceived as extending well beyond the realm of one's concrete experiences.

[3] George Polya, *Mathematical Discovery: On Understanding, Learning and Teaching Problem Solving*, vol. 1. New York: John Wiley & Sons, Inc., 1962, p. v.

The essence of mathematical knowledge is a system of concepts or ideas. If these are perceived as a system, their intrarelationships will be evident. If they are learned as disparate ideas, the unity of the knowledge will not be evident. Hence, the process of educing the ideas as a system and the process of sensing them as a whole are both important to use in attempting to develop mathematical competency. This can best be done by means of problem-solving activities.

13.5   DEVELOPING COMPETENCY with PROBLEM SOLVING

The report of an action research project concerned with the development of problem-solving abilities indicates that considerable growth can be accomplished in that regard. About 2000 pupils in grades 4, 5, and 6, together with 61 teachers and a small group of consultants, gave special attention to certain aspects of problem-solving procedures for a period of four months. The results are surprising. The pupils achieved an average gain of nine tenths of a normal year's growth in their measured ability with verbal problem solving. "Some entire classes averaged a gain of more than two years, indicating that within these classes there were children who gained considerably more."[4] Eight phases of procedure and pertinent materials were identified and utilized in this project: (1) Identifying "What is the question?", (2) Analysis of the problems independent of number, (3) Children writing their own problems, (4) Estimating and judging problems, (5) Graphic structuring, (6) Labeling the answer to a problem, (7) Identifying "On what does the answer depend?", and (8) Mental arithmetic.

Four types of problems are discussed by Hildebrandt in the Twenty-fourth Yearbook of the National Council of Teachers of Mathematics. "First there are those which involve the use of one or more simple mathematical principles and concepts but deal with phenomena or experiences with which the student may not have had much previous contact. . . .

"A second type of problem is one which may require a certain amount of experimentation and assembling of pertinent data before convincing the student that a solution is possible. . . . The third type of problem arises from situations which result from changing the conditions of a simpler one, for example, by adding another *dimension* to the problem, or requiring the study of a complete generalization or abstraction. . . . A fourth type of problem is the one which leads to the formulation of

[4] Leslie Beatty, *Teacher's Guide to Problem Solving In Arithmetic.* (Report of an Action Research Project in San Diego County School Districts). San Diego, Calif.: Office of the Superintendent of Schools, 1959, pp. 1–2.

general principles, or to the conjecturing and eventual proof of specific theorems."[5]

In his discussion of the problem-solving process, Dr. Hildebrandt treats eight levels as follows: "(1) Presentation, (2) Attention, (3) Observation and Exploration, (4) Classification, (5) Further Exploration, (6) Formulation, (7) Generalization, and (8) Verification and Application."[6]

13.6 TYPES of PROCEDURES THAT FACILITATE PROBLEM SOLVING

When a child solves problems that are his own, he usually shows considerable insight and ability in solving them. The problems are important to him, and he wishes to solve them. An important aspect of teaching is that of identifying the kinds of problems that children solve and sensing the procedures that they use in solving them. This knowledge helps to equip the teacher so that he can create situations wherein the learner uses his problem-solving ability in new situations. The art and science of teaching calls for creating a problem-solving setting that has an element of personal flavor well mixed with mathematical content. The illustrative lessons in this text utilize problem-solving types of activities.

There are many procedures that facilitate problem solving. The following are some of the ones that teachers have found to be helpful.

DEVELOPING MATHEMATICAL RELATIONSHIPS

The process of sensing, discovering, experimenting, stating, applying, and testing basic mathematical relationships is one of the most significant types of problem solving. The heart of mathematical experiences is the building of mathematical concepts, and building the concepts should be a problem-solving process. To challenge children to perform this type of problem solving, the teacher must first analyze the concepts and the skills with computation which underlie mathematics in the elementary school. He should then determine the specific relationships that he plans to teach. On the basis of such analysis and by application of the basic principles of learning, a teacher is in a position to challenge a high level of problem solving in his classroom. Deriving formulas,

[5]E. H. C. Hildebrant, "Mathematical Modes of Thought," *The Growth of Mathematical Ideas, Grades K–12*, The National Council of Teachers of Mathematics, Twenty-fourth Yearbook. Washington, D.C.: The National Council of Teachers of Mathematics, 1959, pp. 373–376.

[6] Ibid., p. 377.

rules, principles, procedures, and concepts are significant problem-solving activities.

ORAL DISCUSSION DURING PROBLEM SOLVING

Oral discussion during problem solving may help the learner identify basic procedures for problem solving. Experimentation, discussion, and many types of learning-laboratory situations contribute extensively to solving problems. How one goes about solving problems and finding various ways for solutions, pupil competition in finding efficient ways to solve problems, and the creating of a high level of interest may be products of the oral discussion program. In many instructional programs, there is an over amount of written work. A fine balance of oral and written problem-solving activities provides opportunity for democracy to operate in a classroom. The child who may not be too astute in written problem solving may do very well in problem solving in the setting of oral discussion, and the learner who is weak in problem solving in the setting of oral discussion may be strong in written. Successful performance in one type of problem solving should facilitate improvement in the other type.

USING PROBLEM-SOLVING MATERIAL FOR ALL SUBJECT FIELDS

Developing problems that grow out of other fields offers excellent opportunity for problem solving. Material for mathematical problem solving exists in every subject field. Unlimited possibilities for good problems are available. The material is there, but it is of little mathematical significance unless the teacher senses and makes use of it. The following illustrate the types of problem ideas that abound:

(a) Ideas of longitude and latitude to interpret a coordinate system

(b) The use of a neighborhood map to interpret relative positions, parallel streets, directions, basic points of origin for measuring direction, and so forth

(c) The selection of referents such as the population of one's school to make comparisons with the population of one's city, state, country, continent, world.

MAKING USE OF PUPIL-FORMULATED PROBLEMS

The good use of pupil-formulated problems calls for good teaching. Pupil-formulated problems are often trite and are copied from the pattern of the textbook variety problem. This is likely to be true when the teacher directs pupils to make up problems without properly guiding the activity. Teacher guidance includes helping pupils sense pertinent ideas and directing their problem solving. The following are examples of profitable settings.

1. The children in Mr. B's room have sensed the importance of zero as a point of origin in developing ideas of directional (signed) numbers. When they noted other basic points of origin, they were excited about them and related them to the concept of zero. The teacher led the children to interpret many such points of origin and through his guidance a bulletin board indicating their problem-solving activity developed.

2. Mr. Howard's children studied coordinate graphs.[7] He challenged the children to interpret many things in their community through writing a description of the idea, writing an equation to fit the idea, and making a graph to describe it. The children used examples of situations such as: The rate at which a nearby dam was filling was noted.

Statements were written to describe the increase and factors of significance for graphing it were discussed. A vertical line was used to indicate the number of gallons per minute flowing into the dam, and a horizontal line was used to indicate the number of minutes being considered.

3. A similar type of problem was made concerning the time that it takes to fill a given swimming pool.

4. Figure 13.1 indicates some of the examples developed by the children: A 6-hour hike was taken by the children. Read the graph and tell the following:

(a) At the rate shown on the graph, how many miles did they hike per hour?

(b) What is the slope of the line of the graph?

(c) Write an equation that describes the trip.

USE OF PROBLEM SOLVING TO MASTER COMPUTATIONAL FACTS

Mastery of number facts and skills should be a matter of problem solving for the teacher and for the learner. The teacher's problem solving

[7] Lesson from Ben Howard, Chula Vista School District, Calif.

consists of things such as identifying the concepts which underlie the specific computational work that he wishes his pupils to master, identifying the specific computational skills, and teaching them through a problem-solving procedure. Reports from teachers indicate that pupil

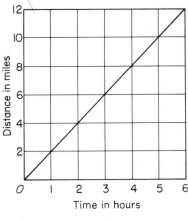

Fig. 13.1

mastery of types of examples and number facts and skills may be accomplished with fewer examples used and greater efficiency when the problem-solving approach is used.

Similarly, when the method of problem solving is used by the learner, greater mastery and a decrease of time needed for mastery result. The following are examples of using a problem-solving approach:

1. Making generalizations of higher decade facts through interpreting the primary facts that one knows. If the child has learned the primary combinations for addition, for example, he may be challenged to generalize the higher decade facts that he will need in the multiplication process. For example, $16 + 5$, $36 + 5$, and $56 + 5$ can occur as higher decade addition facts with multiplication. If the learner knows the primary combination, $6 + 5$, it is a simple process for him to generalize that since $6 + 5 = 11$, $16 + 5 = 21$, $36 + 5 = 41$, and $56 + 5 = 61$, and so forth. Many learners do not formulate such generalizations without the help of a teacher.

2. The method of problem solving may lead to the use of the properties of the decimal number system. Problem solving leads one to use the commutative, associative, and distributive principles of the system. For example, Sue, a pupil in second grade, did not know the answer to $6 + 5$. Her problem solving led her to apply the associative principle for addition. Although she did not use the following algorism in her

written work, she did use the principle in her problem-solving process.

$$6 + 5 = ? \qquad (6 + 4) + 1 = 6 + (4 + 1)$$
$$6 + 4 = 10 \qquad 10 + 1 = 11$$

PROCEDURES TO TEACH COMPUTATIONAL TECHNIQUES

Interpretation of computational techniques such as regrouping for subtraction and for addition, adding common fraction numbers, and dividing by decimal fraction numbers should be problem-solving activities. Development of reasons for all computational techniques should evolve through interpretation of the system of concepts that underlie them. When this procedure is used, the development of the techniques constitutes an important type of problem solving.

USE OF PICTORIAL MATERIAL (GRAPHS, CHARTS, TABLES, MODELS, DIAGRAMS)

The use of materials that facilitate sensory stimulation is important in problem-solving activities. We quantify many types of stimuli — aural, tactile, kinesthetic, visual, thermal, and so forth. Using many avenues by which a learner may perceive an idea is an important consideration. The following examples illustrate the way some teachers have used sensory approaches in their program for problem solving.

Rolling a wheel to determine circumference-diameter relationship.

Evolving number ideas and understanding numerical relationships may be facilitated by many procedures. One of the excellent aids is counters. Counters are concrete, tangible objects that can be moved about and observed in various groupings. Kinesthetic, tactile, and

Making models to help solve problems.

visual processes are given special consideration. Verbalization is used when the learner tells about his sets of counters. When the child writes the story of his grouping of counters, that sensory avenue is added to the others. The child utilizes again and again the one fundamental process (counting). He counts into (adds) when he forms one group of counters, and he counts out of (subtracts) as he forms two or more groupings of his counters. Subtraction and addition are thus experienced as directional counting. Similarly, his problem solving should lead him to experience the commutative and associative principles of addition, and many other problem-solving activities.

Counters that are easy to manipulate and of a size that the learner can get the "feel" of should be used. Some of the small disk counters which are sold commercially are so thin that they are of questionable value. Blocks, tiles, good-sized beads, and objects that can be manipulated easily should be selected.

USE OF ANALOGOUS PROBLEMS

Sue wanted to know why people were so concerned about getting pictures of the "back side of the moon." She said, "We are told that the moon goes around the earth every month. Why can't we see all sides of it as it goes around?"

Someone said, "Whenever the moon is shining it always looks the same. So we must see only one side."

Another child said, "Maybe there isn't any difference. Maybe it is like a ball. It looks the same from any direction."

Someone pointed out, "That isn't true! The 'Man in the Moon' wouldn't look the same from every direction."

Bill said, "That's an idea! Why don't we make a moon with a face on it and see how it works so that the face is always seen?"

They used a basketball and drew a face on one side. Then Bill carried the ball around the room always keeping the face toward the center of the room.

Sue said, "We never did see the side of the ball opposite the face. Didn't the ball turn?"

Joe said, "Sure it turned. The face looked in opposite directions. It can't do that without turning."

Jane said, "Oh! I see what happens! Look! The ball turns around once while it goes around the room. That way the same side always faces the middle of the room. That must be the way the moon does!"

Mike said, "It must be like the earth. It rotates on its axis and also revolves around the sun."

Jill said, "But the earth rotates on its axis every day and it takes 365 days to go around the sun."

Jack said, "I get it! The moon rotates and revolves around the earth at the same time. One rotation takes the same time as one revolution."

ESTIMATING AND CHECKING THE REASONABLENESS OF ANSWERS

Estimating answers and comparing the results of actual computation with the estimated answer is part of problem solving. Problem-solving exercises may be devoted to estimating the answers to problems in which no specific computation is used. Making judgments concerning the nature of the answer may be noted in the problem-solving exercises in many of the illustrative lessons in this text.

Similarly, after a problem has been solved, checking on the reasonableness of the answer may have special merit for certain types of problem solving. For example, problems whose solutions involve com-

putation with decimal fractions, common fractions, volume relationships, and so forth, may be studied to determine the reasonableness of
the solution.

USING ANOTHER PROCEDURE TO SOLVE A GIVEN PROBLEM

It is sometimes desirable to select another way to solve a given problem after one answer has been determined. Selecting another way to
solve it may offer greater accuracy and also stimulate greater insight
into mathematical relationships. Certainly a procedure of solving each
problem in several ways would not be desirable, but with some problems sensing a number of ways to solve them and selecting the most
efficient way has merit.

ILLUSTRATIVE LESSONS

Lesson 1. Procedures for measuring (kindergarten level)
Lesson 2. Balance-weight relationship (kindergarten level)
Lesson 3. Time-distance-speed relationships
Lesson 4. Direct and inverse proportion as observed in interpreting
pitch of sound

Lesson 1
PROCEDURES FOR MEASURING
Kindergarten Level

Easter vacation was approaching, and Jim was worried about whether
the rabbit that the children had at school had food enough to last during
vacation. The following statements and actions took place:

Jim: I don't think that we have enough rabbit feed to feed our rabbit
during Easter vacation.

Teacher: I think that we do, Jim.

Jim: But I want to be sure. I can measure how many cups it takes,
but I cannot count the days.

Teacher: Try counting them for me.

Jim: I can say the names of the days we will stay home on vacation,
but I cannot say and count them together. Will you help me?

Teacher: What do you want me to do?

Jim: You count the days while I say the days. [Jim named the days.]
Saturday, Sunday, Monday, Tuesday, Wednesday, Thursday, Friday,
Saturday, Sunday.

[The teacher counted 1, 2, 3, 4, and so forth, while Jim named the days.]

Jim: That is 9 days. Now I can measure up 9 cups."
[Jim tried to count and measure. It took so long for him to fill the cup that he lost track of how many cups he had counted.]

Jim: Teacher, I get all mixed up. I forget how many cups I have counted while I get my next cup filled.

Teacher: What do you think that we should do?

Jim: Please, may I have those rocks Robert brought for our science table?

[The teacher gave Jim the rocks. He counted out 9 of them. Then as he measured a cup of feed, he put one rock at a time into a box until he had all 9 rocks in the box.]

Jim: Yes, teacher, we have enough feed for the rabbit during vacation, and some more left, but I don't know for how many days. That will be more rocks than I have, I just know.

Lesson 2
BALANCE-WEIGHT RELATIONSHIP
Kindergarten Level

Sandra and Janet were on a seesaw. Janet was high in the air and Sandra was practically sitting on the ground.

Can we balance? Which way should Bill move?

Sandra: Wait a minute, Janet. I'll help you.

[Sandra proceeded to crawl out on the seesaw towards Janet's end of the board until she reached the place where Janet could descend. By shifting themselves forward and backward, the two girls were able to find positions where they could seesaw.]

Grade One Level

[Similar situation with Nancy and Mary on a seesaw. Nancy was the heavier, and she sensed that she was too heavy for Mary. Mary, about the same time, sensed that she was too light for Nancy. Nancy moved forward.]

Mary: Nancy, don't move so far. I can move back a little. There's a little room for me to go back.

These are illustrations of a procedure for balancing an equation. Weight times distance from the fulcrum must equal weight times the distance on the other side of the balance.

Lesson 3
TIME-DISTANCE-SPEED RELATIONSHIPS
Grade Five Class

Purpose of lesson: To lead the children to refine their concepts concerning direct and inverse proportion by evolving problems using time-distance-speed relationships.

Materials used for lesson: Charts, maps, an atlas, and road maps.

Background of children: The children had a good background of understanding of divisor-dividend-quotient relationships and of multiplier-multiplicand-product relationships.

Lesson Procedure

[The charts depicting the ideas shown below were placed on the bulletin board, and the children were asked to discuss them.]

Chart 1   *Chart 2*

$$\text{variable})\overline{\text{variable}}\,\text{constant} \qquad \text{rate of speed})\overline{\text{time}\atop\text{distance traveled (constant)}}$$

Craig: Chart 1 is easy. We talked about a constant dividend and a variable divisor when we studied division. When you keep the dividend constant and vary the divisor, the answer varies in the opposite way.

Bryan: If you make the divisor larger, the answer gets smaller. If you make the divisor smaller, the answer gets larger.

Craig: If you make the divisor 5 times as large, the answer gets 5 times as small. They change in the same way (amount).

Sarah: The answer is called the quotient.

Teacher: Chart 2 tells about speed, distance, and time. If the rate of speed is variable and the distance traveled is constant, what can you tell about the time needed for travel?

Donald: When distance traveled is constant, the faster the speed, the less time it takes. The slower the speed, the more time it takes.

Mary: I'd rather go fast when I go on a trip. I'd rather fly than go by train or car.

Teacher: If you could travel from Los Angeles to New York with all expenses paid, which of the means of transportation shown on Chart 3 would you choose?

[Teacher put up Chart 3.]

Chart 3

AIRPLANE	TRAIN	CAR
time	time	time
speed) distance	speed) distance	speed) distance

Louise: I'd go by airplane. I like to go fast, and I like to fly.

Peter: I'd go by car. I like to take time and see the country. When you fly, you don't get to see much that's interesting.

Harold: Train travel is fun. I think I would go by train. There is more to see than if you fly.

Craig: About how far is it from Los Angeles to New York?

Bryan: We could find out by looking in the new almanac that we have in your room.

Teacher: That is a fine suggestion, Bryan. I suggest that you look up the distance and then that you make up some problems about time, distance, and speed. Write out your problems on a piece of paper, and be ready to ask the class to solve them. We shall use the first part of our class period for that tomorrow. You may want to set up your problem as a division problem or as a multiplication problem.

Part of the period for mathematics was devoted to letting the children work in groups or individually make up problems concerning time, distance, and speed. The teacher helped children look up information and made recommendations so that there would be a variety of types of problems. The next day the children presented and discussed the probelms that they had evolved.

Peter: I found that it is farther from Los Angeles to New York by automobile than it is by airplane. It is 2624 miles by air. To find how many miles by automobile, I had to figure how many miles from San Francisco to New York and then how many miles from San Francisco to Los Angeles. My first problem is this.

[Peter had his problem written out in the form shown below:]

It is 3173 miles from San Francisco to New York. It is 404 miles from San Francisco to Los Angeles. How many miles is it from Los Angeles to New York?
How many miles less is it by airplane than by car?

Irene: The teacher suggested that we (group of three children) could consider that it is about 3000 miles from Los Angeles to New York. In our problem, we have planned the distance by airplane, by train, and by car to be the same distance. We know that they are not the same distance if you go directly from Los Angeles to New York.
[The members of Irene's committee had their problems written out in the form shown below:]

airplane)$\overline{3\ 0\ 0\ 0}$ miles   train)$\overline{3\ 0\ 0\ 0}$ miles

If the (rate of) travel by airplane is twice as fast as by train, what will be true about how long it takes to travel 3000 miles?
What will be true if the train goes 4 times as slowly as the airplane?

Richard: Our committee plans to go by jet plane Our problems are about jet plane, regular plane and car. A jet plane should be able to average 500 miles an hour, a regular plane about 250 miles an hour, and a car about 50 miles an hour.
[The members of Richard's committee of four children wrote their problems out in the form shown:]

JET PLANE	REGULAR PLANE	CAR
500)$\overline{3\ 0\ 0\ 0}$	250)$\overline{3\ 0\ 0\ 0}$	50)$\overline{3\ 0\ 0\ 0}$

If you travel 3000 miles, how long will it take by jet plane? By regular plane? By car?
How many times as many hours does it take to go by regular plane as by jet?
How many times as many hours does it take to go by car as by jet?
Regular plane is 5 times as fast as car. What about the time it takes to go by regular plane compared with car?

Christina: In our committee, we made multiplication problems. In our problems, you are to compare plane travel and car travel. The multiplicand shows how fast we travel. The multiplier tells about the number of hours.

[The members of Christina's committee of four set up their problems in the form shown below:]

PLANE TRAVEL
2 0 0 (miles an hour)
×   1 0 (hours)

CAR TRAVEL
5 0 (miles an hour)
× 1 0 (hours)

Car travel is how many times as slow as plane travel?
If you travel 10 hours, how many miles will you go by plane?
If you travel 10 hours, how many miles will you go by car?
How many times as many miles will you go by plane as by car?

Other problems were presented, but these illustrate the nature of the problem solving that the children did. From problems such as the ones presented here, the following generalizations were formulated by the children:

Concepts of Inverse Proportion
(a) If the distance traveled is constant, an *increase* in average speed of travel produces a *decrease* in the time it takes for travel.
(b) If the distance traveled is constant, a *decrease* in average speed of travel produces an *increase* in the time it takes for travel.
(c) If the distance traveled is constant, average speed of travel and the time it takes for travel are inversely proportional.

Concepts of Direct Proportion
(a) If the time for travel is kept constant, an *increase* of average speed produces an *increase* of distance traveled.
(b) If the time for travel is kept constant, *decreasing* the average speed *decreases* the distance traveled.
(c) If the time is kept constant, the average speed of travel and distance traveled are directly related.
Also:
(d) If the average speed of travel is kept constant, *increasing* the time for travel leads to *increasing* the distance traveled.
(e) If the average speed of travel is constant, a *decrease* in amount of time for travel leads to a *decrease* of the distance traveled.
(f) If the average speed of travel is constant, the time for travel and the distance traveled are directly related.

Lesson 4
DIRECT AND INVERSE PROPORTION AS OBSERVED
IN INTERPRETING THE PITCH OF SOUND[8]
Grade Six Class

Purposes of lesson: (a) To challenge the child to sense the operation of direct and inverse proportion in interpreting the pitch of sound[9]; (b)

[8] Adapted from a plan by Lawrence Foster in "The Quantitative Relationships of Mathematics and Music," an unpublished paper.

to facilitate the interpretation of the operation of direct and inverse proportion in many other areas within the child's experiencing.

Materials used for lesson: For Part I and Part II of the lesson, the materials used are shown in Figs. 13.2 and 13.3.

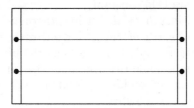

Fig. 13.2 Board with two strings stretched on it.

Background of children: The children had reached a high level of understanding of the operation of direct and of inverse proportion through developing the ideas with numerical computation and with simple ideas that they explained.

Part 1

When weight and other factors (material used, thickness of string, and so forth) are constant, the length of a string determines the pitch of sound

Fig. 13.3 Board with three strings stretched on it. The tighter the string, the higher the pitch; the looser the string, the lower the pitch.

The following ideas were evolved in the early stages of experimentation: When other factors are held constant,
    (a) the longer the string, the lower the pitch,
    (b) the shorter the string, the higher the pitch, and
    (c) the length of string and pitch of sound are directly related.
The following ideas of direct proportion were discovered and stated: When other factors are held constant,

---

[9] Pitch of sound refers to highness and lowness of sound. Middle C has an absolute frequency of 256 cycles per second; C below middle C, 128 cycles per second; C above middle C, 512 cycles per second.

(a) *increasing* the length of the string *increases* lowness of pitch, and

(b) *decreasing* the length of the string *decreases* lowness of pitch.

The following ideas of inverse proportion were discovered and stated: When other factors are held constant,

(a) *increasing* the length of the string *decreases* highness of pitch;

(b) *decreasing* the length of the string *increases* highness of pitch;

(c) when the string is made twice as long, the pitch is twice as low;

(d) when the string is made twice as short, the pitch is twice as high;

(e) when the string for middle C is made half as long, the pitch will give C an octave higher.

Part 2

When the length of the string, the material used, the thickness of the string, and other factors are held constant, the pitch of sound depends directly upon tension on the string (weight).

The following ideas were evolved in the early stages of experimentation with the effect of weight on a string when other factors were controlled: When other factors are held constant,

(a) the tighter the string, the higher the pitch of sound,

(b) the looser the string, the lower the pitch of sound, and

(c) the weight on the string is directly related to the pitch of sound.

The following ideas of direct relationship were discovered and stated: When other factors are held constant,

(a) *increasing* the weight on the string *increases* the highness of pitch;

(b) *decreasing* the weight on the string *decreases* the highness of pitch;

(c) weight on the string and pitch of sound are directly related.

The following ideas of inverse relationship were discovered and stated: When other factors are held constant,

(a) *increasing* the weight on the string *decreases* lowness of sound;

(b) *decreasing* the weight on the string *increases* lowness of sound.

Part 3

The idea was discussed that the thickness of string and pitch of sound are directly related when other factors are held constant.

The thinner the string, the higher the pitch;
the thicker the string, the lower the pitch.

Note: There are many ideas in the field of sound that illustrate the operation of proportion. Two examples are:

The pitch of sound varies inversely with the length of the column of air when other factors are constant.

The pitch of sound varies inversely with the width of the column of air when other factors are held constant.

Discussion Questions

1. What is implied for instruction by the statement, "there is only one way students can learn to solve problems — by solving problems and studying the process"?

2. What is meant by the term "heuristic"?

3. Is it truly possible for one to have an idea and not to be able to express it? What does your answer imply for teaching?

4. Is it true that there are different kinds of problem situations that call for solutions? What does this imply for teaching?

5. What is meant by "sensing a problem"? Why is it important how a problem is sensed?

6. What difference does it make whether or not the student is personally interested in finding an apt solution to a problem?

7. Is problem solving characteristic of other phases of the curriculum or is it peculiar to mathematics?

8. Select two types of problem-solving procedures that are discussed in this chapter and develop an illustration for each of them.

9. Select a specific problem for a class to consider. Write a description of the problem and discuss how you plan to develop problem-solving experiences

Suggested Readings

Ausubel, David P., "Some Psychological and Educational Limitations of Learning by Discovery," *The Arithmetic Teacher*, vol. 11 (May 1964), pp. 290–302.

Banks, J. Houston, *Learning and Teaching Arithmetic*, 2d ed. Boston, Mass.: Allyn and Bacon, Inc., 1964, Chaps. 13 and 14.

Beatty, Leslie, *Teacher's Guide to Problem Solving in Arithmetic*. Report of an Action Research Project in San Diego County School Districts. San Diego, Calif.: Office of the Superintendent of Schools, 1959.

Blecha, Milo, "Helping Children Understand Verbal Problems," *The Arithmetic Teacher*, vol. 6 (March 1959), pp. 106–107.

Burch, R. L., "Formal Analysis as a Problem-solving Procedure," *Journal of Education*, vol. 136 (November 1953), pp. 44–47.

Buswell, Guy T., *Patterns of Thinking in Problem Solving*. University of California Publications in Education, vol. 12, no. 2, pp. 63–148. Berkeley, Calif.: University of California Press, 1956.

Corle, Clyde G., *Teaching Mathematics in the Elementary School*. New York: The Ronald Press Company, 1964, Chap. 15.

Corle, Clyde G., "Thought Processes in Grade Six Problems," *The Arithmetic Teacher*, vol. 5 (October 1958), pp. 193–203.

Dutton, Wilbur H., and L. J. Adams, *Arithmetic for Teachers*. Englewood Cliffs, N.J.: Prentice-Hall, Inc., 1961, Chap. 7.

Harding, Lowry R., "Evaluation of Mathematical Meanings and Understandings," *Emerging Practices in Mathematics Education*. National Council of Teachers of Mathematics, Twenty-second Yearbook. Washington, D.C.: The Council, 1954, pp. 355–364.

Hartung, Maurice L., "Advances in the Teaching of Problem Solving," *Arithmetic 1948*. Supplementary Education Monograph No. 66. Chicago, Ill.: University of Chicago Press, 1948, pp. 44–53.

Henderson, Kenneth B., and Robert E. Pingry, "Problem-Solving in Mathematics," *The Learning of Mathematics*. National Council of Teachers of

Mathematics, Twenty-first Yearbook. Washington, D.C.: The Council, 1953, Chap. 8.

Irish, Elizabeth H., "Improving Problem Solving by Improving Verbal Generalization," *The Arithmetic Teacher*, vol. 11 (March 1964), pp. 169–175.

Kersh, Bert Y., "Learning by Discovery: What Is Learned," *The Arithmetic Teacher*, vol. 11 (April 1964), pp. 226–232.

Koekner, Robert H., "Twenty Methods for Improving Problem Solving," *The Arithmetic Teacher*, vol. 5 (March 1958), pp. 74–78.

Luchins, Abraham S., "Mechanization in Problem Solving: The Effect of Einstellung," *Psychological Monographs*, vol. 54, no. 248, 1942.

Marks, John L., C. Richard Purdy, and Lucien B. Kinney, *Teaching Arithmetic for Understanding*. New York: McGraw-Hill Book Company, Inc., 1958, Chap. 12.

McSwain, E. T., and Ralph J. Cooke, "Essential Mathematical Meanings in Arithmetic in Quantitative Thinking, Computation, and Problem Solving," *The Arithmetic Teacher*, vol. 5 (October 1958), pp. 185–192.

Pace, Angela, "Understanding and the Ability to Solve Problems," *The Arithmetic Teacher*, vol. 8 (May 1961), pp. 226–233.

Petty, Olan, "Non-Pencil-and-Paper Solution of Problems," *The Arithmetic Teacher*, vol. 3 (December 1956), pp. 229–235.

Phelps, Seth P., "When Facts Are Interpreted," *Childhood Education*, vol. 8 (February 1950), pp. 259–262.

Polya, G., *How To Solve It*. Garden City, N. Y.: Doubleday & Company, Inc., 1957, Chap. 1 and Preface.

Polya, G., *Mathematical Discovery: On Understanding, Learning and Teaching Problem Solving*, vol. 1. New York: John Wiley & Sons, Inc., 1962.

Riedesel, C. Alan, "Verbal Problem Solving: Suggestions for Improving Instruction," *The Arithmetic Teacher*, vol. 11 (May 1964), pp. 312–316.

Sauble, Irene, "Development of Ability to Estimate and to Compute Mentally," *The Arithmetic Teacher*, vol. 2 (April 1955), pp. 33–39.

Spitzer, Herbert F., and Frances Flournoy, "Developing Facility in Solving Verbal Problems," *The Arithmetic Teacher*, vol. 3 (November 1956), pp. 177–182.

Sueltz, Ben, "The Measurement of Understandings and Judgments in Elementary Mathematics," *Mathematics Teacher*, vol. 40 (October 1947), p. 279.

Thorndike, Robert L., "How Children Learn the Principles and Techniques of Problem Solving," *Learning and Instruction*, National Society for the Study of Education, Fifty-ninth Yearbook, Part 1. Chicago, Ill.: University of Chicago Press, 1950, pp. 192–215.

Thorpe, Cleata, "The Equation: A Neglected Ally of Arithmetic Processes," *Elementary School Journal*, vol. 60 (March 1960), pp. 320–324.

Unkel, Esther R., "Children are naturals at solving word problems. They love to solve puzzles. They love to explore," *The Arithmetic Teacher*, vol. 8 (April 1961), pp. 161–163.

Van Engen, Henry, "Teach Fundamental Operations through Problem Solving," *Grade Teacher*, vol. 79 (April 1962), pp. 58–59.

Ward, Morgan, and Clarence E. Hardgrove, *Modern Elementary Mathematics*. Reading, Mass.: Addison-Wesley Publishing Company, Inc., 1964, Chap. 10.

14

Errors with Numerical Computation

14.1 INTRODUCTION

The adage, "To err is human," is probably true, but as in the case of other human characteristics, that tendency needs to be controlled. Along with the increased emphasis upon the development of mathematical competencies and with the introduction of mathematical language tasks earlier in the program, there is need to give serious attention to the errors that learners make. The following are important considerations:

ERRORS CAN BE EDUCATIONAL

The fact that it is possible to learn through making errors must not be overlooked. However, in order for mistakes to be educative, they must be recognized as such and used by their makers as guides for changing their ideas and their modes of behavior. This is the very essence of the procedures of discovery and invention.

INSTRUCTION MAY PRODUCE ERRORS

When teacher-dominated "tell and do" procedures are utilized, the learner's efforts are largely centered upon memory and recall. If he has perceived well what he was shown or told, and if he can recall and apply the information as directed, he has achieved as expected. He need not have "mentally digested" the diet nor have sensed its pertinency beyond the period of ingestion. He may perform very much as a mechanical recorder receiving impressions faithfully and reproducing them on demand — a type of academic regurgitation.

Errors noted under such conditions may be due to incorrect materials of instruction, to the pupil's misreading what was shown or told him, or to quirks in his processes of memory or recall. Such errors may or may not be sensed by their makers, since their attention is centered largely on "doing as they were told."

ERRORS MAY BE MERELY "PROVISIONAL TRIES"

When instructional procedures are governed by democratic concern for understanding and for personal responsibility for the aptness of one's behavior, the student is expected to be alert to sense errors in his behavior. He is led to make "provisional tries," in order to learn whether or not what he thought would work really does work. Errors will be made but will be recognized as such and studied to determine why they are in error and why they were made. This is the essence of the idea that one "learns to do through doing." It is the essence of mathematical development.

ERRORS ARE INEVITABLE

Errors are inevitable, and it is important that educational procedures be devised to utilize them effectively. This calls for careful observation and for diagnostic procedures. It entails a more systematic organization of instructional materials and more analytical measurement of pupil progress in the development of ideas and of competencies in their effective expression for communication. Errors may reveal instructional deficiencies quite as truly as they reveal learning deficiencies.

14.2   MANY TYPES of ERRORS

Too often errors are thought of as though they were all of a kind, and all bad. However, a more tenable conception recognizes wide differences among them, differences that need to be observed and given proper consideration.

ERRORS MAY BE MERELY EXPRESSION ERRORS

Some errors reveal that their maker probably has correct ideas, but that he is lacking in skills to express them. The treatment of such inadequacies involves language-skills development.

ERRORS MAY BE EVIDENCE OF FAULTY READING

Other errors suggest that the maker has misread the situation and consequently has used an inappropriate mode of response. The expression techniques used may be effectively performed, but they were unsuited to the conditions of the problem. Such mistakes are fundamentally different from those characterized by mere language expression deficiencies. Inadequacies with the reading of a situation give rise to inadequate ideas. Treating such a condition is quite a different matter from that of treating the poor expression of a good idea.

ERRORS MAY BE ERRORS OF TECHNIQUE

There are errors that reveal inadequacies in the use of techniques. The procedural plan being followed may be an appropriate one, and the work may be accomplished accurately except for some important step that was performed incorrectly. The process of revealing such steps and making clear how they should be treated is an important aspect of instructional guidance.

SOME ERRORS ARE NUMBER FACT ERRORS

A student may make errors with specific number facts, although all other aspects of his work have been well done. Such errors occur only when the specific number facts are involved. Similar problems or examples not involving those facts will be solved correctly. There are numerous other types of error, some of which appear to have no evident explanation; but, if they recur in the pupil's work, there must be a cause which needs to be uncovered.

THERE ARE GOOD ERRORS AND BAD ERRORS

There are many kinds of errors. Some errors are "good errors" in that they indicate that their makers have progressed substantially in the course of their learning, but the errors reveal clearly where some inadequacy lies. Some errors are "bad errors" because they appear to have no reasonable basis, or they reveal that their makers are basically deficient in their understanding of the needs of a situation, or that they are extremely deficient in their mastery of mathematical language skills or techniques.

ERRORS MAY BE CONSISTENT AS WELL AS PERSISTENT

The fact that errors occur and recur in numerical computations will scarcely be challenged. However, the comparable fact that errors occur and recur with consistency only with certain computational situations may not be so evident. There are literally hundreds of specific factual number combinations. Some of them appear to be much more difficult than others to memorize and recall effectively. There are also hundreds of steps involved in customary calculation procedures. Some of them occur infrequently and are likely to be overlooked unless instruction is very carefully planned to treat them. Disclosing consistency in the errors a pupil makes is an encouraging finding. An error that is made consistently can be revealed to the maker with convincing results.

Persistency in error without consistency is a much more difficult problem to handle. Determining what the nature of an error is, and how consistently a pupil makes it, is an instructional responsibility. This calls for the construction and utilization of test instruments designed specifically for that purpose. Tests designed merely to measure general achievement with regard to a variety of computational situations are poorly suited for this purpose.

14.3   TEACHER-MADE TESTS

Careful analysis of the material to be developed in any learning situation will reveal aspects that are potential sources of difficulty. This is true also of the procedures for instruction. Whatever the procedure, it will make some points clearer than others, and conceivably it will be productive of erroneous responses that are directly related to what was presented or what was omitted from the presentation. Instruction and achievement are dynamically related even when errors are characteristic of the achievement. In a very real sense, erroneous and inept behavior is learned just as truly as correct and apt behavior.

Just as instruction needs to be designed to cope with the inherent difficulties of materials and procedures, so also must tests be designed to measure the degree of success that is achieved. One aspect of teacher competence is that of being able to foresee what is likely to produce difficulty and then to proceed in a manner such as to reduce that potential to the lowest feasible degree. Another measure of competency on the part of the teacher is to be able to identify wherein lies a discrepancy or deficiency on the part of the student and then lead the student to recognize and to rectify his deficiencies.

There is need to recognize that observable deficiencies in behavior are merely peripheral symptoms of misunderstandings or misconceptions. Effective instruction uses the symptoms to disclose the basic difficulty. It is within that area that remediation needs to be achieved. Merely treating the symptom and not treating the causes is poor educational practice.

To the extent that ready-made instruments are available and adequate for revealing the nature of pupil deficiencies, they should be used. But, instruments that were devised for one type of instruction may not serve equally well in other types. They may measure abilities to achieve correct numerical answers, but unless the tasks presented truly represent the difficulties normally encountered by students using the procedures as they were taught, they are not usable for disclosing such difficulties. The teacher needs to examine test instruments carefully to determine whether they really measure the areas of difficulty that his pupils experience. Teacher-made tests carefully designed to disclose sources of difficulty are needed. Such tests serve as instructional guides. They are not intended for administrative purposes.

14.4 SUGGESTED GUIDELINES for TEACHER-CONSTRUCTED TESTS

The following suggestions are intended for teacher reference in designing and administering tests for his own instructional guidance. Such testing differs substantially from that which is designed for comparing achievement with norms that are established on a country-wide basis. Normed tests serve a very different purpose.

1. Center the test upon some well-defined unit of learning. The unit of concern may be a particular idea or a single step of a procedure or it may include a somewhat wider scope, but the specific purpose needs to be clearly evident.

2. Select unit tests with care. The usability of test results for indicating pupil progress with an idea or a technique is a measure of its worth. Testing should not be "busy work." It is a probing and evaluative procedure.

3. Reduce extraneous aspects to the minimum. The sharpness with which the matter to be measured is identified is important. Extra things complicate scoring and may interfere with the testing.

4. Use at least two specimens of each test item. A second exposure serves as a measure of consistency of the pupil's response.

5. Check the nature of the error as well as the incorrectness of the answer. An answer may be incorrect for a variety of causes. Center your attention upon the matter of major concern.

6. Note both individual and group responses. If a weakness is characteristic of a group, instruction needs to be examined. If it is individual only, the personal source of the difficulty needs to be determined.

7. The taking and the scoring of the test should be educational experiences. There is little use for tests that are not of interest to the person taking them or that are without purpose on the part of those who administer them.

14.5   SPECIMEN TESTS DESIGNED for INSTRUCTIONAL GUIDANCE—SMALL UNITS of SPECIFIC MATERIAL

The following tests are designed to measure performance with specific small units of learning. In some instances, they are adapted to a particular mode of performance.

SPECIMEN TEST ONE

This test is a unit test concerned with the placement of the decimal point and the use of zero as a placeholder in the multiplication of mixed decimal and decimal fraction numbers.

Directions

The following examples with multiplication have been solved except for the placing of the decimal point in each product. Place the decimal point where it is needed to make the answer correct.

(a)	(b)	(c)	(d)	(e)	(f)	(g)
1.5	.2 6	1 4	2 4	.3 1	.0 9	.1 8
$\times$ 1 2	$\times$ 1 3	$\times$ 1.2	$\times$ .1 3	$\times$ .8	$\times$ .6	$\times$ .0 6
3 0	7 8	2 8	7 2	2 4 8	5 4	1 0 8
1 5	2 6	1. 4	2 4			
1 8 0	3 3 8	1 6 8	3 1 2			

Description of the Test

The actual multiplications have been kept relatively simple. The purpose of the test is to measure the pupil's understanding concerning the correct position for the decimal point in the product. The decimal fraction expressions are placed in all the possible positions — decimal point in multiplier only, decimal point in multiplicand only, and decimal point in both factors. Examples (f) and (g) entail the use of zero in order to give the decimal point its proper place.

A test such as this may be duplicated and a copy supplied to each pupil. At least two specimens of each type of example should be used. When scoring the test, any improper placement of the decimal point should be noted and compared to determine whether it reveals a consistent mistake on the part of the examinee. The examples may be used in the form above, or they may be used with no computation presented. The objective of the test is to indicate pupil ability in placing the decimal point.

SPECIMEN TEST TWO

This is a unit test concerned with a specific technique. Sometimes pupils persist in applying a specific technique in situations in which it does not apply. Usually such a technique is a part of a particular procedure that has been taught. It may not be appropriate when used with another method of procedure. For example, if regrouping of the minuend is practiced with the subtraction of decimal integers, it is sometimes applied without adaptation in subtraction involving other types of numbers. This tendency has been noted frequently as a source of error in the subtraction of mixed numbers and likewise in the subtraction of denominate numbers. Testing specifically for that kind of performance can be the basis for a unit test. For example:

(a)	(b)	(c)	(d)
5 2	4 . 1	5 $\frac{1}{6}$	5 feet 2 inches
− 3 8	− 2 . 7	− 3 $\frac{5}{6}$	− 3 feet 8 inches

Purpose of the Test

To determine whether regrouping as performed with decimal numbers persists in working with nondecimal numbers.

Description of Test

Example (a) calls for the use of the regrouping technique in the setting in which it was probably learned. Example (b) calls for the use of the procedure when regrouping across the decimal point is involved. Example (c) calls for regrouping, but the numeral is nondecimal in nature. If regrouping is done as in the decimal numeral, the minuend will be regrouped as $4\frac{11}{6}$ instead of $4\frac{7}{6}$. The resulting remainder may appear characteristically as $1\frac{6}{6}$, or as 2 (the $\frac{6}{6}$ accounting for 1), or even as 11 signifying not 11, as it would seem, but "1 and 1 more." Example (d) provides for a recurrence of the regrouping situation, but with the denominate number scale involved. The use of decimal regrouping in such instances is common. Perhaps it is like the phonetic spelling errors in the vernacular, that is, it suggests that more consistency in our language forms is desirable.

14.6   SPECIMEN TESTS DESIGNED for INSTRUCTIONAL GUIDANCE—LARGER UNITS of SPECIFIC MATERIAL

Specimen tests for larger units of instructional material may be developed in the same way as for smaller units, but more test items are involved. This section illustrates a unit test for the subtraction that occurs in long division. Division is not easy, but it can be made easier. One way to make it easier is to determine the things that make it difficult. One of the things is the subtractions that occur in the division process. For example, the subtraction example, 200 − 188, is illustrated as it occurs in a division example:

$$
\begin{array}{r}
2 \\
94) \overline{\ 200} \\
188
\end{array}
\qquad
\begin{array}{r}
200 \\
-188
\end{array}
$$

If the pupil is unable to solve correctly the subtraction example in its subtraction setting, it is unlikely that he can solve it correctly in its setting in division. Hence, that subtraction step needs to be done accurately and readily if the division operation is to be done effectively. Since the subtraction operation is commonly taught prior to that of long division, it is well to assure reasonable competency with the subtractions that are likely to occur in the division process. The subtraction examples which can occur in division are readily identifiable. Their subtrahends are the product of divisor and quotient combinations. The range of minuends with which each subtrahend can occur is also identifiable. It begins with a number equal to the subtrahend and ranges upward to a number that is one less than the next multiple of the divisor which produced the subtrahend.

There are more than 40,000 of such subtraction examples that can occur in division examples having one-digit or two-digit divisors and a one-digit quotient. Approximately one half of the total number of examples have subtrahends that may be produced by two or more divisor-quotient combinations. Since these are presumably most likely to occur in division examples, they are the ones to give special attention in preparation for their use in division.

Assuming that the subtractions are performed by the regrouping, decomposition ("borrowing") procedure, the examples can be typed according to the steps required to perform that operation. These are regrouping in either the units' or tens' positions or in both positions, together with the occurrence of zero involvements.

If another method for performing the subtractions is used, a different set of types will be found. However, it is unlikely that any procedure can be devised that will eliminate entirely the potentiality of difficulty with some of its steps. The fact that variance in such procedures does exist, however, makes it especially important for the teacher-made tests to be devised to cope with them.

SPECIMEN TEST ONE

This specimen test is a unit test of subtraction as it occurs in long division. In order to construct a test for the unit described earlier, there needs to be agreement as to the size of the divisors and the method of procedure employed with the operation of subtraction. No new elements are incorporated by using divisors having more than two digits and quotients of more than one digit. Therefore, the test is limited to such situations. Using the regrouping (decomposition) procedure, there are two general sources of difficulty. They are

(a) regrouping that can occur in the units' position only, in the tens' position only, or in both the units' and tens' positions, and

(b) involvements with zero. Zero appears to present difficulties that are peculiar to it, and that need special consideration in teaching.

Twenty types of subtraction examples have been identified in long division when the presence or absence of these sources of difficulty is used as the criterion of classification.[1] See Table 14.1.

TABLE 14.1
Types of Subtraction Examples That Occur in Long Division, Using Regrouping-Decomposition Procedure in the Minuend.

		SPECIMEN	RANK*
Subset A. No regrouping is required for the solution			
Type 1	There is no zero involvement	187–162	3
Type 2	Number minus zero in units' place	476–440	1
Type 3	Number minus itself in units' place	155–135	2
Type 4	Combination of Types 2 and 3	554–504	4
Subset B. Regrouping required in units' place only			
Type 5	No zero involvement	334–315	13
Type 6	Number minus zero in tens' place	573–504	12
Type 7	Zero minus number in units' place	260–243	6
Type 8	Combination of Types 6 and 7	520–504	11
Type 9	Zero minus number in tens' place	701–693	17**
Type 10	Zero in both units' and tens' places Combines Types 7 and 9	800–792	15

[1] Peter L. Spencer, *A Study of Subtraction Cases Found in Long Division Examples Having Two-Digit Divisors*, Studies in Arithmetic No. 1. Claremont, Calif.: Claremont College, 1933.

TABLE 14.1 continued

Subset C. Regrouping required in tens' place only   SPECIMEN   RANK*

Type 11	No zero involvement	639–588	14
Type 12	Zero minus number in tens' place	308–273	10
Type 13	Zero minus number in tens' place and number minus itself in units' place	302–252	8
Type 14	Number minus itself in units' place	872–792	7
Type 15	Number minus zero in units' place	614–560	5
Type 16	Zero minus number in tens' place and number minus zero in units' place	603–560	9

Subset D. Regrouping required in both units' and tens' places

Type 17	No zero involvement	751–693	16
Type 18	Zero minus number in units' place	740–672	20
Type 19	"Unseen zero" minus number in tens' place	611–558	19
Type 20	"Unseen zero" minus number in tens' place, zero minus number in units' place	210–162	18

* The rank order as given here is the order as determined by the percentage of correct answers. Rank 1 gave the greatest number and Rank 20 gave the least number of correct responses.

** This step of regrouping goes across the tens' place to the hundreds' position, but in so doing a 9 is made available in the tens' place. Hence, no regrouping is required for the hundreds' position unless it is incorporated in the instructional methodology.

Consider the following example:

$$\begin{array}{r} 8\ 0\ 0 \\ -\ 7\ 9\ 2 \\ \hline \end{array}$$

$$\begin{array}{r} {}^{7}\ {}^{9} \\ 8\ \cancel{0}\ {}^{1}0 \\ -\ 7\ 9\ 2 \\ \hline \end{array}$$

The 800 may be considered as 80 tens. We can take 1 ten from the 80 tens leaving 79 tens. The 1 ten may be regrouped as 10 units. The regrouped value of 800 in 79 tens, 10 units. This is the procedure that was used to classify the example as Type 10. The same procedure was used to classify Type 9. The procedure calls for one regrouping rather than the two regroupings that are sometimes used.

The ranking of difficulty of the types has been observed over a period of years. It has remained substantially the same even though considerable improvement has taken place in regard to the total number of correct answers. This seems to indicate that the sources of difficulty are real and inherent, and that ways to cope with them are needed.

The following set of examples contains one specimen of each of the twenty types:[2]

(1)	(2)	(3)	(4)	(5)
4 9 9	7 7 7	4 6 6	3 3 4	2 9 8
− 4 5 6	− 7 2 0	− 4 5 6	− 3 0 4	− 2 7 9

(6)	(7)	(8)	(9)	(10)
1 2 6	7 0	3 2 0	2 0 5	5 0 0
− 1 0 8	− 5 7	− 3 0 4	− 1 7 6	− 4 6 8

(11)	(12)	(13)	(14)	(15)
7 2 8	1 0 9	3 0 3	3 3 0	6 1 3
− 6 9 3	− 9 8	− 2 7 3	− 2 8 0	− 5 8 0

(16)	(17)	(18)	(19)	(20)
5 0 4	4 2 2	7 2 0	3 1 5	1 1 0
− 4 9 0	− 3 9 6	− 6 7 2	− 2 8 8	− 7 4

This set of examples can be logically divided into four subsets according to the nature of subtraction situations involved. Subset A containing examples of Types 1 through 4 includes no regrouping, but it does contain zero involvements. Subset B, composed of Types 5 through 10 requires regrouping for the units' position only together with zero situations. Subset C containing Types 11 through 16 is similar to B except that the regrouping has been shifted to the tens' position. Subset D composed of Types 17 through 20 presents situations involving regrouping for both the units' and the tens' places, as well as "unseen zero" situations.

By using example sets comparable to these at appropriate times during the course of the instructional program, a teacher should be able to direct the learning and measure its progress in such a manner that the subtraction preparation for division will be assured.

As mentioned previously, noting the *nature of errors* is of more value than merely noting that an answer is incorrect. In order to facilitate the scoring of error types, a system of labeling is needed. The system shown in Table 14.2 was devised by a teacher for use with subtraction. It has been used effectively by other teachers and is offered here as an illustration of what has been proved to be a useful procedure.[3]

[2] Ibid. Test made from study by Peter L. Spencer.
[3] James Edward Spencer, *A Comparative Study of Computational Error Types with the Subtraction of Decimal Integers.* Unpublished Master's Thesis, Claremont College Graduate School, Claremont, Calif. 1957.

TABLE 14.2

DESCRIPTION OF ERROR	SPECIMEN	SYMBOL
Solution omitted		*om*
Number minus zero	6 6 −6 0 ——— 4	$n - 0$
Zero minus a number	6 0 −3 6 ——— 2 8	$0 - n$
Number minus itself	5 5 −3 5 ——— 2 1	$n - n$
Error with subtraction combination	2 8 −1 6 ——— 1 3	*s*
Failure to adapt after regrouping	6 3 −2 6 ——— 4 7	*far*
Adapting for regrouping when regrouping not done	6 5 −3 4 ——— 2 1	*asn*
Reversing instead of regrouping	2 8 −1 9 ——— 1 1	*r*
Adding instead of subtracting	6 3 −2 1 ——— 4 4	*as*
Miscellaneous mistakes having no "apparent" basis	6 3 −2 1 ——— 9 8	*m*

With the use of some differential scoring procedure, the location and, frequently, the nature of errors can be spotted. It is not always feasible to infer just what the pupil did, but it is more feasible to locate the situation in which erroneous behavior occurred. Sometimes it is helpful to have the pupil work out comparable situations and report orally what he is thinking as the work is being done.

A study of the consistency with which specific situations are productive of error has proved to be helpful to both teachers and students. That errors are characteristic products of the materials and procedures of instruction is suggested by the percentages of error types that were found in scoring the work of two groups of pupils at the fifth grade level.

TABLE 14.3

CLASS	$o - n$	$n - n$	s	far	r	m	TOTAL PERCENTAGE TYPED
A	19	4	14	25	11	14	87
B	18	16	8	14	9	30	90

This table indicates that 87 percent and 90 percent, respectively, of the incorrect responses of these pupils were of the types identified. However, the performances of the two groups showed some strong similarities, as well as some evident difference. For example, zero minus a number produced practically the same percentages of error for each of the classes. A number minus itself calling for a zero in the remainder produced 4 times as high a percentage in Class B as in Class A. Errors in subtraction facts produced almost twice as high a percentage in Class A as in Class B. This was also the case with errors that were of the nature of failing to make an adjustment in the minuend after regrouping. Mistakes in reversing occurred about equally in both classes, and it is interesting to observe that they constituted only about 1 out of 10 of the mistakes. Class B produced about twice the number of "miscellaneous" mistakes, and it is important to note that such mistakes account for 1 out of 3 of the wrong responses. Surely this is a condition that requires the attention of the teacher of that class. Finding consistency in performance that is related to some discernible step or aspect of a procedure is an important part of teaching.

SPECIMEN TEST TWO

This unit test[4] was made to determine the consistency of performance and the types of errors that more than 700 junior high school students would show with the division of decimal fractions and mixed decimal expressions. These pupils had completed the offering in division as provided in the school system which they attended. A test was constructed which contained two specimens each of 18 types of examples with the division of decimal fractions and mixed decimals. Two forms of the test as identical as possible in their exposures to type examples were used. Only the papers of students who accomplished both forms of the test were considered in the study. Table 14.4 below reports the gross data secured.

[4] Hilda Peterson, *A Study with the Division of Decimal Fractions.* Unpublished Master's Thesis, Claremont College Graduate School, Claremont, Calif. 1951.

TABLE 14.4

Gross Data Concerning Errors With the Division
of Decimal Fractions and Mixed Decimals

TEST FORM	NUMBER PUPILS	NUMBER PUPIL EXAMPLES	NUMBER INCORRECT ANSWERS	PERCENT ANSWERS INCORRECT
A	742	26712	8488	31.8
B	742	26712	7651	28.6

Each of 742 pupils in the seventh and eighth grades of a junior high school accomplished two forms of a test, which included two specimens each of 18 types of examples with the division of decimal fractions. The percentages of incorrect answers given to the separate forms were 31.8 and 28.6, respectively. Consistency of achievement was measured by correlating the scores on the two forms. The coefficient was .9906. Twelve error types were identified and applied in the study of pupil responses in this study. The error types were as follows:

dpom   Decimal point omitted

dpmp   Decimal point misplaced

dq   Divisor-quotient error, usually error
        with number fact

0p   0 not prefixed as required between decimal
        point and other digits in quotient

0s   0 not suffixed as required to give quotient
        proper place value

0i   0 not placed within the number as required
        for place value

rev   Reversed the divisor and dividend

om   Did not attempt the example

inc   Example attempted but solution not completed

exinc   Decimal expression changed to common
        fraction or not carried out

exp   Unnecessary zeros to left of decimal point
        when quotient is decimal fraction

exs   Unnecessary zeros to right of quotient

Table 14.5 identifies the types of examples and reports certain of the error types. The evidence appears to indicate that the errors are closely associated with particular aspects of the procedures used in such examples.

TABLE 14.5
Example Type and Error Occurrence with Division of Decimal Fraction Numbers

EXAMPLE TYPE NUMBER	TYPE SPECIMEN	PERCENT INCORRECT ANSWERS	PERCENTAGE OF INCORRECT ANSWERS REPRESENTING RESPECTIVE ERROR TYPES						
			dpom	dpmp	dq	0p	0i	om	
1	4$\overline{)}$.8	7	52	30	15			3	⎫
2	6$\overline{)}$3	25	57	21	9			4	⎪
3	3$\overline{)}$.09	10	22	34	13	29		1	⎬ Part 1
4	5$\overline{)}$.025	45	7	30	7	18	33	2	⎪
5	4$\overline{)}$.16	24	9	35	4	51		1	⎪
6	14$\overline{)}$3.22	20	20	22	49			7	⎭
7	.22$\overline{)}$3.432	39	8	42	42			4	⎫
8	.333$\overline{)}$.999	45	1	32	67*			1	⎪
9	1.2$\overline{)}$38.64	28	10	44	35			9	⎪
10	.005$\overline{)}$.125	27	3	55	33			9	⎬ Part 2
11	.125$\overline{)}$.025	39	11	43	28	1		16	⎪
12	2.6$\overline{)}$2.73	70	4	18	10**		30		⎪
13	.25$\overline{)}$.2	30	11	50	24			11	⎪
14	.14$\overline{)}$32.2	37	14	53	24			8	⎭
15	.014$\overline{)}$28	54	28	58	9			5	⎫
16	.14$\overline{)}$322	55	24	58	13			5	⎬ Part 3
17	.5$\overline{)}$4525	62	22	55	8	13		2	⎪
18	.75$\overline{)}$15	50	18	64	9			8	⎭

* The high percentage of division errors in this instance is due to the tendency to divide serially. The characteristic answer for this type was 333.
** A considerable number of pupils failed to carry this solution to completion.

The percentages reported are averages of the four responses given by 742 pupils to each of the example types. The percentages reported under the error types were calculated on the number of incorrect answers only.

Example 2 is unlike the examples in the remainder of the test in that it contains no decimal point.

In division of decimal fractions, the placement of the decimal point is a basic factor in the production of error. Table 14.6 below summarizes data concerning the occurrence of errors with the decimal point.

TABLE 14.6

Occurrence of Type Errors in Different Groups of Division Examples

DECIMAL POINT EXPRESSED	PERCENT ANSWERS INCORRECT	PERCENT OF INCORRECT ANSWERS DUE TO EACH ERROR TYPE	
		dpom	dpmp
Neither term	25	57	21
Dividend only	21	22	28
Both divisor and dividend	39	9	41
Divisor only	55	23	59

On first reading, the report is very discouraging to one who hopes for reasonable "functional competency" with the process of dividing decimal fractions and mixed decimals. The percentages of incorrect answers are unreasonably high for pupils at that stage of educational advancement. But, again, as we inspect the responses for type errors and evidence of deficient learning, the interpretation must be changed. From 50 to approximately 80 percent of the incorrect responses were incorrect because the pupil failed to use, or misused, the decimal point. Surely some way can be found to make instruction with the decimal point more functional! The same test was applied to a group of children in the sixth grade, after they had studied decimal fraction expressions for only four days, with results far better than those reported above. The teacher of the sixth grade in the instance just mentioned introduced computation with decimal fractions with division and, believe it or not, with examples having decimal fractions in the divisors only. The instruction proceeded smoothly and without any evidence of confusion on the part of the pupils.

The studies presented in this chapter bring out the idea that pupils are demonstrating much better abilities to accomplish mathematical thinking and computational accuracy than is being credited to them. Failure with a number fact will produce an incorrect solution, but does it also indicate a lack of ability to accomplish mathematical development? Similarly, a misconception regarding any of the many specific steps of procedure in performing a computation will probably produce an incorrect answer. However, *it takes a vast amount of wrong learning to produce the patterns of errors commonly found in pupil responses. The errors must have been learned. If students can learn such errors, they should be able to be taught correct responses!*

14.7 "NOTHING SUCCEEDS LIKE SUCCESS"

The preceding studies indicate the need for heeding the adage, "Nothing succeeds like success." It suggests a good guideline for instruction in general and for mathematical instruction in particular. Since reasonable competence with basic mathematical ideas and skills is deemed to be necessary, it is desirable that this be achieved as effectively as possible and that the achievers develop attitudes of respect and appreciation for what they have accomplished. Instruction that produces feelings of fear or of frustration, or leaves the learner competent only as regards memorized facts and techniques is fundamentally undemocratic. The operator needs to be informed concerning the rational bases for what he has learned.

There is need to "accentuate the positive." Accuracy in expression and in computation is important, but during the course of learning it need not be treated on an "all-or-none" basis. Evaluation of the responses of learners must be done constructively. As pointed out earlier, there are many forms of errors all of which produce "wrong answers." Surely, from an instructional point of view, the nature of the errors is an important matter to note. Merely checking the response for its numerical or expressional accuracy is an easy, but essentially superficial, type of scoring. Identifying *what is right* in the student's responses is as important as noting that the responses are wrong. This does not imply that pupils should be given credit for work that is wrong; but, on the other hand, it is intended to point out that credit should be given for *what is right*.

"Provisional tries" are essential to disclose to the student the true nature of the situation confronting him and also the adequacies and inadequacies of his behavioral responses. Like the proverbial turtle, he can get to where he needs to go only by "sticking his neck out." *Since learning is an emergent process and educating is a procedure of educing or drawing out, the capable teacher encourages pupils to make "trial runs" and to "use their heads" in doing so. This is the very essence of problem solving.*

Self-respect and confidence are built by stressing strengths rather than weaknesses. The tendency to recognize only weaknesses or deficiencies when evaluating pupil performance is a form of continuous "fault finding," which tends to frustrate and confuse the learner. By pointing out what is well done and matching it with what is poorly done, the pupil gets a better measure of his competence. As one pupil expressed this point, "Miss B. showed us how much we had already learned as compared with what there was still to learn, and we saw that it was stupid not to finish the learning."

14.8   SUGGESTIONS for INSTRUCTION

In the following numbered paragraphs, several instruction procedures are discussed.

1. Provide for an "interest potential." Willingness to learn is as necessary as is readiness to learn. Arouse an interest rather than merely assign a task.

The instruction "Solve these examples," is not likely to excite much of an interest potential. There needs to be more of a challenge to the student's intellect. Mr. James found the following kind of exercise productive of pupil interest:

Puzzle! Which set of examples looks to be the easier to do? Solve Set *A* first and then do Set *B*. Then answer the questions.

Set *A*		Set *B*	
1 7 8 − 9 2	1 6 5 − 7 3	9 7 − 2 9	6 6 − 3 7
1 4 7 − 8 4	1 0 8 − 6 3	8 4 − 4 8	9 0 − 3 6
1 5 6 − 7 4	1 7 7 − 8 3	7 5 − 4 7	8 7 − 3 8

How are the examples in Set *A* different from those in Set *B*? What is the same in both sets? Which set was easier to do?

This assignment of seat work was designed to serve the two following purposes: (1) to check on the pupils' skill in performing the regrouping-decomposition technique in subtraction, and (2) to check on the accuracy with which they handled certain subtraction facts in both their "seen" and their "unseen" forms. Notice that the facts are the same in both sets provided the regrouping has been properly done:

$$\begin{array}{r} 1\ 7\ 8 \\ -\ 9\ 2 \end{array} \quad \text{and} \quad \begin{array}{r} 9\ 7 \\ -\ 2\ 9 \end{array}$$

The combinations $17 - 9$ and $8 - 2$ occur in each of the examples.

2. Develop illustrative materials for stimulating inferential reasoning and *leave it available for observation and study*. Since much of mathematical knowledge is derived from establishing references and making comparisons, this procedure should be used with precision. Too often short cuts are introduced which conceal rather than reveal what is to be inferred. For example, consider the following steps concerned with determining the properties of the process of dividing by a common fraction numeral.

$$\frac{5}{7} \div \frac{2}{3}$$

How much is $\frac{5}{7} \div \frac{2}{3}$? Do you know what $5 \div 2$ equals? Is $\frac{5}{7}$ less than 5? Is $\frac{2}{3}$ less than 2?

$$\frac{5}{7} \div 1 = \frac{5}{7}$$

We need something with which to compare. One is nearly always a good reference. Anything divided by 1 is that number. One is an identity element in division.

$$8 \overline{)\,8}^{\;1} \qquad 4 \overline{)\,8}^{\;2} \qquad 2 \overline{)\,8}^{\;4} \qquad 1 \overline{)\,8}^{\;8}$$

If the divisor is made smaller in value, and if the dividend is unchanged, what happens to the quotient?

$$\frac{5}{7} \div \frac{1}{3}$$

Then

$$\frac{5}{7} \div \frac{1}{3} = \frac{5 \times 3}{7}$$

If the divisor is made 3 times as small, the quotient will be made 3 times as large in value.

$$\frac{5}{7} \div \frac{2}{3}$$

Then, it follows that $\frac{5}{7} \div \frac{2}{3}$ will equal

$$\frac{5 \times 3}{7 \times 2}$$

If the divisor is made 2 times as large, the quotient is made 2 times as small. To make the value of a fraction 2 times as small, we make its divisor (denominator) 2 times as large.

Is there any step above which is not true? How does

$$\frac{5 \times 3}{7 \times 2}$$

differ from $\frac{5}{7} \div \frac{2}{3}$?

Does this agree with the statement that "multiplication is the inverse of division?

The answer for the example is 1 and $\frac{1}{14}$. Does this seem like a reasonable answer?

Problem for study. The "reciprocal of a whole number" is one divided by the number. What is the "reciprocal" of $\frac{2}{3}$? Can you work it out from $1 \div \frac{2}{3}$?

Note that the multiplications were merely indicated during the course of the argument. Had they been completed, the cues to the conclusion would have been lost.

3. Pupil discussion supplies clues to their thought processes. Many of the illustrative lessons reported in this book give the statements of pupils that reveal their progress in sensing the situation and in reasoning out what it calls for on their part. Skill in teaching is shown by leading pupils to formulate their own ideas and then testing them for validity. Skillful questioning and skillful use of illustrations can expedite this process.

4. Educe the response that is desired. Teaching is a matter of communicating. Communication has been termed "the logistics of ideas." However, this is not comparable to "logistics" as applied to military operations. In that instance, the substance exists in its own right and can be transferred physically to a designated place. The "logistics" as regards ideas is not a transfer but a procreative process. Everyone must create his ideas for himself. However, educational logistics facilitates this procreative process. The efficiency with which this takes place is directly determined by the skill of the instructor in pointing up the issues and in provoking thought processes that are pertinent to them.

5. Make provision for fixating or "stamping in" the learned matter. The material that is to be learned must be clearly identified. If it is an idea, it needs to be sharply and clearly formulated. Ambiguity or partial accuracy is likely to be evidence of a lack of clear ideas. If the learning is a particular technique, the situations in which it fits need to be identified and also the ones where it does not apply. To know a thing well, one must also know what it is not.

Drill (recurrent experiencing) is important both for the sake of clarifying that which is learned and for the sake of the development of skill in its use. However, tasks performed for drill must be carefully directed. Sheer bulk or "busy work" is not evidence of professional educational services. A few exercises that are really potent are far superior to a large number of those which do not have real function except that of the consumption of time. Each set of examples that a student is asked to solve should have a very direct value to him for the solving. For example, a teacher found that his pupils were having difficulty adding the "carries" in multiplication. He challenged his class to generalize by extending combinations that they had learned. For example: $4 + 6 = 10$. How does it help you to know $14 + 6$, $24 + 6$, $54 + 6$, and $64 + 6$?

After concepts were taught, he developed practice materials which were designed to assist them with that step. First, he determined *what* addition facts could occur in that process. There were 219 of them. Next he set up exercises in addition which contained the more difficult of such examples, that is, 18 + 7, 49 + 6, 54 + 6, and so forth. A sufficient number of these were presented to measure the ability to make additions of that type. Then he presented number sentences which required the pupil to perform a multiplication and then add a designated amount to the product, for example, $(9 \times 2) + 7$; (7×7) + 6; $(9 \times 6) + 6$, and so on. This set of examples repeated the additions given in the first step. They provided a check on the use of the facts in a type of multiplication situation. A final recurrence of the facts was arranged in the following examples:

$$\begin{array}{ccc} 2\,8 & 7\,9 & 6\,7 \\ \times\,9 & \times\,7 & \times\,9 \end{array}$$

Then id order to make sure that the pupils thoroughly understood the occurrence of such an addition step in the multiplication process, he asked them to construct multiplication examples in which 8 would be carried to 54, 5 would be carried to 28, and so on. If the pupil can construct examples which call for the step he is studying, and if he can solve the examples which he constructed, that is pretty good evidence that he knows how to identify the need for that step and how to treat it when it occurs.

6. "Put handles on" what is learned in order to facilitate recall. Providing for the facile recall of what has been learned is as important as providing for its being learned. Too often mathematical learning has been accomplished as disparate techniques, as rules, or principles presumed to be adequate for specific situations. This requires that the performer not only identify the situation but that he recall the specific item of learning which applies. Learnings are retrievable or recallable largely through associations. If we can attach wider significance to the items as we learn them, there will be greater potentiality for their being recalled.

7. Put the learning to use. Applying and extending the learning that one has acquired is a good way to give it significance. When an idea takes wing outside the narrow confines in which it was learned, it generates power. A teacher should open the horizons for ideas to expand continuously.

Discussion Questions

1. Tell how errors help in disclosing the real nature of problem situations.
2. Give instances to show how errors may be produced by instruction procedures or materials.
3. Cite illustrations of errors of expression, errors in technique, and errors of number fact.

4. How do you distinguish between "good" errors and "bad" errors?

5. Refute or defend the statement that consistent errors are as truly evidence of ability to learn as are consistently correct computations.

6. Why does the mere checking of the answers not serve adequately as a guide for instruction?

7. Why is it important that "extraneous" material or steps be noted and controlled in testing for instructional guidance?

8. Tell why zero produces more difficulty than does any other of the digits in the number alphabet.

9. What instructional significance is there to the statement "Nothing succeeds like success"?

10. Why is it important that concern be given to "what is right" in stimulating and directing human learning?

11. How does the learner's "interest potential" affect his learning?

12. To what extent does the injunction "know your stuff" apply to the teacher engaged in remedial instruction?

13. Develop a unit test designed to measure pupil performance for a specific step in arithmetic. Describe the step and write an analysis of your test.

14. Give a unit test. Select one or more of the following activities to study your test results:

    (a) Chart the types of errors that were made.

    (b) Chart insofar as possible the specific number combinations that were worked incorrectly.

    (c) Write an analysis of the errors and write a plan to develop the next step in teaching the unit.

Suggested Readings

Collier, C. C., "Blocks to Arithmetical Understanding," *The Arithmetic Teacher*, vol. 6 (November 1959), pp. 262–268.

Hoel, Lesta, "What Constitutes Remedial Work in Arithmetic?", *The Mathematics Teacher*, vol. 43 (January 1950), pp. 19–24.

Peterson, Hilda, *A Study with the Division of Decimal Fractions*. Unpublished Master's Thesis, Claremont College Graduate School, Claremont, Calif. 1951.

Rappaport, David, "Testing for Meanings in Arithmetic," *The Arithmetic Teacher*, vol. 6 (April 1959), pp. 140–143.

Spencer, James Edward, *A Comparative Study of Computational Error Types with the Subtraction of Decimal Integers*. Unpublished Master's Thesis, Claremont College Graduate School, Claremont, Calif., 1957.

Spitzer, Herbert F., "Techniques for Evaluating Outcomes of Instruction in Arithmetic," *The Elementary School Journal*, vol. 49 (September 1948), pp. 21–31.

Sueltz, Ben A., "Mathematical Understandings and Judgments Retained by College Freshmen," *The Mathematics Teacher*, vol. 44 (January 1951), pp. 13–19.

Sueltz, Ben, Boynton Holmes, and Irene Sauble. "The Measurement of Understanding in Elementary School Mathematics," *The Measurement of Understanding*, National Society for the Study of Education, Forty-fifth Yearbook, Part I. Chicago, Ill.: University of Chicago Press, pp. 138–156.

15

Beyond the Obvious
Lies the Truth

Today's desire for everyone to attain reasonable competence with basic mathematical ideas is well-founded. In the past, instruction has too frequently stressed memorizing verbal statements and manipulative procedures without sufficient regard for what the statements mean or why the procedures were used. As Herbert Spencer so aptly stated, "The rote system, like other systems of its age, made more of the forms and symbols than of the things symbolized. To repeat words correctly was everything; to understand their meaning, nothing; and thus the spirit was sacrificed to the letter."

Teacher-dominated "tell and do" types of instruction produce, at best, only superficial understanding. They do not free the learner to explore, to invent, and to apply the ideas of mathematics in a way that is scholarly and creative. Instead, mathematical statements become the ineffective "ponderous mass" described by a writer in the first century BC who wrote:

> I saw an ass who bore a load
> Of sandalwood along the road.
> And almost with the burden bent,
> Yet never guessed the sandal scent.
>
> So pedants bear a ponderous mass
> Of books they comprehend not — like the ass.

Educational experience can and should develop capable citizens of a democracy by involving each learner purposefully and willingly in a personal rebirth of the ideas that others have conceived and made available to him. A teacher who has developed for himself a meaningful background of mathematics usually has deep-rooted feeling for the ideas he has learned and senses that the concepts have personal meaning and application. Such knowledge leads a teacher to help his pupils learn in a creative, sensitive way — a way that leads them far beyond the obvious to the truth. Or as Kahlil Gibran expresses his ideas about teaching in "The Prophet,"[1]

"No man can reveal to you aught but that which already lies half asleep in the dawning of your knowledge.

"The teacher who walks in the shadow of the temple, among his followers, gives not of his wisdom but rather of his faith and his lovingness.

"If he is indeed wise he does not bid you enter the house of his wisdom, but rather leads you to the threshold of your own mind.

"The astronomer may speak to you of his understanding of space, but he cannot give you his understanding.

"The musician may sing to you of the rhythm which is in all space, but he cannot give you the ear which arrests the rhythm nor the voice that echoes it.

"And he who is versed in the science of numbers can tell of the regions of weight and measure, but he cannot conduct you thither.

"For the vision of one man lends not its wings to another man."

[1] Kahlil Gibran, *The Prophet*. New York: Alfred A. Knopf, Inc., copyright 1923 by Kahlil Gibran; renewal copyright 1951 by Administrators C.T.A. of Kahlil Gibran Estate and Mary G. Gibran.

Index